PHYSIOGRAPHY OF THE UNITED STATES

The Grand Canyon from Point Sublime, North Rim. Compare the section, Fig. 156. (Courtesy of the Union Pacific Railroad.)

PHYSIOGRAPHY
OF THE
UNITED STATES

By
FREDERIC B. LOOMIS
Professor of Geology, Amherst College

DOUBLEDAY, DORAN & COMPANY, INC.
Garden City, New York
1937

PRINTED AT THE *Country Life Press*, GARDEN CITY, N. Y., U. S. A.

PREFACE

This book is the outgrowth of a set of notes used by the writer's classes in physical geography. It is hoped that it will prove helpful not only to students beginning the subject, but also to all whose inquiring minds seek explanations for the varied scenery with which one comes in contact in moving about this country with its great contrasts. The broad outlines of the development of any section are comparatively easy to read if one is accustomed to think in terms of geological processes and times. Unfortunately, the number of people who have become accustomed to reading a meaning in a level sky line, in the tilt of the rocks, or in the general composition of the rocks is small; and the books which may be used as guides in learning Nature's open secrets are very few. In this book it is the author's purpose to start at the beginning, using as few technical terms as possible, so that the student may learn to see the history revealed all around us. In order that he may go still further into the histories revealed in any section, a bibliography is given at the end of each chapter. If he desires to study any region fully it is recommended that he write to the Director of the United States Geological Survey in Washington for the lists of publications on that region.

For those who teach this subject, two items (in addition to the topographic maps, the geological maps, and the folios of the region, all from the Geological Survey) are especially helpful: A. K. Lobeck's Physiographic Diagram of the United States, published by the A. J. Nystrom Company of Chicago; and the *Atlas of American Geology*, by the same author, published by the Columbia University Press. The United States Geological Survey has a collection of 100 typographic maps selected for Physiography; Professional Paper, No. 60, is an interpretation of these maps. In the bibliographies in this book the topographic maps whose descriptions are included in that paper are marked by an asterisk. A fuller treatment of the subject is given by N. M. Fenneman in his *Physiography of the Western United States;* but for the eastern United States there is no recent comprehensive treatment, though Isaiah Bowman's *Forest Physiography* is still a useful book.

The assembling of the material for a book of this sort must be largely compilation, and its success depends on the discrimination used in selecting from the work of hundreds of investigators, as well as on the manner of the presentation. The writer has visited most of the provinces discussed, and has used the interpretations which appealed to him. Ever-increasing new information is coming to light, and new methods are making it possible for heretofore unreached depths to tell at least a part of their story, so that the knowledge of this subject is constantly growing.   As far as possible the latest data have at least been considered.

The author has been met with the greatest generosity in the matter of illustrations.   The source of each illustration is credited in the legend, but the author wishes to express here his thanks to the United States Geological Survey, The National Parks Service, the Army Air Corps, the Canadian Geological Survey, the Virginia Geological Survey, The Union Pacific Railroad, The Luray Caverns Corporation, the *National Geographic Magazine*, to J. H. Bretz and D. W. Johnson, and to his colleague, G. W. Bain, for furnishing him with illustrations.   Also to A. K. Lobeck and the A. J. Nystrom Company for allowing him to use their maps, both directly and as a basis for others prepared for this book.

                                                        F. B. Loomis.

December, 1936

CONTENTS

vii

CONTENTS

PART I

PHYSIOGRAPHIC PROCESSES AND THEIR EFFECTS

CHAPTER I

PHYSICAL DIVISIONS OF THE UNITED STATES

The United States is a belt of country some 1,400 miles wide extending across the North American continent from the Atlantic to the Pacific Ocean. Its surface ranges from below sea level to over 14,000 feet of altitude. Each feature is the result of upbuilding forces, and has been modified from the time of its inception to the present by the opposing destructive agencies. Every physical landscape reveals more or less clearly its history, for him who can read the story.

The major centers of uplift: Provinces.—There are several areas which are now highlands because they have been the centers of recent active uplift and the erosive forces have not had time to wear them away. Other areas, less elevated by the constructive forces, are lowlands. Each area, whether it be the result of a major or a minor uplift, if it has had a unified geological history is known as a *major division*. Each portion of a major division that today presents similar surface characteristics is known as a *province*. In many cases, as we will see in the later chapters, some provinces may be further divided into *sections* because of local differences in appearance.

A major division may include several contrasted provinces. For instance, the Appalachian Highlands are commonly divided into seven provinces (Fig. 1), comprising the Piedmont Province, the Blue Ridge Province, the Valley and Ridge Province, the St. Lawrence Valley, the Appalachian Plateaus, the New England Province, and the Adirondack Province. We are primarily concerned with the study of provinces, and major divisions will be discussed only when including them will contribute to the clearness of the physiographic story.

As the geologic and physiographic history of an area is not limited by political boundaries, several of the provinces of the United States extend into Canada or Mexico, and the country

3

immediately adjacent to the United States is therefore included in some of the descriptions.

Characters of the provinces.[1]—The Laurentian Upland, or Canadian Shield, is an area of ancient rocks, mostly in eastern Canada, that extends into the United States in two lobes, one about Lake Superior known as the Superior Upland, the other to make the Adirondack Province in New York state. The Laurentian Upland is often referred to as the nucleus of North America, as it has been generally above sea level since earliest geological times. Around it has been added more and more of the lower-lying country of the Interior Plains. The New England Province was perhaps the next to come into existence, and is now a highly dissected upland. The Valley and Ridge Province is the center of a fairly early disturbance. It is a belt of highly folded mountains, much of which has been later removed by erosion. To the east of the folded mountains is a belt of much more ancient rocks which were raised along with the Valley and Ridge Province, and which now stand as high as the latter, in some places even higher; this province is known as the Blue Ridge. The Blue Ridge is bordered on the east by a belt of ancient rocks which are now only slightly uplifted and which make the Piedmont Province. Between the Piedmont Province and the Atlantic Ocean, and extending southward and westward bordering the Gulf of Mexico, is the Coastal Plain Province. The surface of the plain is made up of stratified rocks that everywhere dip gently seaward.

On the west side of the Valley and Ridge Province is a belt of less folded, but still uplifted rocks, of the same age as the mountains, which form the Appalachian Plateaus. Westward an old sea floor, made of rocks rich in limestones, makes the Central Lowland and the Interior Low Plateaus. In Oklahoma and Arkansas the lowlands are broken by the Ouachita Mountains, which are similar in character and history to the Valley and Ridge Province but, being widely separated from that province, are designated as the Ouachita Province. Just north of this are the less disturbed but upraised Ozark Plateaus. The Great Plains Province, like the Central Lowland, is on

---

[1]Constant reference should be made to Fig. 1, and to the map in the rear of the book showing the distribution of the provinces and sections in greater detail.

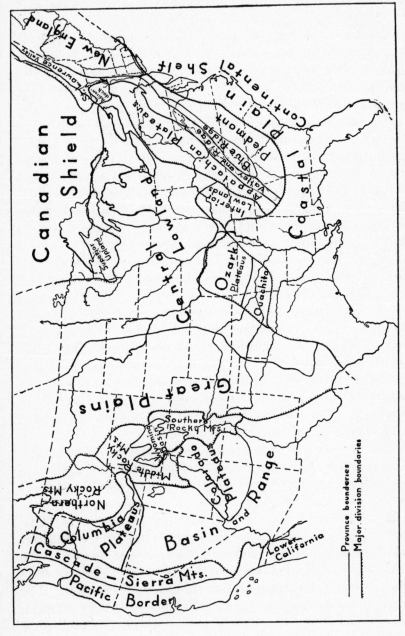

FIG. 1. Physical provinces of the United States. (As prepared by Fenneman for the U. S. Geological Survey.)

little-disturbed marine beds, but in this case the deposits are largely clayey shales. It is a large province extending from the Rio Grande, in a belt some 400 miles wide, far into northern Canada. The Rocky Mountain system including the Southern, Middle, and Northern Rocky Mountains, is a highland composed of granites and other strong rocks, monuments of a great uplift across this part of the continent.

The Wyoming Basin and Colorado Plateaus were involved to a lesser degree in the Rocky Mountain uplift and are composed largely of sedimentary rocks. The Basin and Range Province to the west of the Rocky Mountains is a region where the crust of the earth has been broken into blocks which have been tilted up into shorter ranges, the intervening valleys being mostly filled with the rock debris from the erosion of the adjacent mountains. The Columbia Plateaus were once of similar character but are now buried under tremendous lava flows, averaging half a mile in thickness, and making the surface nearly level over large areas. The Cascade-Sierra Mountains Province is an area of relatively old rocks which has been recently elevated to make these two mountain ranges. The Pacific Border Province is a series of young folded and broken mountain chains, which are even yet in the making.

Around the whole continent there is a shallow area of varying width, extending out from the shore line to a depth of about 600 feet, which is known as the Continental Shelf.

The reasons for the existence of these several provinces may be clearer if we review briefly the geological history of the United States, going back step by step from the present. The geological dates of the various events will be clear if one refers to the time chart on pages 94–95.

The Ice Age.—The most recent significant event in geologic history was the occurrence of the Ice Age, which lasted for about a million years, ending some 25,000 years ago. During the time of the continental glacier snow and ice fields formed in the Hudson Bay region, and as the snow was compacted into ice to a depth of thousands of feet, the ice sheet moved southward and carried with it the loose mantle rock scraped from the surface. The glacier also rounded the surface over which it moved and ground off some of the solid rock.

When the ice melted, the material it carried was dropped, sometimes in ridges (moraines), sometimes as a sheet of boulders and clay (ground moraine), and sometimes as sand or gravel. This material, irregularly deposited, often dammed river courses, making lakes and ponds, and today forms the mantle rock over much of the area once covered by the ice. The extent of the area covered by the continental glacier is shown in Fig. 2.

The Tertiary Period. —During the Tertiary period (i.e., from 1,000,000 back to 55,000,000 years ago) the east and south margins of the United States were overlapped most of the time by the ocean, and the material which forms the upper layers of the Coastal Plain was being deposited. At the same time rivers from the

FIG. 2. North America, showing the areas covered by an ice sheet during some part of the Pleistocene. (After W. C. Alden.)

young Rocky Mountains were spreading from 100 to over 1,000 feet of deposits on top of the Great Plains and the Wyoming Basin on the east side, and also over portions of the Colorado Plateaus on the west side. This material, composed largely of sands and clays, was thickest adjacent to the mountains. In the Basin and Range Province the earth's crust was fractured and the blocks were being tilted to make the mountains of the present time. At the same time the rising blocks were being weathered and the debris was accumulating around the bases of the mountains to make the flat floors of the basins, for the region was arid and the rivers did not run to the ocean.

After the mountain blocks were formed in the Columbia

Plateaus Province there was great volcanic activity. Lava rising from hundreds of openings filled the valleys to a depth of several thousand feet and buried the mountains. This was one of the greatest outpourings of lava the world has ever known. At the beginning of this period the Sierra Nevada Mountains were a plain near sea level, but early in the Tertiary a break occurred along the east side, and this great single block of mountains was slowly tilted into its present position. The

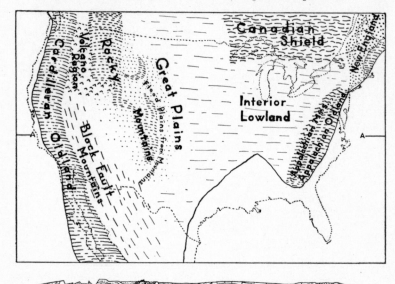

FIG. 3. The United States in early Tertiary (Eocene) times. The section shows the types of rocks encountered on the line A–A.

Cascade Mountains were also a low plain at the beginning of the period, and came into existence as a mountain range rather late in the Tertiary, buckling into a ridge 6,000 to 8,000 feet high. The mountain-building was accompanied by extensive volcanic activity, the row of volcanoes on top of the range being the latest remnants of this. Mt. Rainier is a conspicuous mountain-top volcano. The Pacific Border was under the sea through the greater part of the Tertiary, and thousands of feet of deposits were several times raised, folded, and again depressed under the sea, resulting finally in the series of ranges and valleys that comprise the province. Uplift and movement are still going on in the province.

The Tertiary was a period of continental uplift in the eastern United States; and the Appalachian Highlands, which had been worn down to a peneplain in the Cretaceous period (see below), were re-elevated.

The Cretaceous Period.—The period preceding the Tertiary is the Cretaceous period (55,000,000 to 95,000,000 years ago).

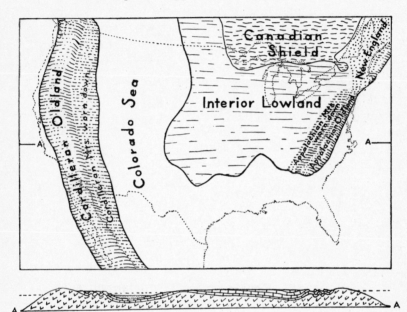

FIG. 4. The United States in Cretaceous times. The section shows the types of rocks encountered on the line A–A.

Its end was marked by the uplift of the Rocky Mountains. Its dominant characteristic was the continuous presence of a great interior sea (the Colorado Sea), stretching from the Gulf of Mexico to the Arctic Ocean, and averaging some 600 miles in width. Into this great basin was washed debris from both the east and the west, but mostly from the west, making deposits in the basin from 5,000 to 15,000 feet in thickness.

While the bottom of this basin sank, clays and sands accumulated over the sea floor, so that the waters of this Colorado Sea were never deep, as is indicated by the fossils preserved in the sediments. This was the time when the dinosaurs flourished; their remains are often found in these Cretaceous beds, especially in the marginal deposits, where it was swampy, or where the rivers were making flood plains. The filling of such a basin was accompanied by the leveling of the mountains from which the material was eroded. Toward the end of the period great swamps developed on the east and west margins of the basin; these later became coal beds.

The eastern half of the continent was relatively low, and streams from the Appalachian Highlands carried deposits to the bordering ocean. These deposits underlie the Tertiary strata of the present Coastal Plain. In the west there were high mountains (the folded Cordilleras) where the Basin and Range and the Columbia Plateaus Province are now.

The period came to an end when the Rocky Mountains were built. The southern and middle portions were folded into nearly parallel ranges, but in the northern section the intrusion from below of great quantities of granite and granite-like rocks has produced a very complicated series of mountain ranges.

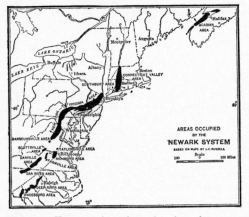

The Jura-Trias Period.—Through the Jurassic and Triassic periods (120,000,000 to 190,000,000 years ago) the North American

FIG. 5. Eastern America, showing the areas which were down-faulted in the Triassic.

Continent generally stood high and the only large areas which were flooded were in the north and west. In the east, which was well above the level of the sea, fractures developed in many sections during the late Triassic. The blocks were raised on one side and lowered on the other, thereby forming depressions. These depressions were slowly filled by gravel and sand brought down by the streams. The deposits, with associated lava flows, varied in depth from 4,000 feet in the Bay of Fundy region to 13,000 feet in the New Jersey and Pennsylvania region.

In the Basin and Range Province the early Cordilleran Mountains were raised into highlands in the early Triassic. The debris from these new mountains was spread as gravels and sands on the desert floors to the southeast. These deposits are seen today in the red and white cliffs of Arizona and Utah.

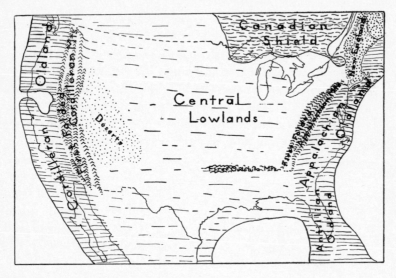

FIG. 6. The United States in early Triassic times. The section shows the types of rocks encountered on the line A–A.

The Palaeozoic Era.—Before the Triassic there was a long period of time, the Palaeozoic (215,000,000 to 550,000,000 years ago), during which North America had an old upland, Appalachia, along its eastern margin, and another, Cascadia, along its western margin. Between these the country was a basin, part of the time lowlands, and part of the time more or less completely submerged by inland seas. West of Appalachia and east of Cascadia portions of this basin were more frequently submerged; they are known as the Appalachian and Cordilleran Troughs. Debris (sands and clays) was washed from Appalachia and deposited in the Appalachian Trough. When

the deposits had accumulated sufficiently the overloaded trough
sank and Appalachia rose.   These movements were repeated
five or six times until from 6,000 to 30,000 feet of sediments
were deposited in the trough, the coarsest and thickest toward
the eastern margin, while the material toward the west was
finer and contained more limestone.   In the later Palaeozoic,

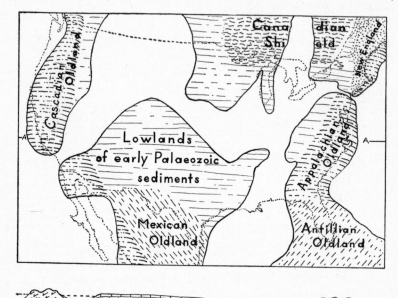

Fig. 7.   The United States in middle Palaeozoic times.   The section shows
the types of rocks encountered on the line A–A.   The line of dashes indicates
sea level.

i.e., in the Pennsylvanian, swamps developed over thousands of
square miles of this area.   From time to time these swamps
were covered by shallow seas, and buried under thin deposits
composed mostly of clay.   When the seas were filled, or
drained, new swamps were formed, later to be buried as the
oceans again occupied the region.   In Pennsylvania there are
29 successive beds of coal made from the swamps of the Pennsylvanian Period.   The Palaeozoic era ended with the folding
of the Appalachian Highland and Ouachita Mountains in the
Permian.

During the uplift of the Appalachian Highland all the eastern half of the United States was raised into a land mass which has since remained above the sea, except that the south and east coasts were submerged in the Cretaceous and Tertiary periods. Deposits then formed underlie the Coastal Plain. Mountain-building occurred in the New England province in the Ordovician and Devonian periods of the early Palaeozoic, so that it became a continental mass much earlier than did the rest of the Appalachian area. The Cordilleran Trough, east of Cascadia, was being filled similarly through the Palaeozoic, but was not folded into mountains until the Triassic.

Pre-Cambrian Lowland.—The sedimentary rocks of the United States are everywhere underlain by gneisses, granites, and other coherent rocks that were developed in the long ages that preceded the Palaeozoic era, and whose history is as yet only partly interpreted. In the late Pre-Cambrian, during a long period of erosion, these oldest rocks were worn down to a lowland of slight relief so that the continent was a great plain. This period of erosion was followed by a period of active mountain-building during which highlands were formed about the margins of the continent. These highlands, known as Appalachia,

FIG. 8. Map to show the uplifted units which came into existence at the beginning of the Cambrian time, and which played major roles in the making of the North American continent.

Cascadia, and the Canadian Shield, were bordered by the Appalachian and Cordilleran basins, in which the earliest rocks of the Cambrian were deposited. The story of the physical development of the continent usually begins with the late Pre-Cambrian

CHAPTER II

THE ATMOSPHERE AND ITS WORK

Functions and composition of the atmosphere.—The air, which surrounds us, has several important functions. It is the medium which brings to the land the water used by animals and plants, and is one of the agents which disintegrate rocks and transport detritus from one locality to another. Air in motion is a source of mechanical power. The oxygen of the atmosphere furnishes energy for animals, and the carbon dioxide which occurs in the air is used by plants in building their bodily structures. The climatic regions of the earth are in large part determined by atmospheric conditions. The atmosphere is made up of several gases; at the earth's surface it has the following average composition:

Nitrogen	77.07%	Water vapor	1.20%
Oxygen	20.75	Carbon dioxide	.03
Argon	.94	Hydrogen	.01
		Helium	trace

The weight, or pressure, of the air at sea level is about 15 pounds to the square inch and is equal to that of 29.9 inches (or 760 millimeters) of mercury. This is the base used in measuring atmospheric pressures.

Mechanical work of the atmosphere.—The solid rocks of the earth, where exposed at the surface, are subjected to the action of many agencies, both chemical and mechanical, which slowly break them into smaller and smaller fragments. The accumulation of loose rock material thus formed on the surface of the land is known as *regolith* and may vary in thickness from a mere fraction of an inch to hundreds of feet. The superficial portion of the regolith may ultimately develop into soil, upon which plants, animals, and men depend directly or indirectly for their food.

The mechanical work of the atmosphere in disintegration is largely due to changes of temperature. All solids expand on heating and contract on cooling. When a rock surface is partly exposed and partly covered or, owing to diurnal changes of temperature, is alternately heated and cooled, it rapidly expands and contracts. Cracks develop between the warmer and cooler portions parallel to the outer surface of the rock. The surface portion thus loosened may flake off, exposing the rock beneath. Thus the rock mass is slowly reduced in size. This process is known as *exfoliation*.

Further, most rocks are composed of several minerals, and each mineral has a different coefficient of expansion. Granite, for instance, is composed of quartz, feldspar, and mica. Upon heating, the quartz expands twice as much as does the feldspar, and tiny cracks develop between the quartz and feldspar grains. Repeated expansions and contractions, as day changes to night, and summer to winter, result not only in shattering the rocks, but in opening passages which water may enter. Whenever water freezes in the cracks, or between the rock crystals or grains, it expands by one-tenth of its bulk, thus further breaking up the rock mass. In the cracks thus formed seeds of trees may take root and, as they grow, may further pry rocks apart, thus making it possible for water to penetrate deeper into the rocks.

The wind is an agent of erosion and of transportation, especially important in arid climates. When the wind is strong it may remove rock fragments from their places of origin and deposit them elsewhere in the form of sand dunes or loess. Wind-carried sand may be recognized by the fact that the particles are worn smoother than are sand particles carried by water. Sand dunes are common surface features in many desert regions and on certain lake and ocean shores. Wind may also act as an erosive agent, sand-blasting and polishing rock surfaces by blowing particles of sand against them.

Wind-blown dust has been carried from the Cascade and Sierra Nevada Mountains into the Basin and Range Province, partly filling the valleys, while dust from the Rocky Mountains has been carried far to the eastward and deposited in the form of *loess*. Loess deposits of varying thickness, but rarely exceeding twenty feet in depth, are found in the Mississippi Valley, especially in Kansas, Nebraska, Missouri, and Iowa. Large areas of China are covered with very thick accumulations of loess. The finer ash from active volcanoes may be carried many miles by the wind and may accumulate in thick beds, as has occurred several times in the geologic past.

Chemical work.—Both air and water decompose rocks chemically. Water, absorbing oxygen and carbon dioxide from the air, becomes slightly acid and dissolves the more soluble minerals and cementing materials of which the rock is composed. Feldspar, for instance, is readily broken down chemically, the potassium (or sodium or calcium) element going into solution and being carried away in the water, leaving a residue of kaolin (clay) which may be mixed with relatively insoluble quartz particles. The lime of limestone is also soluble in water which is slightly acid and may be entirely removed by solution, leaving only impurities like sand or clay as residues. Many sandstones are cemented with lime, and when this is removed break down into sand.

Many rocks contain some form of iron either as a cement or as a component. Iron tends to unite with oxygen, especially when in solution in water, and thus forms limonite or iron rust which, being soluble, may be carried away in the water.

The chemical work of the atmosphere and of water in the atmosphere or in the surface rocks is the most widespread cause of rock disintegration, for it operates at varying rates over all the surface of the earth not covered by ice or water, while all other erosion agencies are limited in time or space.

Soil development.—As was indicated above, the superficial portion of the regolith may, in course of time, through the action of the atmosphere and water, become disintegrated. When this raw soil, as it may be called, is mixed with humus, it becomes a young soil, capable of supporting some type of plant life. Humus is the term applied to the vegetation that has been decomposed by weathering, or by the action of bacteria or other micro-organisms. Most of the humus in the soil layer is derived from plants growing on the surface. It becomes gradually mixed with the underlying rock particles, partly by the downward movement of water, partly by burial under a new deposit of rock detritus, and partly by the activity of underground animals. Earthworms in humid regions are constantly stirring the soil particles and are an important agent of soil formation.

When about 15 per cent of humus, by weight, has been added to the soil layer, the soil is said to be mature, and for a long time after maturity is reached, new additions of humus may about balance the losses of humic materials due to plant growth. When the humus content begins to decrease proportionally, the soil is old. Soils become old most rapidly where the land is cropped and no effort is made to restore to the soil the humus content that has been used by the growing plants.

Soil structure and texture.—During its formation, a soil will gradually develop a soil profile and become differentiated into three layers, or horizons, usually designated as the A, B, and C horizons. The A horizon at the top contains humus, is mealy or granular in texture, and is readily penetrated by plant roots. It is coarser than the B horizon because much of the finer and more soluble material has been carried downward into the B horizon by the action of water and of gravity. The B horizon contains more clay than the A horizon and has usually a dense columnar structure. The C horizon comprises the unaltered rock material. The A horizon is the zone of leaching, whereas the B horizon is the zone in which the soluble materials from the A horizon are concentrated.

Soil classification.—Soils are classified according to whether or not such a soil profile as has been described has developed. Soils without profiles are called undeveloped soils, and occur in swamps, in deserts, and in alluvial plains where new rock material is frequently added to the surface.

Developed soils are of two general types, according to the lime content of the B horizon. In humid regions where water is moving downward through the soil layer there is no accumulation of lime in the B horizon. Such soils are known as *Pedalfers* (pedo, soil, and Fe, iron) because of the iron obviously contained in them. They vary in character and in color according to the length of time to which they have been exposed to the processes of rock disintegration. In the southern states where the surface is frozen for only a short period each year, the rocks are deeply weathered, the soluble minerals have been dissolved or *leached* out, and the soils are red or brown in color. They approach the character of *laterites*, as the excessively leached soils of hot, humid regions are called.   In the northern states, where a soil profile has developed, the color is grey or brown.   There soils are not so deep as are the soils in the southern states, both because they have not been developed rapidly, and because in the glaciated regions the soils are young.

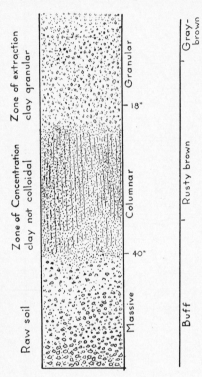

FIG. 9.   Soil profile of a mature upland silt.

In semiarid regions, where evaporation exceeds precipitation, the movement of the water is downward in the soil after a rain and upward at other times.   This results in the concentration of lime in the B horizon at depths varying with the aridity.   Such soils are known as *Pedocals* (pedo, soil, and Cal, calcium—lime). They vary in color according to the depth of the layer of lime concentration.   In the eastern portion of the Dakotas, and thence southward, the soils are black or dark brown.   To the west of this belt, over the Great Plains, aridity increases, the lime layer is nearer the surface, and the soils are described as chestnut brown in color.   In deserts the soils have no profile, the lime layer may be at the surface, and the soil is very alkaline.

Soils are sometimes described as *residual* if they have not been removed from above the parent rock, and as *transported* if they have been removed by gravity, wind, running water, or ice, and deposited elsewhere.   Alluvial soils and glacial soils have been transported perhaps hundreds of miles.

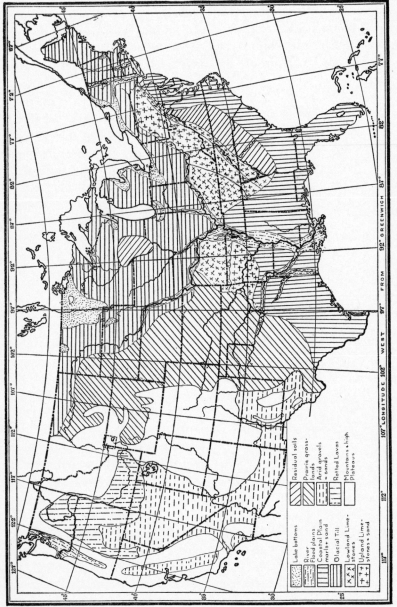

Lake bottoms
River
Flood plains
Coastal Plain
marls + sand
Glacial Till
Lowland Lime-
stones
Upland Lime-
stones + sand

Residual soils
Prairie grass-
lands
Arid gravels
+ sands
Rotted Lavas
Mountains + high
Plateaus

Fig. 10.   Soil map of the United States.

19

Soil fertility.—The latent fertility of a soil depends on several factors: the size and composition of the rock particles, the permeability to water and air, and the amount of humus content. The ideal soil is a mixture of rock particles of various sizes and character which makes loam. Sand is mostly quartz particles, varying in size from 1/25 to 1/200 of an inch in diameter. The insoluble residue derived from minerals other than silica forms clay. Clay is composed of tiny flakes, about 1/25,000 of an inch in diameter, and is relatively impervious to water, while water readily moves through sand. Light, sandy soils are therefore subject to rapid leaching.

Soil fertility also depends on whether the soil is acid or alkaline in its chemical reactions. Soils composed largely of sand are acid, and soils containing an abundance of lime are alkaline. Soils tend to become acid as decaying vegetation forms acids. Lime is, therefore, essential for the growth of most plants in order to neutralize the acids derived from decaying vegetation. The lime from decaying vegetation may be returned to the soil and used by successive generations of plants. When a crop is removed from the area where it is grown, the lime content is lost to the soil, and unless it is replaced the soil becomes poorer in lime and in humus, until it is worn out.

Soil fertility is also lost through the action of running water (Chap. IV) and of the wind. The erosive efficiency of running water is increased if the vegetation cover is removed, whether the cover be forest or grass. The loss of soil from many sections of the Great Plains through the action of the wind is, in part, due to the removal of the original grass cover in the preparation of the land for crops.

CHAPTER III

CLIMATE

In the previous chapter we have seen how the atmospheric processes produce changes in land forms, owing to the effects of temperature, moisture, and winds. The erosional results vary according to the climate of the region in which the land-forms occur. An understanding of the distribution of land-forms—and especially of the minor landforms—in the United States therefore must be based on a knowledge of the distribution of climatic regions and of their characteristics.

Climatic regions are areas where the atmospheric conditions have certain seasonal or annual characteristics over a long period of time. The atmospheric conditions which must be studied separately and in their most important relationships for an understanding of the bases for demarking climatic regions are temperature, pressure, winds, humidity, and rainfall.

Temperature, pressure, and winds.—The temperatures experienced at any place during a year depend on many factors, of which the basal one is the amount of *insolation*, or radiation received from the sun. Of the total insolation emanating from the sun, the earth intercepts about one two-billionth part. This amount is almost constant at the top of the atmosphere, but only about one-third reaches the surface of the earth. A large part is reflected back into space by the atmosphere, and much is absorbed as it passes through the atmosphere.

The amount of insolation reaching any point on the earth's surface varies according to the angle at which the rays from the sun are received, the length of the period during which the sun shines, and the amount of dust and moisture particles in the air. At the equator, where the days and nights are always equal and where the sun is always nearly vertical at noon, the amount of energy received is greater than at any other place, and varies but slightly from season to season.

21

In mid-latitudes, as for instance in the United States, the angle at which the rays of the sun reach the earth at any season varies with latitude, and the number of hours of sunlight varies with the season. Between the 21st of March and the 23rd of September, the number of daylight hours in the Northern Hemisphere increases with the latitude. During the other six months the hours of daylight decrease with increasing latitude.

Whether the solar radiation received will warm the earth and the lower portions of the atmosphere depends on many conditions. Much of the insolation is reflected from the surface of the earth, depending on the character of the surface. The reflection from a water surface amounts to 40% of the amount received. The rest is transmitted to varying depths until it is absorbed. A body of water is thus warmed slowly, but it also cools off slowly, so that regions receiving winds from the ocean have less range of temperature than do regions at a distance from the ocean.

In contrast to water surfaces, land surfaces absorb a large amount of insolation and thus become quickly heated during sunshine hours, especially when the angle at which the rays are received is high. On the other hand, land surfaces lose heat rapidly, either by conduction to the lower atmosphere which is in contact with the heated surface, or by re-radiation into the atmosphere. The heat rays that are re-radiated from the earth do not pass through the atmosphere so readily as the insolation rays. These re-radiated rays are the chief cause of temperature changes in the atmosphere. Over a long period of time the amount of energy absorbed by the earth and changed to heat equals the amount lost in various ways. Otherwise the temperatures of the earth would be constantly increasing or constantly decreasing.

Temperatures are recorded on maps by means of lines known as *isotherms*, showing the location of all points having the same average temperature for the period indicated in the title of the map. Figure 11 indicates the average surface temperatures of the United States for January, and Figure 12 the July temperatures. From a comparison of these maps it will be seen that the isotherms over the land trend southward in winter and northward in summer, indicating that the interior of the continent is colder in winter and warmer in summer than are coastal areas in the same latitudes. Note also the southward deflection of the isotherms in January over the Appalachian Highland, and in July over the Rocky Mountains, owing to the fact that temperatures decrease with altitude. Notice the general parallelism of isotherms to the Pacific Coast; and that along the Atlantic Coast the air over the ocean is warmer than the bordering land in winter and cooler in summer.

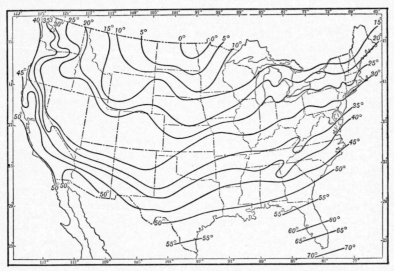

FIG. 11. Average temperatures for January. (After Henry.)

In July the temperatures in southwestern United States are much higher than the temperatures experienced near the Equator. The hottest July temperatures in the world are found in desert regions bordering the area in which the sun is vertical at noon during the northern summer months.

Temperatures vary from place to place and from time to time, in part because the atmosphere is constantly in motion either vertically or horizontally. The air is a fluid, and, like other fluids, flows from where the pressure is greater to where it is less. With increasing altitude pressure decreases, but not at a regular rate. At 17,500 feet the pressure is only half the pressure at sea level.

Horizontal movements of the air produce winds, but where

the movement is vertical, either upward or downward, there is
a calm at the surface of the earth. The center of the wind
system of the world is the permanent calm belt, known as the
doldrums, bordering the Equator. This belt moves north
and south with the seasons and is better developed over the
oceans than over the lands. Within the doldrum belt the
warm surface air expands and pressure decreases. Cooler,
heavier air pushes in under the lighter air and a vertical con-

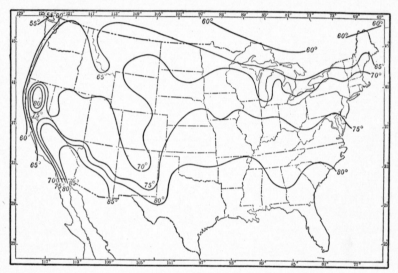

FIG. 12.　Average temperatures for July.　(After Henry.)

vectional movement results. The air moving toward the low-
pressure region on both sides of the doldrum belt produces
permanent winds, known as *trades*.

In the mid-latitude regions of the world, as, for example, in
the United States, the high-level winds are known as *Westerlies*,
because of their general direction. Surface winds, except those
accompanying local storms, like thunderstorms or tornadoes,
vary in direction and in intensity with differences in pressure,
owing to seasonal changes of temperature, or to the passage of
large, moving eddies in the air known as *cyclones*. The strength
or velocity of a wind depends on the rate at which the pressure
changes horizontally. A wind blowing at the rate of 5 miles
per hour means a difference of pressure of 2 thousandths of an

inch in fifteen nautical miles, while a wind of 25 miles an hour means a difference of pressure in the same distance of 3/100 of an inch.

Humidity.—All air contains some invisible water vapor, evaporated from water surfaces or from moist land, or brought to the air through transpiration from plants, as they carry on the physiological processes of growth. Evaporation goes on at all temperatures but is more rapid when temperatures are high. At any given temperature the air can contain only a certain amount of invisible vapor (Figure 13). The amount of vapor present in proportion to what it could hold at a given temperature is termed *relative humidity*. Because the amount of vapor that can be held

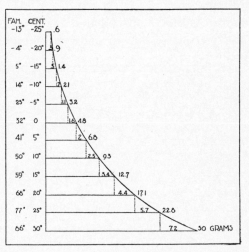

FIG. 13. The moisture content of the air when it reaches the saturation point at various temperatures. The figures in the triangles indicate the amount of water vapor a cubic meter of air can take up in a rise of 5° centigrade, or must precipitate in a fall of 5° centigrade, if the air is saturated.

in the air decreases with decrease of temperature, the relative humidity is often higher at night than during the daytime, though the actual amount of moisture in the air has not changed. When the relative humidity is 100% the air is said to be *saturated*, and any surplus added causes some of the moisture to condense, and to form clouds, fog, dew, frost, rain, or snow.

Clouds are due to condensation of moisture above the surface of the earth and are usually associated with vertical movements of moist air whose temperature decreases as it rises. For instance, surface air having a temperature of 77°F. and containing 20 grams of water per cubic centimeter has a relative humidity of 90%. If this air rises convectionally and is cooled to 50°F. it can hold but 12.7 grams of water per cubic meter. The surplus water condenses in tiny droplets which appear as a cloud. These tiny droplets settle slowly and may be re-evaporated in the lower, warmer air. If, however, the cloud forms at a low level, the smaller droplets, uniting into larger drops as they descend, fall as rain or snow on the surface of the earth.

Dew, or frost, depending on the season, results from the fact that the earth and the surfaces of vegetation, wood, metals, and

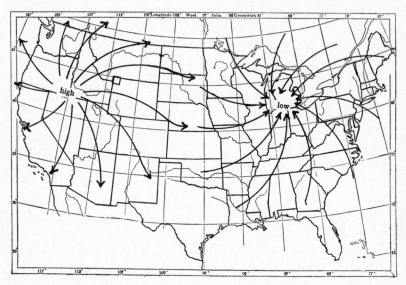

FIG. 14.   A high- and a low-pressure area as seen from above.   Arrows indicate the direction of the wind.

other objects lose heat in the night by radiation. The air in contact with them is in consequence chilled and its relative humidity rises so high that condensation takes place.

Weather and climate.—The climate of any region is expressed in averages of the atmospheric elements described above, and the values of these elements are found by a study of weather conditions. Weather is the combination of atmospheric conditions which exists at a given time and may change in character from moment to moment.

In some parts of the world weather conditions vary but little from one season to another, and the climate is monotonously uniform. Over much of the United States, lying in the westerly-wind belt, weather changes at certain seasons are sudden and often severe. Such changes are associated with the passage of eddies of air with inblowing winds, known as *cyclones*, and of masses of outblowing winds known as *anti-cyclones* (Fig. 14). The cause of such eddies is not definitely known, but they are associated with the distribution of permanent or seasonal areas of low or high pressure.

In the winter months masses of cold air move southward from the permanent high-pressure centers in polar regions or from the cold interior of the continent, forming an anticyclonic center, with low temperatures, with a low relative humidity,

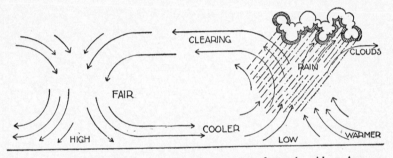

FIG. 15. A high- and a low-pressure area as seen from the side. Arrows indicate the directions of air currents.

and with winds blowing outward from the centers at a speed that varies according to the rate at which the pressure changes in a given distance over the surface of the earth. At the same season the winds over the oceans and the bordering lands are composed of air coming from warmer, lower latitudes, and circling about permanent high-pressure centers in the ocean.

On the lee side of these masses of continental cold air, cyclonic eddies or cyclones develop, into which blows warm, humid air from equatorial regions on one side, and cold polar air on the other. Cyclones form in front of the anticyclonic polar air masses and move eastward across the United States as is indicated in Figure 16. On the easterly side of the cyclonic low-pressure center the warm, humid air usually causes precipitation, as it is cooled both by rising and by mixing with the cold air blowing into the eddy from the opposite direction.

The approach of a cyclone is first indicated by a falling of

the barometer and by increasing cloudiness, and is usually
accompanied by the shifting of the wind to an easterly direction.
Cloudiness steadily increases, and precipitation as rain or snow
usually follows.   A cyclone may be from 300 miles to 1,000
miles in diameter, and in the winter months the center moves
forward, on the average, about thirty miles an hour.   Cyclonic
and anticyclonic areas are better developed in the winter than
in the summer months.   Storms are therefore usually more

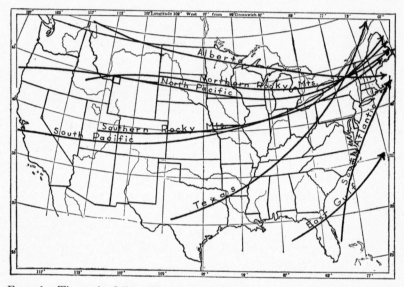

FIG. 16.   The paths followed by storm centers, as compiled by plotting their
courses over a period of years.

severe in winter than in summer, and weather changes are more
rapid and extreme.

In the coldest weeks of the winter, a great polar air mass may
spread southward and eastward over the eastern United States
and cause a period of extreme cold lasting for several days.
The coldest weather occurs during the calm that marks the
center of the anticyclone.

In the summer time, when the interior of the continent is
warm, cyclonic and anticyclonic centers are less well developed, and a long "spell" of warm, humid weather may occur
when low summer pressure occupies most of the continent.

Most of the winter precipitation over the eastern United

States occurs during the passage of cyclones. Much of the summer precipitation results from local convectional movements in thunderstorms, which are caused by the superheating of the humid surface air.

The distribution of low- and high-pressure areas, and of the associated temperatures and rainfall over the United States, is ascertained twice daily by the United States Weather Bureau, and the morning records are published daily in the form of a

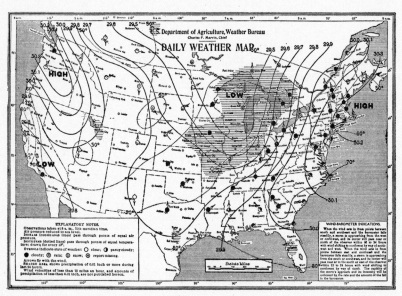

FIG. 17. A weather map such as is published daily by the Weather Bureau.

map (Fig. 17). From a knowledge of the significance of combinations of weather elements, obtained through many years of observation, Weather Bureau officials can forecast with a high degree of accuracy the weather conditions to be expected within the next twenty-four hours in each of the states.

From the accumulated records statistics have been compiled that show for the different sections the average seasonal as well as annual atmospheric conditions. The most useful of these are, perhaps, temperatures and rainfall, particularly those of the growing season.

The growing season varies in length from 250 or more days along the Gulf Coast in Florida and along the southern Atlantic

Coast to less than 100 days in northern Maine, in northern Minnesota, and over most of the Rocky Mountains and Columbia Plateaus.

The character of the growing season is determined by the rainfall as well as by the temperature. On the average, snow covers the ground from two to four months a year north of a line extending westward from northern Connecticut to the Missouri River. The average rainfall of the United States is indicated in Figure 18. The heaviest rainfall, amounting to over 120 inches annually, is on the Olympic Mountains on the peninsula between Puget Sound and the Pacific Ocean. The heaviest rainfall in the East occurs along the Gulf Coast and on the highest mountains of the Blue Ridge, where it is over 80 inches a year. The rainfall is less than 10 inches, and in some places less than 5 inches a year, over most of the Basin and Range Province and in portions of Wyoming, Utah, northern Arizona, and southern New Mexico.

For agriculture the time of the year in which the rain falls is significant. Owing to high temperatures and low pressures, the summer rainfall is greater than the winter rainfall over the Great Plains and the western portions of the Central Lowlands, while in New England, the middle Atlantic Coast, and the northern Appalachian areas the rainfall is about equally distributed through the year. Winter precipitation may accumulate as snow, with the result that with the coming of spring the melting snow, accompanied perhaps by rain, often produces floods in the larger rivers.

A light summer rainfall usually means an abundance of sunlight and a high rate of evaporation. Therefore the ground water table is low in arid regions (page 37). In regions with summer rainfall the ground water table is high, plants can readily secure the water essential for growth, and erosion may be rapid on steep slopes which are not covered with vegetation, or where the rocks are deeply weathered.

Climatic regions in the United States.—Many ways of dividing the United States into climatic regions have been proposed and are in use for different purposes. Some, as for instance that of Köppen, are very detailed and indicate the seasonal characteristics in each section.

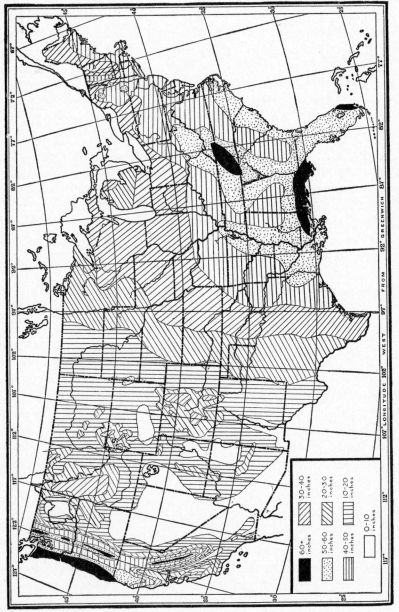

FIG. 18. Average annual rainfall in the United States.

30-40 inches
20-30 inches
10-20 inches

60+ inches
50-60 inches
40-50 inches
0-10 inches

31

The Köppen climatic regions are indicated in Figure 19.[1]   It will be noted that in the eastern United States boundaries extend in a general east-west direction, while west of approximately the 100th meridian, boundaries are roughly parallel to the ocean and the several mountain ranges.

Only Florida has a tropical climate (A) with an average temperature in the coldest month higher than 65°F., and with a winter dry season.   The desert (BW) and steppe (BS) climates which mark west coasts in sub-tropical latitudes the world over, end in the southwestern United States where North Pacific storms bring ample rains along the coast, but extend well to the north in the rain-shadowed interior.   They have a summer dry season (s) west of the Rocky Mountains when Pacific storms are weak; and a winter dry season (w) east of the Rockies, where winter cold prevents appreciable precipitation.   Small areas of steppe climate occur west of the Sierras, in the hot, southern portion of the Great Valley of California and in Washington.

The true desert (BW) is found only in the immediate lee of the high Sierras and in the hot southwestern interior.   Over the higher, more exposed, and, therefore, moister areas, warm (C), or cool (D), temperate climates make promontories or islands in the dry ones of the West.   Practically all have a summer dry season (s), except in the high Sierras and the Rockies (Dfb), which have summer thunderstorms.   These high lands, though marked Dfb, include both the oak (Dfb) and the birch (Dfc) climates, which, however, are here characterized prevailingly by conifers.   The highest summits of the Rockies and Sierras, in general over 9,850 feet in altitude, have no month with a temperature over 50°F. and therefore have a tundra climate (Et).

The Cs or Etesian (often called Mediterranean) climate, a warm, maritime, or semi-maritime type with dry summers, has no broad extent as in southern Europe, but is narrowly confined east to west by mountain barriers.   It is greatly elongated south to north along the coast, however, by the mildness of the Pacific and the mountain ramparts to the east.   The Sierras cut off Cs not far from the Coast because they reduce the rainfall to steppe or desert levels in the lee. Farther east, however, on the piedmont of the high Wasatch Mountains in Utah, Cs reappears with the increased rainfall; and it extends across the plateau in the north where the lower Cascade Range lets more moisture pass and the rain-provoking Rocky Mountain System bends far westward.   This climate appears in three forms.   Csa, the

[1]The map and the description of regions here given are from the Köppen-Geiger *Handbuch der Klimatologie*, Vol. II, Part J, *The Climates of North America*, by R. DeC. Ward, C. F. Brooks, and A. J. Connor, pp. 194–195, and are used here with the permission of the authors and of Gebrüder Borntraeger, the publisher.

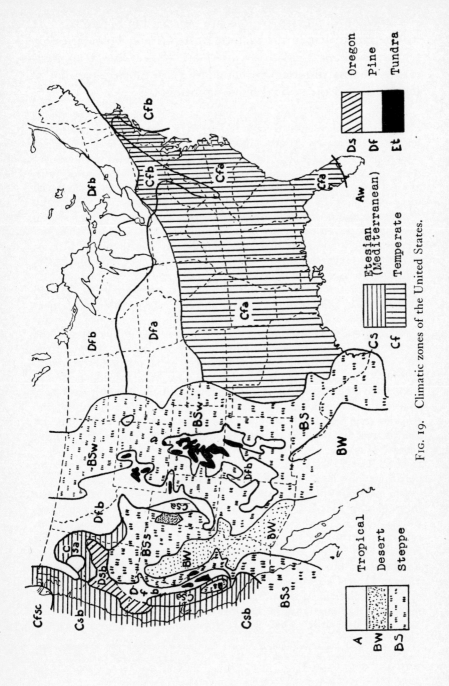

FIG. 19. Climatic zones of the United States.

33

olive type, characteristic of Italy, is a rather dry type found in the
rain-shadows of the western mountains—in the Great Valley of
California, in Utah, and in the Columbia and Snake River Valleys.
The higher plateaus of Oregon, however, become so cold in winter,
less than 25°F. in January (D), and also cool in summer (b), that
they are set off as a separate type (Dsb), called the Oregon climate,
for it is found nowhere else in the world. Csb, the evergreen heath
type, has its most pronounced development at Eureka, California,
where the summers are so cool that the annual range is less than 9°F.
Cfsc, with appreciable rainfall in summer, even though this season is
markedly drier than the extraordinarily wet cold season, extends
from Washington to Alaska.

In the eastern half of the country, broad areas, being without important mountains or hills, have much the same climates. The warm
temperate (C) with all months having an average temperature above
27°F., and with rains at all seasons (f), covers two-thirds of this great
region. Its western boundary is practically the limit of the tall grass.
Throughout, there is no marked dry or wet season; that is, no month
has less than one-tenth as much rainfall as the wettest month (f).
In the South, the temperature of the coldest month averages over
50°F., and pine barrens and cypress swamps are characteristic native
vegetation. Practically all this area has warm summers, July over
72°F. (a). It constitutes the most extensive Cfa climatic region in
the world. In the northeast, a portion of the warm temperate climate, owing to altitude or cool coastal waters, has cooler summers,
with the warmest month averaging less than 72°F. (b). This is the
beech climate (Cfb).

Immediately to the north of Cfa on the plains is a cool temperate
climate, which has colder winters, less than 27°F. (D), though like
Cfa it has no pronounced dry season (f), and is nearly as hot in
summer—July more than 72°F. (a). This Dfa climate is named the
Sioux climate. Cfa and Dfa together include the great Cotton,
Corn, and Winter Wheat Belts.

To the north, stretching from Maine to Dakota, is Dfb, the Canadian climate, with snowy winters and moderately warm summers.
It is the oak climate, with needle-leaved forests in the north and
broad-leaved in the south.

CHAPTER IV

THE WORK OF GROUND WATER AND OF RUNNING WATER

Ground water and run-off.—Rainfall, including melted snow, is disposed of in one of three ways. It may be evaporated and its vapor added to the air; it may sink into the ground, in which case it is termed *ground water;* or it may immediately *run off* and form streams. The proportion of the rainfall which disappears in each way varies with the climate and with the nature and condition of the surface on which it falls. Where precipitation is heavy the run-off is great, especially if the ground is already saturated with water, or is frozen or otherwise impervious; whereas in some dry areas and on loose soil a greater proportion sinks into the ground. Steep slopes have a greater run-off than gentle ones, and on slopes protected by vegetation, whether grass or forest, the run-off is less than on bare slopes. The proportion of rainfall which sinks into the ground varies from 90%–95% in some parts of the West, to about 50% on the Coastal Plain.[1]

GROUND WATER

Ground water performs both chemical and mechanical work. The chemical work consists in dissolving minerals and soluble rocks (page 16). Mechanically the water in the regolith lubri-

---

[1]The measurement of water in its various activities becomes important, and the following units are generally used in this country:

A second-foot is the delivery of a cubic foot of water per second.
A second-foot will cover an acre to a depth of one inch in an hour (43,560 cu. in.).
A second-foot equals 7.48 gallons per second.
One horsepower equals 1 second-foot falling 8.8 feet.
$1\frac{1}{3}$ horsepower equals 1 kilowatt.
To calculate waterpower: $\dfrac{\text{second-feet} \times \text{fall in feet}}{8.8}$

Or for practical purposes, where 80% of theoretical power can be counted on, divide the numerator by 11.

cates the rock particles, especially if they are clayey, so that they readily move downward under the influence of gravity.

When a slope is gentle, regolith saturated with ground water will slowly creep or "flow" downhill. This is known as *soli-fluction*, and it is by this process, in part, that material on valley sides is brought to a river.

If a slope is steep, a mass of rock material may suddenly slide to a lower region in a *landslide*. A great landslide may move so far as to obstruct the drainage in the lowland and form a lake. If successive large slides occur in one locality, the front of a cliff may be bordered by a great area of landslide material whose surface is very rough and irregular. Such a surface occurs in front of a portion of the Vermilion Cliffs in Arizona.

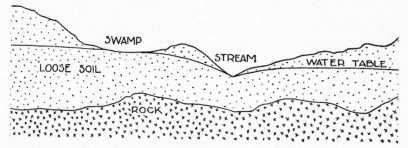

FIG. 20.   The relation of the water table to the surface.

Water table.—Water which enters the ground descends until it reaches a level where all the spaces in the soil, or rocks, are filled with water. The top surface of this accumulation of water is termed the *water table*. In regions of heavy rainfall the water table is only a few feet below the surface of the soil (5 to 20), whereas in arid regions it may be 200 or more feet below the surface.

Since water moves slowly through the interstices in the regolith or rocks, the top of the water table is not horizontal but is always tending to become so. Thus the top of the water table follows somewhat the contour of the land, curving upward under hills and downward in valleys; but at the same time it is true that the water table is farther below the surface on a hill than in a valley. In some places the water table coincides with the surface of the land. This results in a swampy area. Or if the surface of a hollow in the land lies below the top of the water table, a lake or pond is formed.

A stream flowing through an area may have one of two effects on the water table. A stream in a humid region is usually in a valley lower than the general level of the water table. The water table will then slope down to the level of the stream, the ground water seeping through the soil help- ing to maintain or in- crease the volume of water in the stream. On the other hand, in an arid region where the water table is far below the surface, and where a stream is fed by far-distant sources, the stream will con- stantly lose water by seepage down to the water table. Thus the

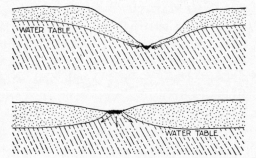

Fig. 21. The relation of the water table to rivers: above, when the water table is higher than the stream, the commonest case; below, when the river is higher than the water table, as often occurs in the Great Plains.

water table will here rise up to the level of the stream, and the stream will decrease in size with increasing distance from its source in the mountains. Such streams as the Platte River and others of the Great Plains are of this type.

Wells and springs.—The position of the water table is greatly affected by the presence of impervious or less pervious layers of soil or rock. While water moves freely in sand or loose soil, and less freely in compacted soil, there is practically no move- ment in clay or shale. In sandstone the rate of flow has been measured and found to be from 15 inches to 12 feet a day.

In a humid region, where the water table is normally near the surface, a *well* is the usual means of supplying water to a family in the country. A well is an opening, either dug or driven to a depth below the lowest level that the water table is likely to reach in a dry season.

A *spring* occurs where the ground water, seeping downward to an impervious layer or mass of rock, follows the top of the impervious material to the point where it comes to the surface on a slope.

An *artesian well* is an opening drilled deep enough to reach water confined in a tilted pervious layer between two impervious layers. The middle, pervious layer, usually a sandstone, must be exposed on at least one of its edges so that surface water may slowly move along the bed through the interstices between the rock particles. Such a water-holding stratum is known as an *aquifer*. An aquifer may extend many miles from the place where it is exposed, and may be buried,

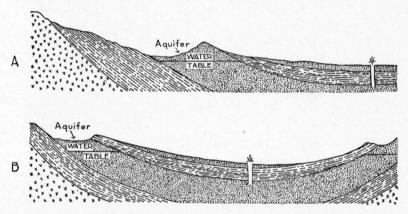

FIG. 22.   The conditions suitable for artesian wells: A, around a dome as in the Black Hills; B, in a structural basin.

with its two confining layers, many feet below the surface. For instance, the Dakota sandstone is exposed in the Black Hills in a wide belt, where the water table is but 25 feet to 30 feet below the surface. This sandstone, overlain by less pervious Cretaceous shales, slopes down from the Black Hills and underlies the Great Plains in every direction. For a hundred or more miles out from the Black Hills wells from one to two thousand feet deep are drilled into the sandstone, and water rises through them to the surface (Fig. 22) under hydrostatic pressure.

The term *artesian* is sometimes applied inaccurately to deep wells drilled into granite or metamorphic rocks in the expectation of securing water which is flowing in crevices and fissures. Under these conditions there is no certainty that water will be

FIG. 23. Stalactites and stalagmites in Luray Caverns. (Courtesy Luray Caverns Corp.)

found; but in regions with real artesian conditions water is assured.

Chemical work of ground water.—The chemical work of ground water is most obvious in regions underlain by limestone rock. Limestone is but slightly pervious, but it is usually broken by numerous joints. Water moving through the joints dissolves some of the lime and soon opens passages which may become the channels of underground streams. As these channels enlarge they may form caverns, often of great extent, such as the Mammoth Cave in Kentucky. Water seeping through the overlying rock comes out on the ceiling of such caverns in drops. If evaporated, each drop leaves a little deposit, mostly of lime or gypsum, thus in time developing on the ceiling icicle-like formations termed *stalactites*. If drops fall to the floor of the cave, rising cones, called *stalagmites*, are built up.

Caverns are mostly near the surface because underground channels cannot be dissolved below the level of the mouth of the stream. Therefore the overlying layer of rock is oftentimes thin and may break, or cave in, making a more or less circular depression on the surface, called a *sink hole*. Sink holes are numerous in many sections of the southern states and especially in central Florida, which is honeycombed with underground streams. Hundreds of lakes in Florida, having neither inlets nor outlets on the surface, are water-filled sink holes. These lakes are clear and rise and fall independently of the rainfall, for their source is the ground water and underground streams.

Ground water is an important factor in the fertility of a region, for besides supplying the necessary moisture for plant growth, it dissolves mineral substances and other plant foods. If a region is underlain by a stratum of rock containing large amounts of soluble minerals, fertility may be destroyed by the chemical action of the ground water. The ground water may contain so much of one mineral, such as iron or sulphur, that where it comes to the surface it forms what is called a *medicinal spring*.

Ground water not only dissolves minerals but also deposits them in the interstices and cracks of rocks at great depths, thereby cementing them.

STREAMS

From the time water condenses as raindrops in the air, it moves under the influence of gravity.   Sheets of water, meeting at the foot of opposed slopes, unite to form a stream which is also fed by water moving through the regolith.   Small streams join one another to form a large stream, or *river*.   As water flows along in a stream it carries with it loose rock material, varying in size and in amount with the volume of the stream and the steepness of the slope, and with the character of the rock material through which it flows.   The sand, gravel, and perhaps boulders borne along by the water become tools which wear away or erode the rocks over which the stream flows. The running water also dissolves some types of rocks, especially limestone.

The erosion cycle.—A stream that has just begun to erode a valley is at the beginning of its life cycle, and its valley is said to be *young*.   Young valleys are narrow in proportion to their depth and often receive special names, such as ravine, glen, canyon, gorge, or arroyo.

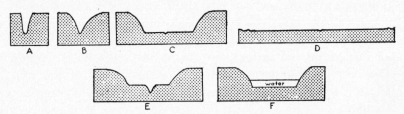

FIG. 24.   Sections to show ages of rivers: A, a young river in an arid climate; B, a young river in a moist climate; C, a mature river; D, an old river; E, a mature river rejuvenated; F, a mature river drowned.

As a main stream cuts its valley deeper, tributaries develop. As a main stream or tributary deepens its valley its headwaters work backward and thus the valley is lengthened as it is deepened.   By the growth of valleys in this way the original land mass becomes dissected and consists of a series of valleys with intervening ridges which form divides between the tributaries.

In time, a river in its lower course cuts down approximately to sea level, or attains the least slope on which it can still flow, which is about 6 inches to the mile.   It is then said to have

reached its *base level*, and to be graded in its lower course. An
obstruction in a river's course, such as a strong layer of rock,
or the barrier holding back a lake, forms a *temporary base level*,
because it will limit the down-cutting of the stream until the
barrier is removed.

When a stream has cut down to the base level, or to a temporary base level, it no longer cuts its valley deeper, and it is

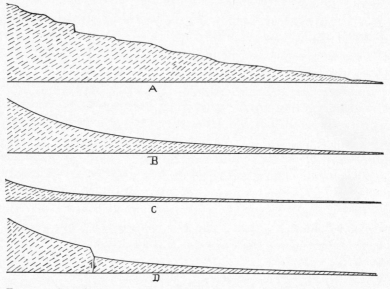

FIG. 25.   Stream profiles: A, a young stream; B, a mature stream; C, an
old stream; D, a mature stream where the profile has been broken by
faulting.

said to have reached *maturity*.   Its valley slowly widens, owing
to the action of many forces, the slopes become more gentle,
and the divides are slowly lowered.   The valley is then said
to be *mature*.

Finally, when a valley is all worn down to a slope as low as
will permit the stream to flow, it is said to be *old*, and the land
surface is termed a *peneplain*.   Any strong rock remnants
which were not entirely removed during the development of
the peneplain are called *monadnocks*, after Mt. Monadnock in
southern New Hampshire.   When old age has been reached
the cycle of erosion has been completed.   However, few rivers
pass through their cycle of development without interruption,

for a number of conditions may affect the rate at which a river may wear down its valley, as will be seen in the following pages.

1. **Young rivers.**—A young river is characterized by its narrow V-shaped valley, by its irregular course, and by an uneven vertical profile (Fig. 25). It wears away weak rocks faster than it does strong ones and waterfalls or rapids with a steeply sloping bed develop where the water flows from a strong onto a weak rock. Where strata of strong rock are underlain by weak rocks the weak rocks are worn away faster, the strong layer is undermined, and its edge is slowly worn back, as is illustrated by Niagara Falls (Fig. 97).

Transportation and deposition.—The principal work of a stream in carving out a valley is to carry away the material which it has eroded or which has been fed into it from the valley sides (page 15). The amount and the coarseness of the material transported will depend on the volume of the stream and on its rate of flow. In general clear streams carry but little detritus, except that which is in solution or rolled along the bottom. Muddy streams are heavily loaded with material suspended in the water. The following indicates the size of particles carried by streams when flowing at different rates:

At $\frac{1}{6}$ of a mile an hour a stream will transport clay.
At $\frac{1}{3}$ of a mile an hour a stream will transport fine sand.
At 1 mile an hour a stream will transport gravel the size of a pea.
At 2 miles an hour a stream will transport gravel the size of one's thumb.
At 3 miles an hour a stream will transport stones the size of a hen's egg.

Coarse materials while in transit are battered against each other and the stream bed, and are gradually reduced in size. Minerals with good cleavage can stand but little of this battering, and so feldspars, mica, and some less common minerals are soon reduced to fine particles. These particles may be so dissolved by water that only a residue of clay may be left. For this reason the proportion of clay in a long river steadily increases downstream. Quartz sand is very resistant and is carried far.

The load of detritus carried to the ocean by the Mississippi

River is close to 400 million tons a year, which is about 1/5,000 of its water discharge. That carried by the Potomac River is 5.5 million tons, about 1/3,575 of its discharge. That of the Rio Grande is 3.4 million tons, about 1/290 of its discharge. Even such a stream as the Rio Grande is not carrying a capacity load. It is a muddy stream, as is the Mississippi River, while the lightly loaded Potomac River is clear. To the 400 million tons carried in suspension by the Mississippi River must be added 136 million tons carried in solution. This represents a lowering of the whole drainage basin of the Mississippi by a foot in about 6,000 years.

The total amount of detritus carried in solution is usually expressed in parts per million parts of water, and varies in different streams—the Hudson having 108 parts per million, the San Joaquin 183, the Mississippi 203. In the case of the Mississippi River this equals 79 tons of material from each square mile of the drainage basin annually. The material in solution consists largely of either calcium or sodium carbonates; calcium, magnesium, or sodium sulphates; sodium chloride; iron oxides or silica. In regions of heavy rainfall carbonates predominate, while in arid regions the sulphates are greatest in quantity.

Alluvial fans.—On steep slopes young streams often take up such excessive loads that when the slope is lessened and their speed is reduced they deposit the coarser material in the form of a semicircular *alluvial fan*. Alluvial fans are frequently found where young tributary streams flow into a more gently flowing main stream. As time goes on the top of a fan may be built up and its front built forward so that the slope of the fan becomes less steep. Along the foot of mountain slopes, several alluvial fans may expand laterally until they meet and form a *compound alluvial fan*. Such compound fans occur in great numbers in the Great Valley of California and in many valleys in the Basin and Range Province.

2. **Mature rivers.**—Mature rivers flow at a slower rate than do young streams, the slopes of the valley walls are more gentle, and the soils of the valleys are usually deeper and of finer texture. When rivers have become graded to the base level, or to a temporary base level, their rate of flow in their lower

courses is so reduced that they become overloaded. They
then deposit portions of the detritus on the sides of the valley
in the form of flood plains.

Flood plains.—The detritus carried by mature rivers is finer
in texture and the proportion of material in solution is greater
than in young rivers.
There is also a great
variation in the vol-
ume of water, and the
effects of high water
are marked because
mature rivers are close
to base level and the
rate of flow cannot be
greatly increased. In
times of excess flow a
mature river overflows
its channel and its
water spreads across
the *flood* or *alluvial*
plain and adds a new
layer to the surface of
the plain. Deposits are first dropped immediately adjacent to
the channel, and thus a ridge is built along either side of the
channel. This is a natural *levee*, from which the flood plain
slopes away from the stream (Fig. 72). The deposits next to
the stream may, in periods of lower water, be partly carried
away and terraces may be left on the sides of the channel.

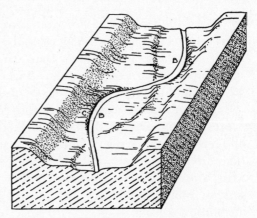

FIG. 26. A mature river valley with a stream
beginning to meander. It is cutting at C and
filling at B. Terraces are seen to the left
and right of B.

A stream, flowing through a flood plain, is deflected first to
one side and then to the other, and forms curves known as
meanders. Each meander tends to become larger until in the
course of time two meanders may nearly meet. The neck of
land separating them may become so narrow that in time of
flood it may be cut through. The course of the river is thus
locally straightened and the abandoned curve becomes an
oxbow lake. In a meandering stream the greatest current is on
the outside of the curve, so that the outer bank is eaten away
and carried downstream, while at the same time deposits are
left on the inside of the curve. Thus a *terrace* may be built at

a slightly lower level than the bank which is being eaten away on the opposite side of the stream.

3. **Old rivers.**—Old rivers are very meandering and sluggish, and have reduced their entire drainage basins approximately to a level surface or peneplain. The surface of a peneplain has no relation to the position or relative strength of the rocks beneath it; it is covered with a deep soil, composed partly of alluvial sediments and partly of the decayed underlying rock. A peneplain can develop only when the country on which it is formed has stood at a given level for a long time, possibly ten to fifty million years, depending on the amount of rainfall and the strength of the rocks. Generally before a peneplain is completely developed, the land will rise or sink; hence there are few complete peneplains, but many partially complete ones.

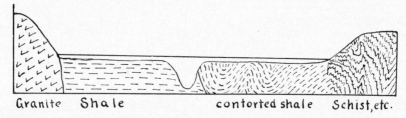

Granite   Shale   contorted shale   Schist, etc.

FIG. 27. Cross section of the St. Lawrence Valley below Quebec to show, first, a mature valley between the granites on the north and the schists on the south; second, a deep inner valley due to rejuvenation; and third, both valleys now drowned.

Rejuvenation and drowning.—If, during the cycle of river development, the land is raised, the strength of the stream is immediately increased, and it becomes rejuvenated and begins to cut a young valley again. If rejuvenation takes place when a mature river has established a meandering course, the result is a narrow V-shaped valley with a winding course set into a broader upland.[1]

If a region is lowered in reference to the sea level, the lower courses of river valleys may be flooded by ocean waters. Such valleys are said to be *drowned*. The lower St. Lawrence River

---

[1] The term *rejuvenated* is sometimes incorrectly applied to a region in which the normal cycle of erosion has been interrupted by a glacial period or by volcanic flows. The rock materials left on the surface by ice or by volcanoes may completely obliterate the earlier drainage lines, so that a new cycle has to be begun.

is a valley which in the Miocene was mature. Then in the Pliocene it was elevated and a young valley carved in it. Finally under the ice the valley was depressed and is now drowned (Fig. 27). The lower Hudson, Delaware Bay, Chesapeake Bay, San Francisco Bay, and many other bays in America are drowned river valleys. Drowned young valleys are known as *fiords*, drowned mature valleys are often called *estuaries*.

Deltas.—When a stream flows into standing water, either a lake or the ocean, its carrying capacity is checked and it must deposit its load. If there are no strong tides or currents to remove these deposits, they accumulate to form a *delta*. The coarser material of a delta is dropped close to shore, the finer

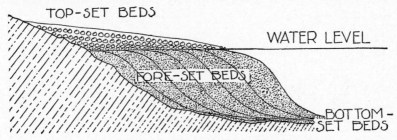

FIG. 28. The formation of a delta.

farther out. The first deposits will conform to the slope of the bottom. As the coarser material piles up, its front slope will vary in steepness with the character of the detritus carried. New layers are constantly being laid down on this sloping front, making what are known as the *fore-set beds*. The finer materials (generally of clay) are deposited along the bottom in front of the delta. These are the *bottom-set beds*, which will later be buried by the advancing fore-set beds. As the delta grows forward, the incoming stream has to flow over a nearly horizontal surface, and, its speed being lessened, the coarsest material is dropped on the upper surface of the delta, making the *top-set beds*. These are always nearly horizontal, and of coarse material, and serve to aggrade, or build up the bed of the stream so that it can carry its material across the top of the delta.

The beginning of a delta is opposite the mouth of a stream, but as it grows in height its top-set beds extend upstream and may block the main channel. The stream will then be diverted to a new course across its delta and discharge its load at a new point. Large deltas may have more than one channel across the delta top, in which case the various branches of the main stream are called *distributaries*.

LAKES

Lakes are bodies of standing water held back by a barrier. They usually indicate an undeveloped drainage system, though, as we have seen, in mature and old drainage systems abandoned meander curves may become lakes.

Lakes may be caused in many ways—by deposits of tributary streams, by the formation of barrier beaches, by volcanic action, by the action of the wind, by obstruction of sink-hole openings, by landslides, by faulting, and by the action of ice.

Lake Pepin on the upper Mississippi River is due to a barrier of deposits built across the Mississippi by the Chippewa River. Lake Tulare in the upper San Joaquin Valley is similarly caused by alluvial fans built out from opposite sides of the main valley. Barrier-beach lakes occur when standing water builds a beach across a lagoon (page 57). Chilmark Pond on the Island of Marthas Vineyard in Massachusetts is a small lagoon lake. Lava flows may block drainage lines and cause lakes to form. Such is the origin of Harney Lake in Oregon and of the extinct Payette Lake in Idaho. Lakes may occur in the craters of extinct volcanoes, as is illustrated in the case of several small volcanic cones in Arizona, and of Crater Lake, Oregon, which lies in the large basin of an old volcanic crater. Lakes in depressions formed by wind erosion are numerous in many dry regions (page 15), and may occur where, in a semiarid grass-covered region, a break occurs in the grass cover. Such wind blow-outs were once thought to be the result of buffaloes wallowing on a moist spot of land. Sink holes, when blocked either naturally or artificially, become lakes, as has already been noted (page 40). Landslide and fault lakes are rare. In 1925 a landslide in the Gros Ventre Mountains of Wyoming formed a lake. The Warner Lakes in Oregon and Reelfoot Lake in Tennessee were caused by earth movements along fault lines.

The larger number of lakes in the United States were formed as the result of ice action. Hence lakes are most numerous in the northern part of the country recently covered by the continental glacier (page 64). Ice-formed lakes are of many types. The greater number occur in depressions in glacial deposits. In Minnesota, Wisconsin, and Maine they are to be numbered by the hundreds, some of them containing several hundred square miles. To the great number now existing may be added the thousands which have been drained since the ice receded, and whose former presence is recorded by delta and alluvial deposits and abandoned beaches. In some instances the Ice Sheet gouged out the bed rock so that lakes are now found in the depressions. Alpine or mountain glaciers form depressions or cirques at the heads of the basins in which they accumulate, and when the ice melts away cirques become occupied by lakes known as *cirque lakes*. Numerous cirque lakes occur in the Rocky Mountains, especially in Glacier National Park.

Lakes without outlets are frequently found in dry regions, owing to the fact that the rainfall is not sufficient to maintain flowing streams. Great Salt Lake, for instance, once flowed out to the Snake River, but its level is now far below that of the barrier.

The extinction of lakes.—Lakes are but short-lived surface features, for they may be destroyed in one of several ways. They may be drained as the barrier that holds them is worn down by the overflowing water; they may be filled by wind-blown or water-borne deposits; they may be obliterated by being changed into swamps through the accumulation of rock detritus and plant remains; or their water may be evaporated.

Great Salt Lake is the remnant of a former much larger fresh-water lake (page 276) whose waters have been evaporated; it contains at least 18 per cent of salt in solution.

As the vegetation in swamps dies and falls into the water it is partly decomposed by bacterial action, and the remainder forms a brown or black mass known as *peat*. Peat deposits are sometimes dried and used for fuel. If buried by later rock detritus, the peat is gradually compressed and changed into *coal*.

The cycle in arid regions.—Thus far we have discussed the cycle of changes from youth to old age as it occurs in regions of moderate to heavy rainfall. In regions of light rainfall such as Nevada, Utah, western Texas, and New Mexico, many rivers do not flow to the sea, but evaporate or sink into the ground. The rainfall usually comes in torrential showers, and the heavy run-off rushes down the slopes gathering a heavy load of detritus, especially where there is little or no vegetation cover. The coarser sediments are left at the foot of steep slopes in broad alluvial fans, and valleys are thus gradually filled perhaps to a depth of several hundred feet. Such filled valleys are called *bolsons*. In some cases streams carrying coarse detritus will continue for some distance along a valley, and, eventually disappearing, will leave behind deposits of sand. Such a deposit is called a *wash*.

In many valleys filled with fine-grained water-borne or wind-borne detritus, the hollows may become shallow lakes after a heavy rainfall. Such lakes, known as *playa* lakes, occur by the hundreds in the drier portions of the United States. As the water evaporates or sinks into the ground the lake disappears, perhaps leaving a crust of salts precipitated on the surface.

In arid and semiarid regions, where the mechanical work of the atmosphere is much greater than the chemical weathering, rounded profiles are much less common than in humid regions. The edges of exposed rock layers are characterized by angles. Steep cliffs are common, as are isolated and perhaps fantastically shaped erosion columns.

BIBLIOGRAPHY

Clarke, F. W., *Data of Geochemistry*, Bulletin of U. S. Geological Survey, No. 770, 1924.

Meinzer, O. E., *Occurrence of Ground Water in the United States*, U. S. Geological Survey, Water Supply Paper, No. 489, 1923.

CHAPTER V

THE OCEANS: THE WORK OF STANDING WATER

The oceans.—The waters of the several oceans cover approximately 71 per cent of the surface of the world, to an average depth of about 13,000 feet. The floors of the several oceans generally slope gradually to a depth of about 600 feet at the edge of the *Continental Shelf* and then rapidly increase their slope to great depths (page 99). The portions of the oceans over continental shelves are known as *epicontinental seas* (Fig. 29).

The oceans, which are the largest source of the moisture found in the air, are constantly being replenished by rains and by the water borne to them by rivers. Rain water is pure water, but as it moves through the soil as ground water or passes over the rocks of the earth in streams, it dissolves some of the minerals from the rocks. Streams which reach the ocean have, during all the geologic ages, been adding minerals to the ocean waters, so that now every hundred pounds of sea water contains about $3\frac{1}{2}$ pounds of dissolved solids. The average composition of the mineral content of the ocean water is as follows:

Sodium chloride (salt)	77.8%
Magnesium chloride	10.9
Magnesium sulphate	4.7
Calcium sulphate	3.6
Potassium sulphate	2.5
Calcium carbonate	.3
All other solids	.2

These proportions do not represent the relative amount of different chemicals removed from the land, but the amount which the plants and animals have not built into their structures. Mollusks, corals, bryozoa, and other animals, as well as such plants as algae, make their shells or skeletons largely from the calcium carbonate in the sea water. Silica is withdrawn by sponges, radiolaria, and diatoms, and built into their skeletons.

The work of standing water.—All bodies of water are level, except as their surface may be roughened by the wind. Shore lines of any body of standing water, whether of the ocean or of lakes, are therefore changed in horizontal profile by the work of the moving water, whereas the erosional processes on land result in profiles with inclined lines. The movements of standing water may be in the form of waves, tides, or currents.

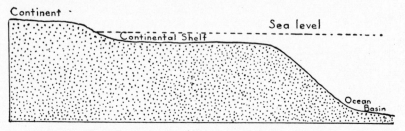

FIG. 29.   The Continental Shelf.

Currents and tides.—Owing to differences in the temperatures of ocean water in low and in high latitudes, to differences in density, and particularly to the effect of constant winds, the water of each of the several oceans of the world is always in motion in a great eddy which moves clockwise in the Northern Hemisphere and counterclockwise in the Southern Hemisphere. The direction of the movement is due in part to the influence of the rotation of the earth, and in part to the presence of continental barriers.

The great ocean currents have no erosive effect. They do not change the shape of the shore line, but they do help distribute over the ocean floor the fine detritus brought from the land by streams, by the wind, and by waves. Ocean currents carry food to plants and animals living on the ocean bottom, and they modify the winds blowing over them both in moisture content and in temperature. Thus, indirectly, they affect the climate of lands lying to the leeward.

Smaller currents near the shore are due to the flow of water with the incoming and outgoing tide, or to waves which strike the shore obliquely (page 56). *Tides,* which are semidiurnal movements in the oceans and in some lakes, do not accomplish any erosive work on the shore line, but they do aid in the distribution of detritus over the ocean floor.   Where the ingoing or outgoing tidal waters of a large bay are confined to narrow channels, the flow of water is so rapid that the channel bottom may be deepened by the *tidal scour*, as it is termed.   It is to make tidal motion more effective in preventing the deposition

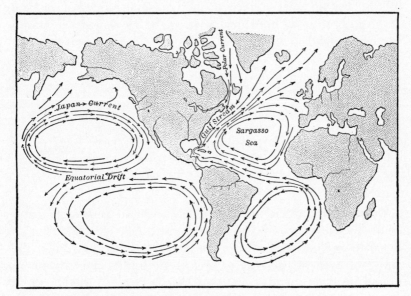

FIG. 30.   An outline of the currents in the oceans.

of river-borne detritus near the shore that jetties are often built at the mouths of streams.

Waves.—Waves due to the wind are the great agency by which the shore lines of the ocean, of lakes, and even of broad rivers are changed in form.   Wind by its friction starts the surface particles of water in motion, and this motion is gradually transmitted downward until the water is stirred to a great depth.   Wave motion rarely extends below 200 or 300 feet, but in exceptional cases it may stir the detritus on the ocean bottom approximately to 600 feet—that is, to the edges of the Continental Shelf (page 99).

The motion imparted by the wind to each particle is an orbital one.   In deep water each particle moves in a circle, except when the wind is blowing, each adjacent particle toward the right moving successively in a circle of the same size, until the particle B is a full cycle behind particle A (Fig. 31). The amount that each circle is behind is expressed by the line A–B. The top of the wave moves to the right as each particle in turn reaches the top of its orbit. The height of a wave is the distance from the top to the bottom of an orbit. The length of a wave is the distance from one crest to the next crest.

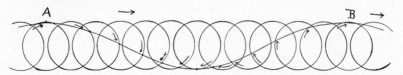

FIG. 31. Diagram to illustrate the movement of water particles, in circles, to form waves. The wave is indicated by the line A–B.

If there is a wind, the orbits are distorted in the direction of the wind movement. As a wave moves into shallower water, the orbits toward the bottom come in contact with the bottom and those particles are held back, resulting in the front of the wave gradually steepening until the top "breaks." At this point the motion ceases to be wholly cyclic and the water moves toward the shore as a *wave of translation.*

Ocean-floor deposits.—A wave of translation moves up the strand until its energy is exhausted; it then flows back down

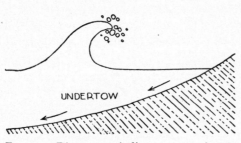

UNDERTOW

FIG. 32. Diagram to indicate a wave breaking, and its relation to undertow.

the slope and part of its water flows under the next incoming wave, thereby creating an outgoing movement along the bottom, the *undertow.* The strength of the undertow is proportionate to the height of the incoming waves and the steepness of the slope. The undertow gradually drops its load, the coarser sands and gravels near shore, and the finer muds and clays in deeper water. The final deposition of these shore materials depends on the strength of the undertow. Storm waves have a stronger undertow and will carry coarse detritus farther from the shore than will less strong waves. Thus a vertical section at any point may show an alternation of coarse and of finer material. The result of wave transportation and deposition is a uniform slope out to the depth of 600 feet, or to the edge of the Continental Shelf (page 99).

Beyond the edge of the Continental Shelf the ocean bottom is covered by fine *oozes*, composed largely of the shells and skeletons of plants and animals which lived near the ocean surface. These may be mixed with volcanic or meteoric dust, or with dust blown from a distant continent. In the deepest portions of the ocean the oozes contain no organically derived material. The fact that no deep-sea deposits have been found in the rocks exposed on the continents indicates that the deeper portions of the ocean are practically permanent in their position. On the other hand, rocks on the continents are like the rocks now being deposited in the shallower portions of the ocean.

The work of waves.—While the work of waves is largely accomplished by means of the tools (pebbles and sand) with which they attack the strong rocks, the force of the water itself is significant, especially when it is driven into fissures and cracks. Water weighs approximately 62 pounds per cubic foot. When set in rhythmic motion in waves, the water acts as a battering ram, alternately exerting a great pressure and releasing the pressure on the coast rocks several times a minute. It has been found that fair-weather waves on the coast of Scotland exert a pressure of 611 pounds per square foot, while in time of storm the force of the

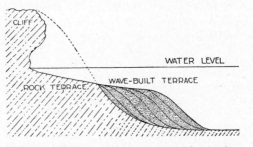

FIG. 33. Diagram to show the undercutting of cliffs and the building of both a rock terrace and a wave-built terrace.

water produces a pressure of 2,086 pounds per square foot.

Irregular shore lines.—The erosive work of waves is best seen on irregular coast lines with alternating strong rock headlands and bays where weaker rocks occur. On such a shore line wave work is most effective on headlands. By means of the

stones and sand set in motion by the waves a cliff is first undercut, forming a cave (see Fig. 33). When the cave has been
cut back far enough so that the overlying rock falls of its
own weight, a new face is formed on the cliff, and the fallen
material receives the force of the waves. Until that loosened
material is removed the cliff will not be cut into again by the
waves. In this stage of development a shore may be said to be
young.

As a cliff retreats under the attack of the waves there is
developed a rock terrace which is extended seaward in a wave-
built terrace formed of detritus carried seaward by the undertow. As a terrace gets wider, waves will break farther from
the shore, their cutting power is decreased, and the cliffs will
be worn back only by weathering and may ultimately cease to
exist.

During the time the cliffs are being worn back by the waves,
part of the detritus is borne by the waves into the re-entrants
and deposited as beaches, with the coarser material near the
headlands and the finer material near the center of the beach.
The movement of material along the shore is partly due to the
fact that waves strike the shore obliquely and set up currents
parallel with the shore.

When the detritus is carried out into deep water and deposited in the lee of a cliff, a *spit* is formed. If the spit extends
out far enough into deep water, secondary currents may deflect
it and it will form a *hook*. When spits built between two
islands or from an island to the mainland meet, they form a
tombolo; when built between two headlands, they form a *bar*
when they meet.

Regular shore lines.—When a continental shelf becomes
exposed as a coastal plain, the new shore line is practically
straight, or regular. The same condition is found when glacial
outwash plains (page 133) meet the ocean. In both cases the
rocks attacked by the waves are unconsolidated and weak, and
the offshore slope is likely to be gentle. As a result, waves, in
time of storm, build a shoal where they break offshore. This
shoal is after a time raised above the height of average waves
and becomes a *barrier beach*, behind which is a lagoon. Barrier
beaches with lagoons—called sounds on the southern Atlantic

coast—are characteristic of the coast line of the Atlantic Coastal Plain, and of southern Long Island, to mention the best-known regions.   Such barrier beaches, owing to the influence of currents near the shore, are often separated by capes, or cusps, built of beach materials.   Cape Fear and Cape Hatteras are instances of capes formed in this way, and are bordered offshore by shoals which may ulti-mately be built above the level of the water.

A shore with barrier beaches and lagoons is a *young regular shore*. Gradually a barrier beach is carried back toward the land by the work of the waves, and the interior lagoon, per-haps changed into a swamp, is slowly reduced in size. When the la-goons have all been removed and the waves are attacking the rocks underlying the plain, the shore line is *mature*.

Elevated shore lines. —The position of the continents in reference to sea level is slowly but constantly changing. If a coast is raised, the features due to wave and current work at the

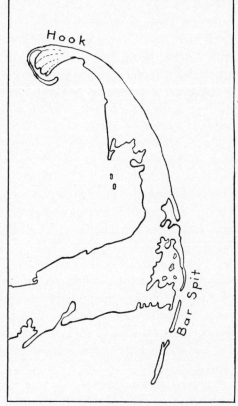

FIG. 34.   The outer part of Cape Cod, show-ing a hook, a bar, and a spit.

former level may be found high above the present sea level.   On the California coast a series of abandoned shore lines is found at various elevations up to 1,500 feet.   Elevated shore lines are also found about lakes which have been drained, as have many glacial lakes in the northern United States (page 175), or from which water has been evaporated, as happened in the case of Lake Bonneville, the ancestor of Great Salt Lake (page 276).

In some cases elevated shore lines, both ocean shore lines and lake shore lines, are not horizontal but slightly inclined— an obvious evidence that the land has been differentially raised since the beaches were formed.

CHAPTER VI

GLACIERS AND GLACIATION

Classes of glaciers.—Glaciers are masses of ice which form on areas where for a long period of time the annual snowfall is not all melted. The snow is slowly compressed to ice, and when the mass becomes sufficiently great it "flows" to lower levels. There are two types of glaciers: those formed over broad areas in high latitudes, termed *continental glaciers* or *ice sheets;* and those of limited area, formed in high altitudes, as on mountain tops, and termed *alpine glaciers*. The first type is illustrated by the Greenland Ice Sheet, and the second by the glaciers in Glacier National Park. The present-day glaciers are but remnants of continental glaciers which existed in recent times, geologically speaking.

The formation of alpine glaciers: névé.—Above the *snow line*, where snow lies the year around, the light flaky snow becomes granular as a result of alternate thawing and freezing. Such granular snow is termed *névé*. Gradually the lower layers of névé are compressed into ice by the weight of the overlying snow. This ice is more or less layered because successive falls of snow are separated by layers of windblown dust.

When the ice has accumulated to a depth of some hundreds of feet, it begins to "flow," like a thick liquid, though remaining actually a solid. The glacier, thus formed, moves from the névé field down the most accessible slopes, being more and more exposed to melting temperatures, and finally ends where the ice is melted as fast as it moves forward. If the ice is melted back faster than it moves forward the glacier is said to retreat, or, preferably, recede. When the opposite condition exists, the glacier advances.

The rate of movement of alpine glaciers varies with the mass of the glacier as well as with the steepness of the slopes and the season of the year. The rather small glaciers of the Alps move

from one to three feet a day; the larger ones in Alaska at times
from 60 to 70 feet a day.   The movement is differential, being
faster in the middle than on the sides or bottom.   While that
part of the ice which is under pressure acts as if plastic, the
surface ice is brittle and breaks under strain, so that as a glacier
moves over a steeper slope, cracks or *crevasses* are formed.
These close again as the glacier comes to lesser slopes.   Water
flowing into crevasses and again freezing and expanding is one
of the causes of glacial motion.   Detritus on the surface of the
ice, by falling into crevasses, becomes imbedded in the body
of the glacier.

The work of a valley glacier: *Cirques.*—Around the edge of a
névé field there is usually a depression between the ice which
is moving to make the glacier, and the snow or rock above the
névé field.   This is the *bergschrund.*   Here the exposed rock,
especially during the summer months, alternately freezes and
thaws, and becomes mechanically broken up.   The rock fragments are drawn in under the névé field, and gradually there is
formed a deep-walled basin, or *cirque*, deeper at the center than
at the margin where the glacier leaves the basin.

Cirques are seen only after the ice has disappeared from the
basin.   In rugged regions formerly covered by snow and ice
fields, cirques form very striking landscape features, with their
steep walls surrounding a curved basin, in which may lie a
picturesque lake.

Glacial erosion and glacial deposits.—As a glacier moves
through a valley it is constantly receiving rock materials which
slide or roll onto its surface from the valley sides.   It also
abrades the bed rock by means of the rock fragments which are
frozen into the bottom of the ice.   In this process scratches or
striae may be made on resistant rocks.   Such striae often may
be seen long after the glacier has disappeared.   They are evidences of the former presence of the ice and indicate the general
direction of ice motion.

By glacial erosion a V-shaped valley becomes U-shaped in
cross section.   If a valley is completely filled with ice, tributary
streams will flow from the valley sides out onto the surface of
the ice.   Such tributary streams, not being able to cut down
their beds rapidly, will form waterfalls when the ice in the main

Fig. 35. Chickamin Glacier, Alaska. The névé field is to the right, the glacier flowing to the left, with a tributary glacier joining it, so that the lateral moraines unite to make a medial moraine. (After R. M. Wilson, U. S. G. S.)

valley has melted away. These valleys are described as *hang-ing valleys*, of which that of Bridal Veil Fall in the Yosemite Valley is an excellent illustration.

The detritus transported by an alpine glacier may ultimately be deposited on the sides of the valley as a *lateral moraine;* on the bottom of the valley as *ground moraine;* or at the end of the ice as a *terminal moraine.* In some cases two lateral moraines of adjacent valleys may join to become a *medial moraine.*

The fragments of rocks of many kinds carried by a glacier and deposited in moraines are of all sizes from boulders tens of feet in diameter to rock powder so fine that it will remain suspended in quiet water for several days. This heterogeneous accumulation of ice-borne material is known as *till* and when deposited in a moraine is unsorted. Moraines have a rough and irregular surface, in the hollows of which water may accumulate, and on which may be many boulders, if the rocks have not been entirely broken up during their journey.

Continental glaciers or ice sheets.—When snow fields have formed over great areas they make continental glaciers, or ice sheets, which move slowly outward from the centers of accumulation, and may be so thick as to override highlands.

In geologically recent time a continental glacier spread from centers east and west of Hudson Bay, over Canada, New England, and the states north of the Ohio and Missouri rivers.

The Labrador Ice Sheet extended from northern Labrador southerly over New England and into the sea east of Long Island. The northern portion of Long Island is occupied by the terminal moraine left by this ice sheet. This moraine crosses to the mainland at Perth Amboy, N. J., and may be followed across New Jersey, Pennsylvania, and Ohio, almost to the Ohio River. Newfoundland and Nova Scotia seem to have been covered by independent and lesser ice sheets.

The Keewatin Ice Sheet originating west of Hudson Bay covered the central portion of the continent, its southern boundary being approximately marked by the Missouri River and thence west in Montana almost to the Rocky Mountains.

The Cordilleran Ice Sheet covered the Cordilleran Highlands of Canada and extended into Washington and Idaho. During the Ice Age certain ranges in the Rocky Mountains and the

Cascade Mountains had localized snow fields from which alpine glaciers developed. Northwestern Alaska and the Arctic Islands seem to have been free of ice during the Ice Age.

The Ice Age began early in the Pleistocene, about a million years ago, and the ice-covered area expanded for perhaps a hundred thousand years. During the Pleistocene, the ice sheet alternately retreated (or may have entirely disappeared) and advanced four times. The periods of retreat are known as

FIG. 36. Boulder Glacier and cirque wall at the head of Bowman's Valley, Glacier National Park. (After Campbell, U. S. G. S.)

interglacial periods, when the climate was as warm as that of the present day, or perhaps warmer. The last retreat began about 25,000 years ago and probably is not yet complete. The surface features produced during the earlier advances and re-treats were largely obliterated during the last advance. In Illinois, in Iowa, and in a portion of Indiana, deposits of an early advance form the surface, because the last advance did not cover the area. Elsewhere the glacial effects seen are mostly due to the latest, or Wisconsin, Ice Sheet. There were earlier continental glaciers in the Permian and Proterozoic periods.

Effects of the Continental Glacier.—Inasmuch as the Continental Glacier covered all the highlands in the area it occupied, its erosive effects were produced under the ice. The

method of erosion was similar to that of alpine glaciers, but on a
larger scale. Through the action of the ice and the rock fragments contained in it, preglacial soil and regolith were removed,
and in many areas the underlying bed rock was deeply scoured
and fluted. The result was a rounding of upland areas, which
gave the glacially eroded country a rolling surface. Where the
bed rock was eroded, the result in some cases was a series of
nearly parallel rounded surfaces which have been compared
to the backs of a flock of sheep, and called *roches moutonnées*.

Ice-laid deposits.—The deposits made by the ice without any
water action are composed of till and were left in the form of
moraines or *drumlins*. At the extreme front of the ice sheet
terminal moraines were formed in a general east-west direction
and across the main lines of drainage. Back of the terminal
moraine are many secondary moraines, marking places where
the ice front halted for a time during its retreat, or places to
which the ice temporarily readvanced. Much of the surface
between the terminal moraines is covered by ground moraine.
Drumlins are lenticular hills of till with the longer axes approximately parallel to the direction of ice movement. They were
probably formed when the advancing ice overrode the morainal
material at its front. Groups of drumlins occur in Massachusetts, New York, and Wisconsin.

The deposition of morainal material in the valleys obstructed
the drainage lines. Many streams were diverted to new
courses, and lakes by the thousands were formed in depressions
after the retreat of the ice. Many of these lakes have been
drained, but the beach and bottom deposits formed in them
are a witness to their former existence. Lakes are most
numerous in the portion of the glaciated area from which the
ice disappeared latest. In front of the edge of the ice and
between it and the divides farther south, temporary lakes were
formed and later drained as the ice edge retreated. The present
Great Lakes have developed from such a series of earlier lakes.

Water-laid deposits.—Rainfall, together with the melting
ice, caused streams which quickly modified the surface in front
of the ice edge. Lakes were formed back of the moraines which
became partly filled with gravels, sands, and clays. Streams
cut through the moraines, drained the lakes, and being heavily

overloaded with detritus, deposited gravels in front of the moraines. By the coalescing of the deposits from several streams, an *outwash plain* many miles in length and breadth was formed in many places. Southern Long Island is such an outwash plain.

Streams under the ice and near its front often become overloaded and build up the beds of their channels. When the

FIG. 37. The hanging Valley of Yosemite Creek, and Yosemite Falls, from Glacier Point. (After Matthes, U. S. G. S.)

bordering ice walls are removed, the gravels slump down, and long irregular ridges of sand and gravel, known as *eskers*, are left.

The ice lasted longest in the lowlands, where it became stagnant and melted away with little forward motion. Depressions between the ice and the bordering valley sides became lakes into which deposits were washed from the ice on one side and the land on the other. When the ice disappeared such deposits were left on the hillsides as *hanging shores*. In some cases the ice itself was buried by such deposits of gravels, and when the ice disappeared these gravels slumped in and formed a rounded depression without inlet or outlet, known as a *kettle*

Fig. 38. Front of the ice sheet in Greenland, suggesting how the country must have appeared as the great Pleistocene Ice Sheet was retreating from New England or any other irregular part of the country. (Courtesy of Charles A. Lindbergh. Copyright, *National Geographic Magazine*.)

hole. Kettle holes may also have been formed where a block of ice was surrounded by gravel deposits and on melting caused a depression in the surface.

Existing glaciers.—Today Greenland and Antarctica are covered with ice sheets which are regarded as remnants of the Pleistocene glaciation. Alpine glaciers exist in many parts of the earth, particularly in the Alps, in the Himalayas, in Norway, in New Zealand, and in parts of North America. These are found in the higher parts of the Northern Rocky Mountains as far south as Yellowstone Park, and are numerous in Glacier National Park in Montana and in Jasper National Park in Canada. A few glaciers still remain in Mt. Rainier National Park and farther north in the Hozomeen and Okanogan Mountains. The glaciers of the St. Elias and Fairweather Mountains in southern Alaska are noteworthy.

BIBLIOGRAPHY

Antevs, E., *The Last Glaciation*, American Geographical Society, Research Series, No. 17, 1928.
Coleman, A. P., *Ice Ages, Recent and Ancient*, 1926.
Wright, G. F., *The Ice Age in North America*, 4th edition, 1900.

CHAPTER VII

ROCK STRUCTURES AND THEIR SURFACE EXPRESSION

Rocks have thus far been referred to as if they had not been changed since their formation, except as they have been consolidated or eroded. In most places rocks on or near the surface have been elevated or depressed, folded or broken, or possibly greatly metamorphosed (page 89). Changes in the position and attitudes of stratified rocks indicate that since their formation they have been moved, owing to disturbances in the earth. Such movements are due in general to two causes, the one associated with the contraction of the mass of the earth, and the other with the adjustments involved in maintaining equal pressure at the various points on the earth's surface, in spite of the shifting of great quantities of detritus from the highlands to the lowlands, or from the continents as a whole to the oceans.

All the movements of the rocks of the earth are referred to as *diastrophism*. When these movements affect large parts of a continent they are *epeirogenic* (epeiros = continent); and when they affect lesser areas they are *orogenic* (oros = mountain). Both types of movement are complex, and their effects cannot always be differentiated.

The contraction of the earth.—The temperature at the center of the earth is very high (probably well over 3,000°C.), while that of space is −273°C. As the earth cools, its mass contracts. Such contraction can only be compensated by a wrinkling of the earth's surface. The primary folding of the earth's surface accounts for the ocean basins and continents, and probably for some of the mountains. These wrinkles have a maximum difference in height between the ocean floor and the highest mountain of a little over twelve miles, and are not large relative to the earth's radius of 4,000 miles.

A part of the earth's contraction is to be attributed to compacting of the materials of which it is composed, and also to the readjustments which take place when lava and gases escape from the interior.

Isostacy.—Local uplifts or depressions would tend to disturb the balance of pressures within the earth to an amount that can be readily calculated. The fact that where it has been carefully measured, the deviation either does not appear, or is less than expected, has led, together with other facts, to the *theory of isostacy*. According to this theory, when masses of rock material are moved as a result of erosion and deposition so that pressures are greatly increased in one area and decreased in another, equilibrium is restored by a flowing of the subsurface rocks from the overloaded areas to the underloaded areas. This adjustment seems to take place at about 30 to 40 miles below the surface.

The following phenomena also are best explained by the theory of isostacy. Certain basins, like the trough in which the rocks of the Valley and Ridge Province were deposited, have been filled with stratified rocks to a depth of over 30,000 feet, though at no time was the water in the basin more than a few hundred feet deep. This is shown by the character of the sediments themselves, and by the character of the animals entombed. Apparently the Appalachian trough, as it was loaded, sank repeatedly until finally a readjustment of pressures took place beneath the surface, the motion was reversed, and the rocks were folded.

In contrast, over 30,000 feet of rocks have been removed from the tops of the Rocky Mountains, and yet today they are as high as they ever have been. Apparently the Rocky Mountains have risen repeatedly, as one layer after another was worn from their tops—the present top being a peneplain which must have been formed near sea level.

The sinking of the Appalachian trough was due to the flow of rock away from beneath that region, whereas the Rocky Mountains were uplifted because rock material flowed in beneath this underloaded area from some near-by basin.

Mountain-building.—In the history of any mountain region there is first a long period of sedimentation in a continental basin or on a continental margin; secondly there is a period of more or less acute folding and the beginning of a mountain system. This is followed by a wearing down of the folds to or near sea level. Other periods of elevation and erosion follow, each uplift being somewhat less marked than the preceding one. These changes may extend through several geological periods; but eventually a balance will be attained and the height of the region will become relatively stationary.

Rock-folding takes place in response to horizontal pressures; and layers of rock which covered broad areas are compressed into narrower areas. For instance, the rocks of the Valley and Ridge Province have been reduced in width from 50 miles to 25 miles. Surface rocks when compressed are usually folded into simple folds, while the deeper layers of rock, being compressed by the overlying rocks, and often metamorphosed, form more complex folds, the weaker layers often being crumpled into secondary or tertiary folds. Some of the deeper rock folds are thick in one place and thin in another, suggesting that rocks are plastic under great pressure. Folds are the result of slow movements prolonged over hundreds (or thousands) of years.

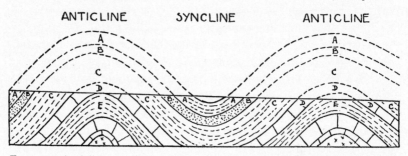

Fig. 39. Anticlines, and a syncline. Letters indicate beds from young to old.

Folds.—A simple upward fold is called an *anticline* and a downward fold is a *syncline*. A complex of folds which together form an arch is an *anticlinorum*, and the converse is a *synclinorum*. If the two sides of an anticline (or syncline) are equally inclined to a plane through the middle, it is said to be *symmetrical*, otherwise *asymmetrical*. Where the strata are bent on one side of the median plane but not on the other, the fold is a *monocline*.

Subsequent erosion may remove some of the weaker material, leaving the stronger rocks standing out in relief as escarpments. If the folds have been worn down to a uniform surface, their former presence may be recognized by noting the arrangement of the different rock layers. A given series of beds will be found in order from young to old, and then back to young, in the case of an anticline, while in the case of a syncline the order is from old to young and back to old (Fig. 39).

Unconformity.—When deposition is interrupted by an uplift, erosion at once removes some of the exposed material. If this

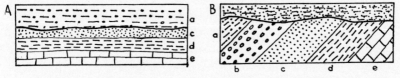

FIG. 40. Unconformities: A, disconformity; B, nonconformity.

area is then again depressed so that deposition is renewed, a break in the sequence of layers, termed an *unconformity*, indicates that a time interval elapsed between the deposition of the lower and overlying layers. If the beds above the unconformity are parallel to those below, this is termed a *disconformity*. If, however, during the interval of elevation, the beds were not only eroded but were also folded or faulted, the overlying later beds will not be parallel to those below. This is a *nonconformity*, and generally represents a longer time of elevation of an area than does a disconformity (Fig. 40).

Faults.—When rocks have been subjected to great pressure, or to differential pressure, they may break. A break in rocks, but with no movement along the line of breakage, is termed a *fissure*. When, however, one block has moved in relation to the adjoining one, the movement is called a *fault*. The surface between the two broken blocks is the *fault plane*. Faults may represent minor movements of inches, or major movements of several thousand feet. The movements may be vertical, horizontal, or inclined. The vertical downward or upward movement is the *throw*; the amount of movement at right angles to the fault plane is the *heave*; while the horizontal movement parallel to the fault plane is the *shove* (Fig. 41). When a fault

is anything but vertical, one block rests more or less on the
other.   In this case the supported wall is called the *hanging
wall*, while the other is the *foot wall*.   These terms are used
mostly in mining.   A fault is said to be *normal* when the hanging wall has slipped down relative to the foot wall, and *reversed*
when the hanging wall has slipped upward.   In some cases the
fault plane has a very low angle and the hanging wall may be
pushed far up over the foot wall, making what is termed a *thrust
fault*.

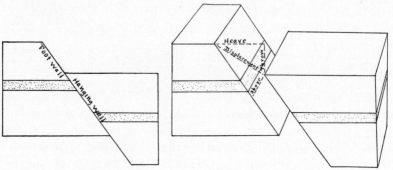

FIG. 41.   A block faulted, to show throw, heave, and shove.

Faulting results from strains set up by the differential movement of adjacent areas of the earth's surface, so that generally
in a fault area there will be sets of faults intersecting each
other at approximately equal angles.   This may be illustrated
by straining a piece of glass.   If the pressure is applied so as to
bend the glass, one or more parallel breaks will result; but
if a twisting pressure is applied, the breaks will develop in
two series intersecting each other at approximately equal
angles.

A series of faults may occur in a fault zone, and the displacement may be by a series of steps, the total movement being the
sum of movements on the adjoining fault planes.   In some
cases minor faults branch off from the major one.

Dip and strike.—*Dip* and *strike* are terms applied both to
fault planes and to the beds of folded rock to express the amount
of inclination and its direction.   *Dip* is the angle made by any
plane (bed of rock or fault plane) and the horizontal plane.
Strike is the line of intersection of a dipping bed or plane with

the horizontal plane. Strike is then a horizontal direction and is expressed in terms of the compass, such as N. 23° W. (that is, a line trending 23 degrees to the west of north). Dip is an angle, say 15 degrees, and its direction is always at right angles to that of the strike. This dip could be either side of the line of strike, but it is usual to indicate that it is downward on either the northerly or southerly side of the strike by using the initial N. or S., as 15° N., meaning that the rocks dip downward on the northerly side of the strike.

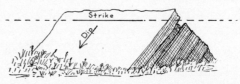

FIG. 42. Diagram to show the relation of strike and dip.

Fault expressions.—If a mass of rocks is raised on one side of a fault plane, weathering will slowly etch out the weaker rocks, and the stronger rocks will be left in relief as an escarpment facing the fault plane. If the rocks forming the escarpment are inclined, the rocks will be worn backward in the direction of the dip as they are worn down, and in the course of time the receding escarpment may be at some distance from the fault plane.

After a long period of erosion it may be possible to detect the presence of a fault only by mapping the distribution of rock outcrops. If a bed suddenly ends, it is the evidence of a fault. If the beds are repeated in their regular order, a fault more or less parallel to the strike of the beds is indicated. If, on the other hand, there is a horizontal off-setting of the beds, the fault is more or less parallel to the dip of the beds (Fig. 43).

The magnitude of movements on fault planes is illustrated on the east side of the Sierra Nevada Mountains, where the fault is hundreds of miles long, and where thousands of feet of vertical movement have taken place. The movement on such a fault does not all take place at one time; intervals between movements may be from 25 to more than 50 years. Movements of from one to fifteen feet have been measured on fault planes after a violent earthquake. The famous San Francisco earthquake of 1906 was the result of a horizontal movement of from ten to twenty-one feet on the San Andreas fault, along which there has been a total movement of some 600 feet, mostly in prehistoric times.

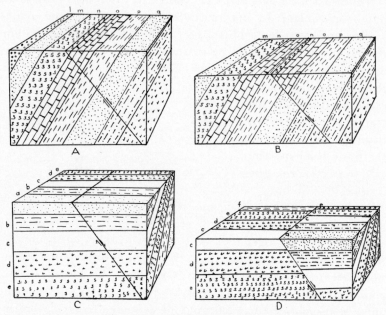

FIG. 43.   Diagram to show the surface effects after the faulted area has been eroded to a level surface: A and B, when the direction of the fault plane is approximately parallel to the strike of the rocks; C and D, when the direction of the fault plane is approximately at right angles to the strike of the rocks.

Stream adjustment.—As we have already seen (page 41), during the development of the cycle of erosion in a river system valleys acquire vertical and horizontal profiles which may be described as young, mature, or old.   Similarly, major land-forms—plains, plateaus, and mountains—may be described as young, mature, or old, according to the aspect they present and the extent to which they have been worn away.

In a plain or a plateau underlain by nearly horizontal rocks, the drainage pattern is *digitate*, tributaries running into larger streams at acute angles, as do the veins of a maple leaf.   If the surface rocks have been folded or faulted and are of varying strength, the streams become adjusted to the structure and the stream pattern is *trellised*.   How a trellised system of drainage will develop may be most simply illustrated by considering the effects of the elevation or rejuvenation of a region worn down to a peneplain.

Suppose that a peneplain has been depressed below sea level, has been covered by 100 or more feet of strata, and is then raised, say 1,000 feet, on its inner edge. Rivers would extend their courses to reach the retreating shore line, and new rivers would form on the coastal plain and follow its slopes to the sea.

Such streams are termed *consequent*. When these streams have cut down through the strata into the underlying rocks of the peneplain, their courses would have no relation to the strength or weakness of these rocks or to the structure. Such a stream is said to be *superimposed*, and its valley might have a youthful cross section where it had cut a *water gap* through a strong rock layer.

With the further passage of time tributaries

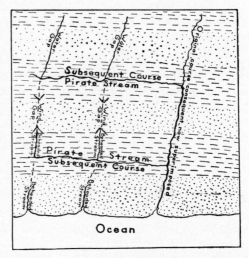

FIG. 44. Stream adjustments in a country of rocks of varying strength. Strong sandstones are dotted, and intervening limestones are hatched.

of the larger streams would gradually extend themselves headwards along the belts of weak rocks at right angles to the main stream. Such a stream is termed a *subsequent* stream. As a subsequent extends its basin, it may encroach upon the drainage basin of another consequent and divert to itself the upper portion of this second consequent. This is *stream piracy*. The path originally followed by the stream that has been *beheaded* may be indicated by a wind gap in the strong rock ridge bordering the weak rock subsequent valley.

The Potomac River is an example of a superimposed stream, its original course being consequent to a surface since removed by erosion. Its tributary, the Shenandoah River inside the water gap at Harpers Ferry, is a subsequent stream, the valley being in limestone between ridges of strong sandstone. It pirated or beheaded the headwaters of several superimposed streams as it elongated southwesterly. An *antecedent stream* is one which has maintained its course through uplifts across its path. Very few streams are today interpreted as antecedent.

Surface expression.—As streams adjust themselves to the different strengths of rocks, varied types of surface result. In a region like the Valley and Ridge Province, or the Appalachian Mountains, the sandstone layers resist erosion, while the shales and limestones yield readily. These rocks were folded in two to three long anticlines with intervening synclines. After being peneplained, the region was raised, and now an outcropping layer of sandstone makes a long ridge, while the limestones make the valleys occupied by subsequent streams. In the Coastal Plain, where the layers of sedimentary rocks are only slightly tilted, strong layers form ridges with a long gentle slope toward the ocean and an abrupt slope inward toward the old land area whence came the deposits of which the Coastal Plain is composed. Such a ridge is termed a *cuesta*. (See Fig. 71.) The Southern Rocky Mountains are bordered by sedimentary rocks tilted at a high angle. Some of the upper (later) layers are stronger than the lower (earlier) layers and make steep ridges paralleling the mountain range. They are termed *hogbacks*.

Distribution of strong and weak rocks.—In general, in the uplifted areas of a continent which have reached or are approaching maturity, the strong rocks make the elevations, the weak rocks the valleys.

The resistance to weathering and other erosive forces shown by various rocks depends on their composition, on the character of the binding cement, and on the amount of open spaces in the rocks. Lavas are generally very resistant, as are also such metamorphic rocks as gneiss and granite, while slates and schists are less resistant. Sedimentary rocks, especially limestones and shales, are generally weak. Sandstones vary in strength. When the cementing material is any type of lime they are weak; when silica is the cement, sandstones become one of the strongest of rocks.

The Canadian Shield is composed of highly metamorphosed rocks and old lavas. New England is largely underlain by ancient metamorphosed rocks, with some localized lavas. It also contains some areas of limestones and poorly cemented sandstones, which mark the lowlands. New England is almost completely bordered by shales along the St. Lawrence and Hudson River valleys.

The whole Coastal Plain is composed of recent and relatively weak sedimentary rocks of Cretaceous and Tertiary age. The Piedmont Belt and Blue Ridge Province, like New England, are mostly composed of old metamorphic rocks with insets of weak sedimentary rocks. From the Blue Ridge to the Great Plains the rocks are older marine sediments, dominantly shales and limestones, with some beds of sandstone. Where these sandstones are brought to the surface by folding, they make ridges or mountains as in the Valley and Ridge Province, or in the Ozark and Ouachita Mountains. The eastern portion of the Great Plains is underlain by weak Cretaceous shales, but the High Plains are mostly composed of poorly cemented sandstones, and owe their height largely to their recent elevation rather than to their strength. The ranges of the Rocky Mountains are formed mostly of granites, while the valleys are on sedimentary rocks which were enfolded with the crystalline rocks when the mountains were raised.

The recently elevated and highly dissected Colorado Plateaus are made partly of sandstones and partly of shales, neither highly resistant. In this province there are also numerous young lava cones and flows. The Basin and Range Province includes ranges of old and resistant rocks and basins filled with recent and largely unconsolidated detritus (page 275). The Columbia and Snake River Plateaus are composed of lavas of relatively recent age and are highly resistant to erosion. The Cascade and Sierra Nevada mountains owe their present elevation partly to being composed of strong rocks—lavas in the former case and metamorphic rocks in the latter—and partly to their youth. The Pacific Border Province is made of weak sedimentary rocks which have been recently elevated. The Puget and California troughs are largely due to faulting or folding.

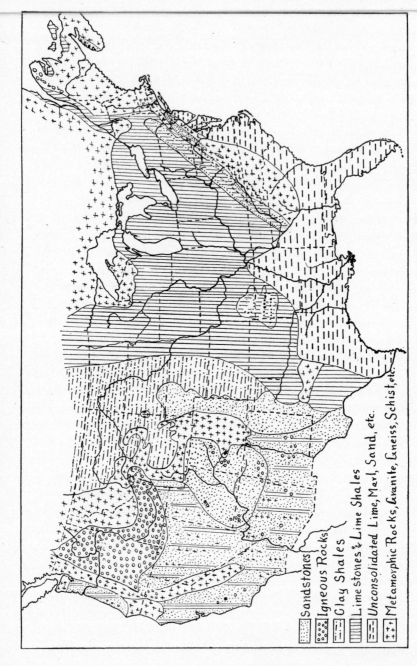

Sandstones

Igneous Rocks

Clay Shales

Limestones & Lime Shales

Unconsolidated Lime, Marl, Sand, etc.

Metamorphic Rocks, Granite, Gneiss, Schist, etc.

Fig. 45. The United States, showing the dominant types of rocks in the different parts.

MAJOR AND MINOR LANDFORMS

The physiographic history of many sections of the United States is extremely involved for several reasons, and in some instances the minor features in a landscape may be so obvious as to obscure somewhat the major features characteristic of the section as a whole.   The present surface may be the result of several periods of elevation, separated by periods in which an erosion cycle has been partially or wholly completed.   Evidences of two or more cycles may be differentiated in some areas, the work of the younger cycle being the most obvious.

Furthermore, no province has uniform characteristics throughout, though it may be readily classified because of its major outlines.   Owing to differences in the resistance of rocks, a cycle of erosion may have been better developed in an area of weak rocks than in one of strong rocks.   Lowlands practically surrounded by strong rock ridges may occur within a mountain area; plains or plateaus may be deeply dissected and have many low and broad valleys inset below their upland surfaces; residual masses of rock may rise sharply above the general level of a region.   Indeed the local landscape in any region may be a mosaic of contrasted minor features which together give it individuality.   Certain minor modifications of major landforms occur so frequently that they deserve special mention.

Mountains.—Mountain areas may, as has been suggested above, include intermontane lowlands due either to differential elevation of the mountain mass or to the subsequent erosion of areas of weak rocks.   Mountains that seem rugged in outline from the valley floors may at higher levels have a wholly different aspect.   For instance, at an elevation of about 10,000 feet the skyline in the Southern Rocky Mountains is approximately level, and records a former peneplain surface.   Above this erosion surface rise many monadnocks to elevations of about 14,000 feet, and below it have been carved many striking young valleys.

In many mountainous areas the present courses of the streams are not adjusted to the belts of strong and weak rocks, indicating that their original courses were determined by conditions which no longer exist. For instance, the Green River rising in the Wyoming Basin flows out through the bordering Uinta Mountains, in which it has cut a youthful and tortuous canyon 3,000 feet deep. As a result the Green River Valley, like many other valleys in mountainous areas, is youthful in some sections and mature in others. Its course is that of a superimposed stream which has not had time in the present cycle to develop mature profiles except on areas of weak rocks.

In many mountain areas valleys youthful in cross section have stretches in which the streams are cutting rapidly and others in which the streams are aggrading their beds. A strong rock barrier or an obstruction of glacial deposits acts as a temporary base level to which the stream is graded. Longitudinally a valley would thus consist of a series of aggraded deposits, known as intervales in the White Mountains, and of rapids, thus causing highly contrasted landscapes within a short distance.

In mountain areas which have been block-faulted along a series of nearly parallel fault planes, the aspect to be seen from an intervening valley depends on whether the escarpment along a fault face, or the more or less gentle back slope of a fault block is observed. This contrast is particularly characteristic in the Basin and Range Province.

In narrowly folded mountains like the ridges of the Valley and Ridge Province, the contrast between the maturely developed longitudinal valleys following the strike of the weaker rocks and the young cross valleys where streams have cut water gaps through the ridges is very striking.

Plains and plateaus.—Plains and plateaus often present many local variations in their surface features—either elevations above the upland surface, or depressions below that surface. Elevations may be monadnocks left during an earlier cycle of erosion, masses of rock protected from rapid erosion by strong rock covers, recent accumulations of lava poured out during the present cycle, or glacial deposits, moraines, or beach accumulations formed during the Ice Age. Lava deposits or strong rock layers may so protect the surface that mesas and buttes are left in relief, especially in a semiarid region. Glacial deposits, though of very slight relief, are by contrast conspicuous elevations above the upland surface of the glaciated portion of the Central Lowland.

A plain or plateau deeply dissected by youthful streams may present a very rugged appearance when viewed from the valley floors. This is well illustrated in the case of the Allegheny Plateau of West Virginia. Another illustration may be found in the ridges which form divides between tributaries of the Colorado River. Because of their height and the steepness of their slopes these ridges present mountainous aspects when viewed from the level of the river, but from the plateau surface seem like hills of small stature.

In regions where the rocks are nearly horizontal and the surface rocks resistant, valleys are cut largely by the headward growth of tributaries which remove the weaker underlying layers and gradually undercut the cover. Flat-floored valleys surrounded by steeper slopes which culminate in vertical escarpments result. The Cumberland Plateau in Tennessee has many such *coves*, as they are termed, which give the upland surface a very irregular margin. In many sections of Arizona and New Mexico canyons formed by headward erosion interrupt the surface of the plateaus; they are often called box canyons because they are surrounded by escarpments.

In plains composed of relatively weak rocks, as for instance in the Atlantic and Gulf Coastal Plain, the larger rivers quickly cut down close to grade and develop broad-floored valleys sharply inset below the upland level. Where the slope of the surface of the plain is greater than that of the graded river, relief increases upstream, at least in the case of the streams that flow across the Coastal Plain from the inland. Tributaries may slowly develop and the plain is thus cut into a series of strips of upland extending from inland to the ocean, and separated from each other by broad-floored valleys.

In low-lying plains composed of limestone rocks, sink holes develop (page 40) and the surface expression consists of hollows, possibly containing water, and of rounded intervening hillocks. The relief is slight and the surface is rolling. Where the limestone area is sufficiently elevated so that underground channels carry the drainage, the roofs of the channels may, in the course of time, fall in, thereby revealing the stream flowing in a narrow canyon. If a portion of the roof remains as a span across the valley it forms a natural bridge.

Where, in a limestone region, the bed rock is revealed on the sides of sinks and open streams, the region is said to have a *karst* surface, so named for a region in Yugoslavia. A region characterized by sink holes, such as portions of Florida, Alabama, and Kentucky, is in the early stages of the development of a karsted surface.

Composite surface characteristics.—In any region where evidence of more than one cycle of erosion is present, the surface is said to have had a composite physiographic history. The most readily interpreted instance is where monadnocks rise above an elevated peneplain surface, as is true in many portions of southern New England. In many instances river valleys may have a mature profile on the higher sides of the valley, and a young cross section nearer the stream, thus indicating a recent rejuvenation of the streams by an uplift of the land surface. If the latest motion of the land was downward, the lower portions of the valley may be drowned. A similar result follows the tilting of the land, as is illustrated on the south side of Lake Ontario, where all the valleys have become embayed, while on the north side of the lake a portion of the lake bottom is exposed as a plain.

The composite origin of present surface features is well illustrated in the valley of the Lower Connecticut River, which previous to the Ice Age had cut deeply into the elevated peneplain. During the recession of the ice sheet, lakes were formed in the course of the stream, and were partially filled with lake deposits. Today the lake beds and associated beaches are revealed in the numerous terraces that rise in a series of steps, in some cases numbering more than twenty, above the present valley floor. In places, the present Connecticut River became superimposed on the underlying bed rock as it cut through the overlying lake deposits, and rapids or falls developed. The most recent change has been a depression that has drowned the valley for about forty miles from the mouth.

The composite history of a region may often be interpreted in more than one way. In such cases the exact interpretation may depend on the securing of more complete and detailed data over all the area which has had a similar history. Not all sky lines with elevations that are of nearly the same height are necessarily evidences of the former existence of a peneplain, and not all broken profiles in the cross section of a valley are necessarily due to rejuvenation. Such profiles may be the result of the presence of a temporary base level, or may be due entirely to differences in the relative strength of the rocks at different heights above the stream. The field worker must therefore draw inferences from careful observations and must not be misled by preconceptions as to what the history of a region should be.

CHAPTER VIII

VULCANISM

Vulcanism includes the study of forces within the earth and their effects. It includes particularly volcanoes, hot springs, geysers, and the effects of heat on the rocks near the surface of the earth.

Volcanoes.—A *volcano* is essentially a vent through which liquid rock, or lava, has been brought to the earth's surface,

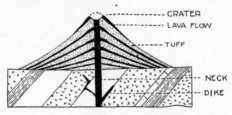

but the term is usually applied to the conical mass of erupted material which has accumulated about the more or less circular vent or *crater*. Volcanoes vary in size from small cones only one to two hundred feet in di-

FIG. 46. Section showing the various components of a volcano.

ameter and of like height to great masses such as Mauna Loa in Hawaii, the base of which is about 100 miles in diameter, and on the ocean floor 14,000 feet below the surface, whereas its summit rises to 13,800 feet above sea level. Such volcanoes as Chimporazo (20,700 feet) and Mt. Rainier (14,400 feet) rise to greater heights, but their bases are on platforms 6,000 to 10,000 feet above sea level.

Distribution of volcanoes.—In general, volcanoes are associated with orogenic movements, especially faulting and folding, and therefore frequently occur in series along a fault line. Volcanoes are found on ocean floors as well as on the land, but always in regions undergoing active uplift. The most recently active volcano in the United States is Mt. Lassen in northern California. Along the crest of the Cascade Mountains are many volcanic cones, including Mt. Rainier, Mt. Hood, Mt. Shasta, and Mt. Baker, which were formed in Pliocene and Pleistocene times.

In the Columbia and Snake River Plains there has been volcanic activity from Miocene to recent times, and numerous eruptions occurred from Eocene to Pleistocene times in the Rocky Mountains. A number of recent volcanoes, and some of earlier periods, occur on the Colorado Plateaus. In New England, volcanic activity is recorded in rocks of the Ordovician and Devonian ages. In Triassic times extensive lava flows occurred in connection with faulting in several basins extending from Nova Scotia to North Carolina.

Temperatures in the earth's interior.—The energy behind volcanic eruptions, hot springs, or geysers is generated by the high temperatures in the interior of the earth. Observations in mines show a uniform increase in temperature with increasing depth, varying from 1°F. for 28 feet, to 1°F. for 130 feet, a generally accepted average being one degree for each 60 feet. In the ancient rocks the increase is slower, while in the younger volcanic rocks it is more rapid. At the average rate of increase for 60 feet, the temperature at a depth of 33 miles would be 2,880°F. (1,600°C.)—sufficient to melt any rocks, especially if water vapor is present. At the same rate the temperatures at the center of the earth would reach 350,000°F. There are, however, many reasons for believing that the rate of increase becomes less as the depth and pressure become greater, and we do not know what the extreme interior temperatures may be.

Volcanic eruptions.—Volcanic eruptions may bring lava to the surface, in which case the flows are said to be *extrusive*, or the lava may be deposited within the rocks near the surface, in which case they are known as *intrusives*. Extrusive flows may be centered about a single vent or series of vents when volcanic cones are built up, or they may flood the surface of the land from fissures. Such fissure flows cover some 200,000 square miles of surface in the Columbia Plateaus.

Lava.—The interior of the earth is not to be thought of as molten, or even as containing masses of molten rock, but rather as being rigid and under great pressure. When readjustments of pressure take place, and the pressure is reduced locally, rock masses may become liquid and be squeezed to the surface along the lines of reduced pressure.

This liquid material is melted rock, containing water vapor, carbon dioxide, hydrochloric acid, and sulphurous acid; it is termed *magma*. At points where vapors collect the rocks are more easily melted, the vapor pressures are localized, and the area becomes one of disturbance. The water and other vapors were not derived from the earth's surface, but were original constituents of the earth's mass.

When the melted rock reaches the surface through a volcanic vent the contained gases and vapor (or part of them) escape and rise in a cloud, while the liquid rock or *lava* builds up a cone about the vent. It is difficult to measure the temperature of lava as it escapes, but temperatures ranging from 1,350°F. (750°C.) to 1,900°F. (1,060°C.) have been measured in Hawaiian eruptions. Both these temperatures are well below the melting point of quartz, which is one of the constituents of lava. After lava has cooled, much higher temperatures are required to remelt it, indicating that the presence of the water vapor and of certain alkalies were important factors in the making of the original magma.

When a volcanic vent becomes sealed by hardened lava, pressures may be built up until sufficient to break the seal. Then an explosive eruption occurs, and rocks and even molten lava may be hurled to great heights, accompanied by earthquake vibrations that may be felt around the world. When the erupted material falls as solid fragments, the largest are termed *bombs*, those of gravel size, *lapilli*, and the finer material *volcanic ash*. The coarser material falls near the vent, helping to build up the volcanic cone, but the finer material may be widely distributed by the winds, some of the finest remaining in the air for weeks. When a deposit of volcanic ash becomes cemented, the resulting rock is termed *tuff*.

A flow of lava may or may not follow an explosive eruption. Many volcanoes, like those of Hawaii, are not of the explosive type. The mass of lava in the crater rises and falls, and from time to time flows out through cracks in the volcano and, as it solidifies, helps to build up the broad cone.

Calderas and explosion pits.—After a cone has been built, a violent explosion may blow off the whole, or most, of the top, or the lava under the cone may be withdrawn so that the top of the cone slumps in. In either case, a great basin with steep bounding walls is formed. Such basins are known as *calderas*. The active cone of Vesuvius is a small cone built up from the floor of a caldera, and Crater Lake in Oregon occupies a caldera.

Occasionally, an explosion of gas and steam may produce a hole with a low rim composed of fragments of country rock but with no lava. Such an *explosion pit* is found at Kilbourne Hole in western Texas.

Intrusives.—A magma may rise and be intruded, or injected, into cracks or cavities below the surface, so that it is revealed at the surface only when the overlying rocks have been eroded off. A fissure of any width filled with lava is a *dike*. If the rising magma lifts overlying beds and spreads out between

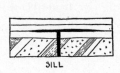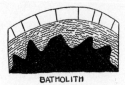

SILL   LACCOLITH   BATHOLITH

FIG. 47.   Types of intrusions.

them it makes a *sill*. If the mass accumulates in a more or less hemispherical mass and domes the overlying rocks, it is a *laccolith*. Where intrusive or extrusive volcanic deposits have been eroded away, the filled passage through which the material came remains as a *plug*, or *neck*.

A large mass of magma may rise under a mountain fold, melting into itself quantities of the adjacent rock, and its escaping vapors altering (or metamorphosing) the rocks for a distance on all sides. Such a mass is termed a *batholith*, is coarsely crystalline in character, and is exposed only after thousands of feet of overlying material have been removed. Smaller masses, or lobes of the main batholith, are termed *stocks*.

Lava structure.—The composition of lavas varies greatly, but feldspar, quartz, and either pyroxene, amphibole, or olivine are generally present. If a lava cools quickly it has a glassy texture and is called *obsidian*. Where the lava cools slowly, as in the interior of flows, the resulting rocks become a mass of interlocking crystals the size of which depends on whether the time of cooling was long or short. The surface of a lava stream is usually cooled while gases are still bubbling out of the mass and is frothy or vesicular in character. As a mass of lava moves, the surface hardens while the interior is still liquid, and the hardened crust is continually breaking, permitting the interior to escape. Because the exterior of a flow hardens

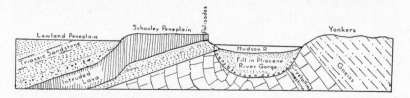

FIG. 48.   Section across the Palisades opposite Yonkers, N. Y., to show the columnar lava sill and its relation to the adjacent country.

first, shrinkage cracks may develop and extend through the mass. Such cracks are generally irregular in form, but in some cases, especially in large flows, they may extend regularly inward, producing a columnar structure such as is seen in the Palisades of the Hudson River, and in the Devil's Tower.

Intrusive flows, when exposed at the surface, may be recognized by the fact that the upper surfaces have no steam holes or other frothy char-

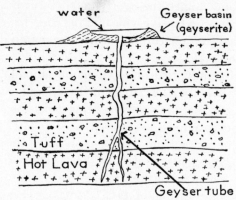

FIG. 49.   The structural conditions producing a geyser.

acteristics; and that the overlying (or contact) beds have been more or less altered or *metamorphosed* by the heat and gases contained in the lava.

Hot springs and geysers.—The role of water in connection with vulcanism is important in many ways. In every volcanic eruption great quantities of water are brought to the surface from deep in the earth. For instance, it has been estimated that during an eruption over a period of 100 days Mount Etna discharged water vapor equivalent to 4,600,000 gallons a day, and Etna is only one of many active volcanoes. Dissolved in the water are quantities of such chemicals as sulphur, carbonic acid, silica, mercury, lead, and silver.

The water vapor of intrusive lavas, with various chemicals in solution, penetrates cracks in the rocks or may even reach the surface as a hot spring or a geyser. In passing through the crevices in the rocks, the water is cooled and often leaves part of its dissolved chemicals in mineral veins. When the hot water comes to the surface and is there cooled the contained minerals are deposited, as is illustrated by the lime and silica deposits about the hot springs and geysers of the Yellowstone Park. Arsenic, antimony, lead, silver, gold, zinc, and cobalt may also be brought to the surface by the hot springs.

If a vent is clear, steam or hot water may escape continually; but if the opening is closed by an accumulation of water the steam is partially condensed under the pressure. When a sufficient pressure has accumulated the water is thrown out as water or steam, forming a geyser. When the pressure is released, the water runs back into the vent and later the geyser is again in eruption. The frequency of eruptions and their length are determined by the character of the vent and the amount of escaping water vapor.

Not all hot springs are due to vulcanism. Those at Hot Springs, South Dakota, and Thermopolis, Wyoming, come from red sandstones which contain quantities of a form of calcium sulphate known as anhydrite. The anhydrite is changed to gypsum by contact with water, heat is generated, and the heated water comes to the surface as warm springs.

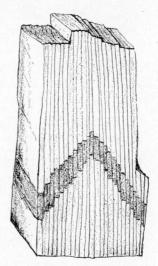

FIG. 50. A piece of slate, showing the folding of the dark band, and the tiny faults developed in the making of the cleavage.

Metamorphism.—Batholithic masses of magma intruded into overlying rocks modify these rocks for perhaps several miles. The adjoining rocks are contorted and compressed. Such alteration is termed *metamorphism*, and is produced far below the surface and under great pressure. Clay or shale is thrown into folds as the result of great pressure, and hundreds of tiny slips form, each at right angles to the pressure. These tiny slips are termed *cleavage*, and the metamorphosed rock thereafter breaks along the cleavage planes. Such a rock is called *slate*.

After cleavage planes have formed they become passageways for vapors which may deposit minerals in the cleavage planes.

Fig. 51. A piece of gneiss. The banded character is a remnant of the cleavages.

When a small amount of mica (or any of several flaky minerals) has been deposited, the rock is then called a *schist*. Generally other minerals, like garnet, staurolite, or otrolite, are also deposited in the cleavage spaces in association with mica, and as the crystals grow the smooth cleavage surfaces of the clay or shale become crinkled. These are also schists. In time other minerals such as feldspar and quartz may be deposited in the schist until there is more of the introduced material than of the original clay. The rock is then called *gneiss*. Gneiss is much harder than the rocks previously mentioned because the introduced minerals have grown through the layers and locked them firmly together.

The progressive changes in metamorphism may be summarized in the following table:

Loose fragments	Cemented rock	Metamorphosed rock
clay	shale	slate—schist—gneiss
sand	sandstone	quartzite
shells, etc.	limestone	marble
peat	bituminous coal	anthracite—graphite

BIBLIOGRAPHY

Allen, E. T., and Day, A. L., *Hot Springs of the Yellowstone National Park*, Carnegie Institution of Washington, Publication No. 466, 1935.

Tyrrell, G. W., *Volcanoes*, 1931.

CHAPTER IX

GEOLOGIC TIME

A time table is essential in geologic study in order to express the relationships of the various layers of rocks and their relative ages. Where stratified rocks are superimposed without any break between layers, it is obvious that the top bed was the last one laid down, and the youngest of the series, and that each lower bed is progressively earlier, or older. As there is, however, no place where beds now visible have been deposited consecutively throughout all geologic time, relative ages can be determined only if the beds in one locality can in some way be correlated with beds found in other places. Similarity of composition is not usable as a basis of correlation, for beds of many kinds are deposited at the same time in different places. For instance, sands, gravels, clays, and limestone are being deposited at the present time along the eastern shore of the United States. Similarity of composition means only similarity in conditions of deposition.

Fossils.—The key to correlation was found in the fossils entombed in the rocks. Their use as time markers is facilitated by the fact that certain groups of animals and plants flourished during one time, then died out, and were succeeded by other and different groups. Rocks containing similar fossils, however widely separated, may with confidence be considered as having been deposited at the same time. These, then, serve as index fossils for the beds in which they are found. The fossil remains of marine animals are the best time markers, for the seas are, and were, continuous, and marine animals have wide ranges of distribution.

Eras and periods.—By the use of this comparative method, a standard geologic time table has been established. (See table, page 94.) Generally six eras and fourteen periods are agreed

upon, and the Tertiary Period is usually subdivided as indicated. To define a period is not altogether easy, because it is
a segment of continuing time. However, it has been found in
Europe and America that certain groups of deposits are separated from both earlier and later groups by a marked unconformity (page 71). To such a group of deposits the term
period is applied. Thus major breaks in continuity of deposition, first generally used to separate periods, have proved
a satisfactory means of delimiting them, especially where the
unconformities indicate world-wide disturbances. But in
some cases transition beds from one period to the next are being
found, and definite boundaries between the periods cannot be
drawn.

Cycles.—A geologic period usually represents a cycle of
changes. Beginning with an elevated continent (North America, for instance) when erosion is dominant, there follows a time
of depression during which the seas flood in over the lowlands
and marine deposits are laid down over them. Finally there
follows another time of uplift and the continent again stands
high with erosion again dominant. These times of uplift result
in forming extensive erosion surfaces, unconformities, which
separate the geologic periods. Mountain-building is frequently
associated with the closing phase of a period—for instance, the
Appalachian Mountains at the end of the Pennsylvanian period,
or the Rocky Mountains at the end of the Cretaceous period.

The age of the earth: *Deposition time.*—Various attempts
have been made to correlate the geologic time table with
astronomical and historical time as expressed in years. The
first estimates were based on the rates of deposition of marine
sediments. The amount of sediment carried to the sea each
year by such rivers as the Mississippi, Rhine, Rhone, and
Nile was measured, and the area on which these sediments were
deposited being roughly known, an average rate of deposition
for sand and mud could be calculated. These studies showed
that the time that has elapsed since the beginning of the Cambrian period must be millions of years. The relative length of
each period was determined; but the time to be assigned to
periods of erosion, as represented by the unconformities, could
not be determined by a study of deposits.

Radium time.—The discovery of radium gave a new and more accurate method of determining the age of the oldest rocks, for radium is associated with uranium on the one side and a form of lead on the other. Uranium is an element found in association with igneous rocks. By the radiation of atoms, uranium changes first to radium and then by a continuation of the process, to lead, at a definite and very slow rate. The ratio is 10,000,000 parts of uranium to 3.4 parts of radium, and 1/2280 part of the original radium is converted to lead each year.

With a knowledge of the amount of uranium and of lead in a given rock, it can be calculated how long the process of reduction has been going on. The determination is a delicate undertaking, but has been made for several igneous rocks of different geologic age. The results of this work are now generally used to express approximately, in years, the dates of certain geological events. The dates are considered accurate to within three per cent as far back as the Jurassic, and to within ten per cent to the beginning of the Cambrian. The time chart following correlates certain major geological events, and gives the time in years, each figure representing the beginning of the period opposite which it is placed.

GEOLOGIC TIME TABLE

Eras	Periods	Characteristic Life	Geological Events	Time in Years
Psychozoic	Recent	Man		25,000
Cenozoic 4%	Pleistocene		Ice Age	
	Pliocene	Age of mammals and of flowering plants		1,000,000
	Tertiary { Miocene			7,000,000
	Oligocene			19,000,000
	Eocene			35,000,000
				55,000,000
Mesozoic 11%	Cretaceous	First grasses / Extinction of the dinosaurs	First Rocky Mountains	95,000,000
	Comanachean	Giant dinosaurs	Western coal swamps / First Coast Ranges	120,000,000
	Jurassic	First modern trees	First Sierra Nevada Mountains	165,000,000
	Triassic	First dinosaurs	Palisades of Hudson	190,000,000

94

Era	Period	Life	Event	Years
Palaeozoic 30%	Permian	Rise of reptiles	First Appalachian Mts.	215,000,000
	Pennsylvanian	Rise of insects, ferns, and seed ferns	Eastern coal swamps	250,000,000
	Mississippian	Rise of echinoderms		300,000,000
	Devonian	First land plants Rise of amphibians	First Schickschock Mts.	350,000,000
	Silurian	First lung fishes and scorpions		390,000,000
	Ordovician	Rise of fishes and corals	First Taconic Mountains	480,000,000
	Cambrian	Rise of mollusks and trilobites		550,000,000
Proterozoic 25%		Primitive invertebrates	Great peneplanation	1,000,000,000
Archaeozoic 30%		Earliest life		1,600,000,000

PART II

REGIONAL PHYSIOGRAPHY

CHAPTER X

CONTINENTAL SHELVES

The distribution of continental shelves.—Bordering each of the continents there is a shelf on which the water gradually deepens from the shore line out to about 600 feet in depth. Beyond the 600-foot line the ocean bottom drops more or less rapidly to oceanic depths of from 10,000 to 15,000 feet. Ideally, owing to the periods of deposition in the Cretaceous and Tertiary periods, a shelf should be rather perfectly developed around the North American Continent, but in relatively recent times (late Pliocene) the whole North American continent was raised more than 600 feet, valleys were carved on the then existing shelf, and a terrestrial aspect was given to the shelf area. Since then there has been a depression along the eastern coast, but not enough time has elapsed for deposits to fill all the valleys. On the west coast a continental uplift is now taking place, but along southern Alaska and southern California large sections offshore have dropped along fault lines.

Along the New Jersey coast the continental shelf is about a hundred miles wide, but widens northward until off Newfoundland it is over 500 miles in width, while southward it narrows to about 15 miles off Cape Hatteras. Off southern Florida the continental shelf widens out as the banks of old Antillia, which, except for the Bahama Islands, is now submerged. On the west of Florida the shelf is approximately 200 miles wide, but is narrower along the north and west sides of the Gulf of Mexico.

On the Pacific coast the shelf is only ten to fifteen miles wide along most of California and Alaska, but north of the Aleutian Islands it widens and is continuous with the continental shelf of Asia. A moderate uplift would make the two continents continuous, as they have been several times in the past.

Submarine valleys along the Atlantic and Gulf coasts.—The outstanding feature of the continental shelf off the Atlantic

and Gulf coasts is a series of submarine valleys, which extend
out to the edge of the shelf opposite the mouths of the larger
rivers.   The submerged valley of the Hudson River is typical.
This river was drowned up to Albany, its rock channel being later
filled with glacial till, sand, and mud.   This rock channel is
600 feet below sea level at Storm King Mountain, and some 800
feet at New York City.   New York Bay, like the old channel
upstream, is filled to a shallow basin; but 12 miles off Sandy

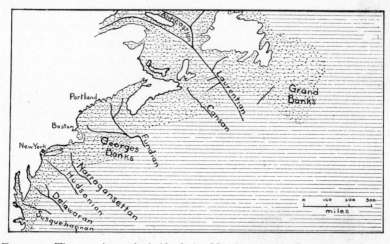

Fig. 52.   The continental shelf of the North Atlantic Ocean in America.
The dotted area is water under 600 feet deep.   The heavy lines show the
submerged valleys.

Hook the valley is again indicated by soundings.   Fifty-three
miles out, where the ocean floor is 90 feet below the surface, the
channel is 180 feet deep and from two to three miles wide.   At
93 miles out the valley assumes the character of a canyon about
a mile wide, which continues on for 23 miles farther to the edge
of the shelf.   On entering the canyon the bottom of the valley
drops to a depth of 800 feet; four miles farther out it drops
again to 1,350 feet, and in the next five miles to a depth of
1,850 feet.

The St. Lawrence River has a similar buried channel.   Where
the Saguenay River enters, the channel is 882 feet deep.   Then
for some 35 miles the old channel is filled so that the water is
only about a hundred feet deep, after which it drops to a depth
of 702 feet, and a little farther down stream to 1,128 feet.   For

some 500 miles through the Gulf of St. Lawrence the old channel is 1,350 feet below sea level, while the water bordering the
channel is but 200 to 250 feet deep.   The main channel is
joined from the north by a channel with two branches: the
one between Anticosti Island and the mainland; and the other
between Newfoundland and Labrador.

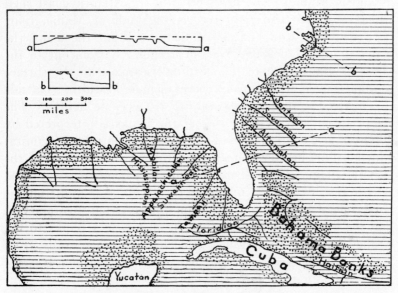

FIG. 53.   The South Atlantic and the Gulf continental shelf.   Dotted areas
are under 600 feet deep; submerged valleys are shown in heavy lines.

These and other submerged valleys (Fig. 52) could be made
only when the present continental shelf was above sea level.
They have been submerged only long enough to be partially
filled close to the shore.   The height of the land when these
valleys were above water cannot be accurately determined.
If the land mass was raised uniformly it may have stood at a
height of over 2,000 feet; but as seems more probable, if there
has been down-warping in this region, the elevation when the
valleys were made may have been over 800 feet, but probably
not more than 1,200 feet.

Along the coasts of Florida and the Gulf of Mexico submerged channels are found opposite each of the major southern
rivers.   The deeper water between the southern end of the

Florida peninsula and the Bahamas is due to a submerged river course which is now followed by the Gulf Stream as it leaves the Gulf. During the Pliocene period, when Florida was continuous with the Bahamas and Cuba, and the Florida River was in existence, the Gulf Stream must have followed a very different course.

Gulf of Maine.—Another section of the Atlantic coast shelf which is of particular interest is the Gulf of Maine, lying between Cape Cod and Nova Scotia. From the shore the water gradually deepens over an irregular bottom out to the George's Banks, where the bottom rises close to the surface to make shoals, which are 100 miles or more in width. Outside the banks the drop is very abrupt to oceanic depths. The steep rise on the westerly side of the banks is interpreted by Johnson[1] as a continuation of that inland-facing cliff (or cuesta) which begins in New Jersey near the western margin of the Coastal Plain. From there the cuesta extends eastward and a little northward. It underlies the terminal moraine on the north side of Long Island and forms the outer part of Cape Cod and the westerly margin of shoals from Georges Banks to the Grand Banks. (See Figs. 54 and 68.) In other words, from New York northeasterly the depression during the Ice Age was greater than the uplift which has occurred since, and this part of the Atlantic coast is still drowned.

South Atlantic coast.—The southern Atlantic coast, like the northern, was raised high above sea level in the Pliocene, depressed during the Ice Age, and raised again since the Ice Age. The last uplift was sufficient to bring a large part of the shelf above sea level to make the Coastal Plain. As a result, the waves break in shallow water and have built offshore beaches at the outer margin of the Coastal Plain, both along the Atlantic Ocean and along the north and west coasts of the Gulf of Mexico. Behind these beaches are lagoons, seldom over 20 feet deep, some of which have gradually become filled with accumulations of sand, shells, and coral remains, first becoming marshes and, in the course of time, firm land.

Gulf coast.—Around the southern end of Florida and about many of the West Indian Islands the clear, warm, saline water

---

[1] *New England Acadian Shore Line*, 1925.

of moderate depth favors the growth of corals, and off the shore these animals have built reefs, which act as protecting barriers to the shore. The west coast of Florida, being in the lee of the prevailing easterly winds, has been but little modified by wave action. Along the north side of the Gulf of Mexico the building of offshore or barrier beaches is progressively more marked as one goes toward the west. The Mississippi River is building a delta out into the Gulf—this being the only place along the shore of the continental United States where the ocean currents do not carry away deposits as fast as they are brought down by the rivers.

North Pacific and Arctic coasts.—The north side of the North American Continent is a drowned area, but the time has been short since the retreat of the Ice Sheet. For this reason and because the Arctic Ocean is covered with ice so much of the time, waves have had but little time to cut cliffs, and the original coast line has been but slightly modified. The two large streams, the Mackenzie and the Yukon, have both begun the building of extensive deltas.

The Aleutian Islands, in part built by volcanic activity, are a much-dissected mountain range, largely drowned at the present time. On the mainland, coming southeasterly from Mt. St. Elias to Mt. Fairweather, the coast rises precipitously against the young St. Elias Range, snow-clad from base to summit, and abounding in glaciers. This range has apparently risen some 5,000 feet in recent times, but the adjacent old sea bottom has not been brought above sea level. This is due to a fault closely approximating the coast line, the block on the west side either remaining stationary or sinking, while that on the east side has risen to make the mountains. From Mt. Fairweather south to Vancouver Island a fringe of mountainous islands forms a belt 50 to 100 miles wide. This belt is a deeply sculptured highland which has sunk some 2,000 feet, and seems to be still sinking.

Middle Pacific coast.—The Pacific coast from Cape Flattery to Point Conception has only a few miles of continental shelf, made by wave action on comparatively weak rocks in very recent times. The whole region has been rising since the Pleistocene, and wave-cut benches are found at intervals on the sides of the Coast Ranges to a height of 1,500 feet. At the

mouth of the Sacramento River a short section has sunk and
the lower reach of the river is drowned, forming San Francisco
Bay. This may be due to the fact that this river has built an
extensive submerged delta, and that the excessive load deposited at this point has caused sinking, whereas all the rest of
the coast is rising.

Southern California coast.—Southern California (from Point
Conception south) is also a rising area; and off the shore there
is a group of islands—Santa Catalina, Santa Rosa, Santa Cruz,
and others which have a different history. The sea bottom of
the region has recently been mapped and a series of remarkable canyons, some as much as 5,000 feet deep and with almost
vertical walls, was found. This is the topography of a high,
arid country. Apparently in late Pleistocene time a large block
of highland country sank at least 5,000 feet, so that only remnants of it remain above the sea to make the islands. Since
then there has been a slight elevation, for there are wave-cut
benches a few hundred feet above sea level on these islands.

California is largely composed of fault-raised mountains,
and apparently there are corresponding down-dropped blocks
off the coast. The continental shelf is about 10 miles wide and
could have been formed by wave action in a short time. The
drop into oceanic depths at the edge of the shelf is so abrupt
as to suggest a fault escarpment, like that of the east face of the
Sierra Nevada.

BIBLIOGRAPHY

Hull, E., *Suboceanic Physiography of the North Atlantic*, 1912.
Shepard, F. P., "Amazing Landscape Lies beneath the Pacific Ocean,"
    Science News Letter, Vol. 26, p. 310, 1934.
Spencer, J. W., "Reconstruction of the Antillian Continent," *Bulletin
    of the Geological Society of America*, Vol. 6, pp. 103–140, 1895.
Spencer, J. W., "Submarine Valleys of the American Coast," *Bulletin
    of the Geological Society of America*, Vol. 14, pp. 207–226, 1903.

CHAPTER XI

NEW ENGLAND

The region to the east of the Hudson and Champlain valleys and to the south of the St. Lawrence Valley, having a unified history, forms the New England Province. It is dominantly an upland surface in which lowlands have been carved where, for any reason, the rocks have been more easily eroded.

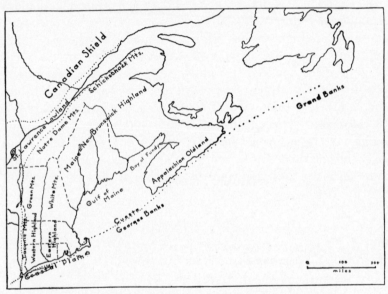

FIG. 54. Orientation map of the New England Province.

History.—In its earliest phase, New England was a basin between the Canadian Shield and the ancient upland of Appalachia. Through the Cambrian and the Ordovician periods great quantities of material, weathered from the uplands, were transported to this basin as sands, mud, and lime. These deposits were especially deep in Vermont and in western Massachusetts, where the sediments amounted to 15,000 feet

105

in thickness. Toward the end of the Ordovician there was a major disturbance in New England known as the Taconic Revolution, and the horizontal sediments were crumpled and upthrust all around the north and west margins, as though

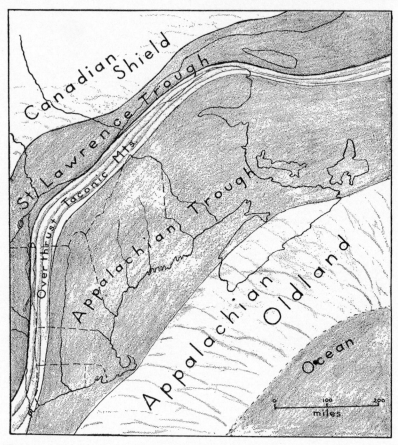

FIG. 55.   Land relations in New England after the Taconic overthrust and uplift.

affected by pressure from the southeast. Not only were the beds crumpled, but they were faulted and overthrust on top of the adjacent undisturbed beds, both to the west and to the north. The line where these overthrust beds meet the undisturbed beds is today known as Logan's Line, which has been traced from east of Quebec to south of Hudson, N. Y. The uplift brought into existence, for the first time, the uplands, now known as the Taconic Mountains, the Western Highland, the Green Mountains, the Notre Dame Mountains, and the Schickschock Mountains—a crescent of mountain ranges lying between the sea which then occupied eastern New England and

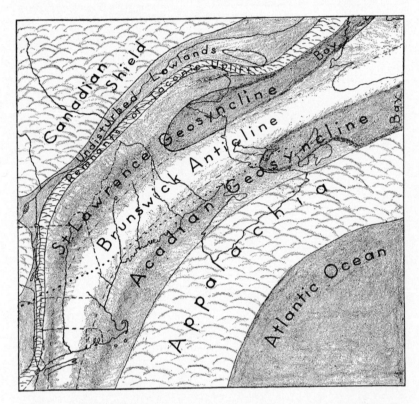

Fig. 56. The New England Province just after the Acadian Revolution. The area south of the dotted line was further disturbed in the Appalachian Revolution. (Modified from Schuchert.)

Acadia and the sea which covered the region now designated as the Valley and Ridge Province and the Appalachian Plateaus.

During the Silurian and Devonian periods, this crescent of mountains was subjected to a long period of erosion and furnished great quantities of sediment which were deposited in eastern Connecticut, in Massachusetts, and in New Brunswick on one side, and in New York on the other side. At the end of the Devonian a second disturbance took place—the Acadian

Revolution—and a great anticline was formed with its axis extending from eastern Connecticut to Newfoundland, with down folds (synclines) both to the north and to the south. The folding was accompanied by great intrusions of granite in batholithic masses which metamorphosed the adjacent rocks into gneisses and schists. At this time there were also great extrusions of lava, especially in the upfolded area, and lesser extrusions in both the Schickschock and Montreal regions.

FIG. 57. Map to show the positions of the various basins which are filled with Pennsylvanian deposits: 1, Narragansett Basin; 2, Boston Basin; 3, New Brunswick Basin; 4, Cumberland Basin; 5, Cape Breton Basin. The broken line outlines the bay which reached into New Brunswick in the Mississippian Period.

The Acadian Revolution brought most of New England above sea level, except for a bay, reaching across Newfoundland into New Brunswick, which was still below the ocean through the Mississippian period (see Fig. 56). In this bay marine sediments continued to be deposited as sands, muds, and limestones. In the upper part of the series, beds of gypsum indicate that the bay was then cut off from the sea and finally dried up at the end of the period.

The basins.—During the Pennsylvanian period there were no further submergences beneath the sea, but there was local warping, which resulted in the formation of several inland basins. Into these debris was washed from the highlands, usually as coarse gravels and sand. The depth of deposits in these basins is very great—6,000 feet in the Narragansett Basin, 10,000 feet in the Cape Breton Basin, and 13,000 feet in the Cumberland Basin (also known as "The Joggins"). These depths indicate that the adjoining lands were high and were eroded rapidly. In the latter part of the period, when the basins were less deep, the character of the filling changed to shales and material of organic origin, the latter indicating swamps. Where the swamps were buried, coal beds were formed. The Boston Basin was filled with coarse material and has no coal. The coal of the Narragansett Basin contains so much shale as to be of little value. Thick seams of coal are mined in each of the other basins.

At the end of the Pennsylvanian period occurred the Appalachian Revolution which brought above sea level all the region lying between New England and the Interior Lowland. New England was again elevated especially in the southern portion. The older rocks, already folded and metamorphosed, were at this time still further distorted. The deposits in the basins were folded, but not metamorphosed. New England was then a very irregular highland, well above sea level, and probably extending far to the east of its present shore line.

Fault valleys.—Following the Appalachian Revolution, New England remained stable for a long time, the highlands being slowly reduced by erosion. By the middle of the Triassic period it was worn down, if not to a peneplain, at least to a country of low relief. Meanwhile tensions had developed in the area extending from New England to Nova Scotia, and a series of great faults occurred, as described on page 10. In New England two great valleys were thus formed, the Bay of Fundy and the Connecticut Valley. In the Bay of Fundy the fault was along the north margin of the present basin, the north side being raised to a mountain range, while the south side sank, and thus produced a basin. In the Connecticut Valley, the fault was near the east side. The block on the east side rose to make a high mountain range, while that on the west sank, making a basin all across Massachusetts and Connecticut. Gravels, sands, and silts were washed from the adjoining highlands into both of these basins, filling them with continental deposits. There were also, in both basins, periodic flows of lava, now seen as sheets of trap interbedded with the stratified rocks.

The Fundy valley attained a depth of some 4,000 feet; the Connecticut Valley, over 10,000 feet. Both these depths resulted from a series of intermittent movements, rather than from a single downward movement. The red color of the sandstones, the mud cracks, and the dinosaur footprints indicate that the climate during the filling of these basins was warm and arid.

After the valleys were filled, and the highlands correspondingly reduced, a second period of faulting took place, which.

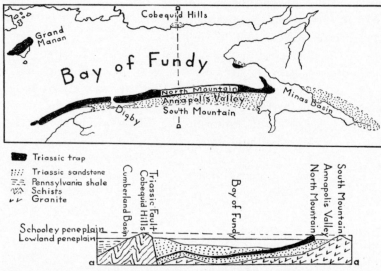

Fig. 58. Map to show the Bay of Fundy in the lowland made in Triassic sandstones. The section shows the relations of the Cumberland Basin to the north, the Cobequid Hills, the Bay of Fundy, North Mountain, the Annapolis Valley, and South Mountain. (After S. Powers.)

broke the large blocks, and also the sandstones and trap, into smaller units. The displacements at this time were generally small, less than 100 feet; but the blocks were so tilted that the originally horizontal beds now dip at angles of 5° to 25°. The date of this second faulting is generally set early in the Jurassic period.

Fall Line Peneplain.—From this time to about the middle of the Comanchean period, New England was stable, and was gradually worn down to a peneplain, known as the Fall Line Peneplain, which extends seaward under the Coastal Plain deposits. Later erosion has removed so much of this lowland that it is preserved only in the even tops of such mountains as the White Mountains. However, the Fall Line Peneplain is clearly seen in adjacent regions, and later events can be explained only by postulating such a plain in New England.

After the formation of the Fall Line Peneplain, New England was depressed and the sea advanced inland at least as far as the middle of New Hampshire, and a relatively thin series of Comanchean and Cretaceous deposits buried the older and stronger rocks of southern New England. A remnant of this cover is to be found under the terminal moraine of northern Long Island (see Fig. 62).

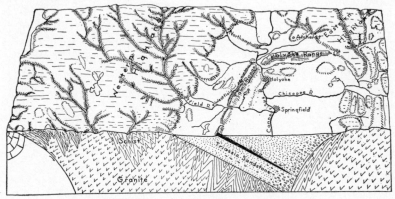

Fig. 59. Block diagram of the Connecticut Valley, showing the inset of Triassic sandstone. (After G. W. Bain.)

Schooley Peneplain.—About the beginning of the Eocene the whole province was raised in a low anticline, the axis of which extended from middle Vermont to central New Brunswick. By the end of the Eocene, erosion had again leveled the surface, except for scattered monadnocks such as Mount Monadnock, Mount Greylock, and the peaks of the Green and White Mountains. This leveled surface is called the Schooley Peneplain and has a wide extent not only over New England, but southward to Alabama and westward to the Mississippi River. Most of the upland surfaces of New England reach the peneplain level, as is indicated by the nearly level sky line to be seen in almost all parts of the province.

Lowland Peneplain.—After the Schooley Peneplain was some 90 per cent complete, it in turn was raised in a low anticline with its axis extending from Vermont to New Brunswick. Erosion again started to make new lowlands wherever the rocks were weak. By the time about a tenth of the country had been reduced to these new lowlands (the lowlands of the present), erosion was interrupted by the Pliocene uplift. In southern New England the lowlands are but 200–300 feet below the Schooley Peneplain, but in central Vermont and Maine the interval between the two surfaces increases to 1,200 or more feet.

At the end of the Pliocene all the New England province was raised, and the streams were thus rejuvenated. In the Massachusetts region the uplift was 1,000 feet or more, and in the New Brunswick region it was still greater. Streams which had approximated grade and were flowing in mature valleys now began to cut deep, narrow young gorges below the level of the lowlands (page 100).

Ice Age.—Following this brief period of gorge-cutting all of New England was buried under the snow and ice fields of the Ice Age, and the work of river erosion was stopped. Ice accumulated to a depth of three or four thousand feet and the land was depressed, perhaps due to the weight of the ice cover, as much, or nearly as much, as it had been raised in the Pliocene. The glacier acted like a great sheet of sandpaper, smoothing out irregularities, rounding the hills, scouring out the valleys, and carrying away the loose soil; but it did not materially alter the larger land features. The farthest advance of the ice is marked by its terminal moraine across Long Island, Nantucket, Marthas Vineyard, and Cape Cod, all of which are underlain by Coastal Plain rocks (page 131).

When the ice sheet melted it dropped till over the whole of New England, which thus forms the surface soil except where it has been worked over in the making of post-glacial lake deposits, deltas, and other water-laid deposits. The retreating ice also left many moraines, generally trending east-west—directly across the general trend of the streams. Thus hundreds of dams were formed across the streams, and behind the dams hundreds of lakes. The larger streams have generally cleared these obstructions from their channels, but there still remain hosts of lakes and ponds, which bear evidence of the short time which has elapsed since the Ice Age. The farther north one goes, the more numerous these lakes are, as the time has been shorter since the retreat of the ice.

Since the melting of the ice sheet the land has risen, some of it even higher than before the Pliocene uplift; some of it not so much, so that in places the sea covers the lowlands formed during the early Pliocene.

Coast line.—Each feature of the New England Province is due to one or more of the events already described. The highly irregular coast line of Maine, Nova Scotia, and New Brunswick is due to the fact that the much-dissected Schooley Peneplain was depressed below sea level during the Glacial Period. Though it has risen somewhat since, the sea still covers the easterly portion, and every valley and lowland made before the Pliocene uplift is drowned. In general, the rocky promontories are the uplands of the Schooley Peneplain, while the inlets and bays mark the valleys and lowlands.

The coast is young in its characteristics, dating only from the end of the Ice Age; but wave action has already begun to modify it. Waves have undercut the headlands, and changed the original sloping surface into cliffs, such as are seen at Marblehead, Monhegan, Schoodic, Grand Manan, Percé Rock, and Gaspé. The material thus eroded has been washed into the coves to make pebble beaches, or has been carried southerly by the alongshore currents. Where indentations are wide, pebble or sand beaches have been formed, but where the indentations are narrow, bars and spits have often been built across the openings. In some cases the waves and currents have built bars or tombolos behind islands, tying them to the mainland or to each other. Marblehead Neck and Nantasket Beach in Massachusetts are good examples of tombolos.

Bay of Fundy.—The Bay of Fundy region represents one of the submerged lowlands. Originally it was one of the Triassic Basins, with the fault line on the north side[1] (Fig. 58). In the Triassic Period this basin was filled by sandstones, with an included trap sheet. Both sandstone and trap were faulted and warped in the Jurassic. Later the Schooley Peneplain was developed over the whole region. When it was raised, the Lowland Peneplain was formed on the sandstone portion, the lava remaining as North Mountain, while the strong rocks to

[1]Occasionally (1638, 1727, 1755, 1927) minor earthquakes have occurred in Massachusetts, the foci of which have been located in the Gulf of Maine and attributed to movements either on this Fundian fault, or on a westward extension of the fault.

the north and south make the Cobequid Hills and South Mountain. The valley formed in the sandstones underlying the trap makes what is known as Annapolis Valley, a sheltered lowland of almost continuous orchards. South of this valley the granite formed in the Acadian Revolution makes South Mountain. Northern outcrops of the trap sheet appear on Grand Manan, Cape D'Or, and Cape Split. The Bay of Fundy is a lowland in the Triassic sandstone above the lava sheet. This lowland was deeply channeled during the Pliocene uplift, then depressed below sea level during the Ice Age, and since elevated to its present level. The peculiar shape of the bay, narrowing as it does toward its head, causes the famous high tides, which at times exceed 40 feet. The water carries along toward the head of the bay great quantities of mud which is there accumulating in the form of marshes and reducing the size of the bay. Filling also seems to be going on in the lower part of the bay.

A little to the north of the Bay of Fundy, but separated from it by a ridge of crystalline rocks, the Cobequid Hills, lies the Cumberland Basin, where shales and coal beds were deposited during Pennsylvanian time. Like the other weak rock areas, this was reduced to a lowland before the Pliocene. After being raised in the Pliocene, depressed during the Glacial Period, and again raised after the disappearance of the ice cover, the surface came to rest just above sea level.

Chicnecto Bay is a flooded river valley which was cut across the Cobequid Hills, and now gives access to the coal layers known as The Joggins.

The Narragansett Basin has had a history similar to that of the Cumberland Basin, but its coal is almost graphite and not commercially usable. Its Lowland Peneplain, formed before the Pliocene, was crossed by the Blackstone and other streams, which cut gorges across it during the Pliocene uplift. In the subsequent uplift following the depression of the Ice Age the lowland surface was raised slightly above sea level but the river channels are below that level, resulting in the deep fingered bay of the present time.

Boston Basin.—The Boston Basin, formed at the same time as the two preceding basins (page 108), was filled with coarse gravel and shale, and contained no coal. These rocks were never so well consolidated as the rocks outside the basin. The Schooley Peneplain developed over it, and then during the Miocene it was eroded to the lowland basin of today. Across the basin flowed the Charles, Mystic, and Neponset rivers. During the Pliocene uplift they all cut deep channels. The

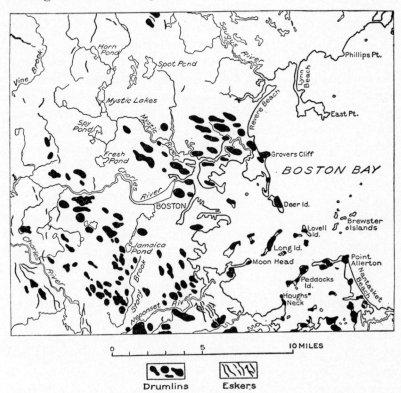

FIG. 60. The distribution of drumlins about Boston. (After La Rue, U. S. G. S.)

region was covered by the ice sheet, depressed, and after the ice retreat raised approximately to its former level. The river channels were partly filled with glacial till, and later with mud brought down by the rivers themselves. Were this fill cleared out, one would find the rock channels 400 or more feet deep. Boston Harbor comprises the flooded mouths of these rivers, but its features are diversified owing to the fact that the retreating glacial ice left a cluster of drumlins, some of them in the harbor, and some of them on land.   Governor's, Winthrop, and Deer islands are drumlins now surrounded by water. Several other islands are also drumlins, which have been modified by wave action.   On the land Breed's, Bunker, and about 180 other hills are also drumlins.

Newfoundland.—Newfoundland, at the mouth of the St. Lawrence Gulf, is made up of the same series of sediments as is New England.   Its heights represent the Schooley Peneplain. In the Miocene the peneplain was uplifted about 800 feet, and the streams cut a series of rather mature valleys trending toward the northeast; but their floors are hardly wide enough to designate them as the Lowland Peneplain.   However, when the Pliocene uplift raised the island (estimated 1,800 feet), these rivers cut deep canyons in the mature valleys.   The Continental Glacier did not reach Newfoundland, but the island had a local ice cap from which glaciers flowed down the narrow river valleys, converting them into U-shaped valleys.   The depression under the ice cap amounted to about 1,000 feet.   When the ice melted the island rose some 400 feet, but the more fully developed valleys are still drowned.

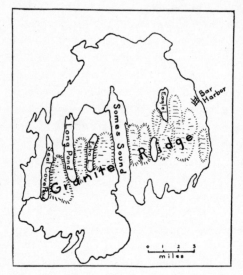

Fig. 61.   Mount Desert Island, showing the glacial furrows now occupied by sounds and lakes.

Mt. Desert.—Among the many islands of the Maine coast, Mt. Desert is peculiar in that along its east-west axis there is a ridge of granite, which rises in several monadnocks above the level of the Schooley Peneplain.   This ridge, athwart the course of the ice movement, forced the ice to concentrate its wear along definite channels; so that it made a series of U-shaped valleys across the island.   When the ice melted, these trenches were filled with water, making a series

of trough lakes, such as Long and Jordan ponds, and Echo
and Eagle lakes.   One trench was deeper than the others and
is now flooded by the sea, forming Somes Sound.   With its deep
rock basin, Somes Sound has all the characteristics of a fiord.

Connecticut Valley.—The Connecticut Valley is the largest
expression of the Lowland Peneplain in New England.   Its
first inception was in the Triassic, when a fault 120 miles long
from east of Greenfield, Massachusetts, to east of New Haven,
Connecticut, caused a downdrop on the west and a rise on the
east.   The fill was mostly conglomerate and sandstone, but
there are three included layers of trap.   The largest flow is the
second one, which in the middle of the valley is 400 feet thick.
There was an earlier flow which, however, is confined to the
southern half of the area; and also a later flow, which is present
in both regions, but is not a continuous sheet.   The Triassic
deposits total some 10,000 feet.   The region was generally
tilted down to the east in the Jurassic.   Both the valley fill and
the mountains on either side were leveled by the time of the
Schooley Peneplain.   When this was raised, the poorly cemented sandstone was soon eroded out, and the Lowland
Peneplain developed over all the surface where the sandstones
outcropped.   The lavas were more resistant to erosion and
stand as ridges above the lowlands.   These have been given
such names as the Talcott, Tom, and Holyoke ranges; East
Rock, West Rock, and Mt. Carmel.   The lesser lava sheets
make lesser ridges paralleling the main sheet.   In places the
continuity of the lava outcrops is broken by the Jurassic faults,
which in one or two cases have caused an outcrop to be repeated.   (See Fig. 59.)

In the region of Amherst, Massachusetts, there is another
type of break in the continuity of surface features.   At Mt.
Tom Junction the main sheet of lava, which to the south outcrops in a north-south line, turns to the east to make the
Holyoke Range.   The change in direction of the outcrop is
accompanied by a change in the dip to the south.   After a gap
of eight miles the lava sheet reappears in Mt. Toby, striking
east-west and dipping to the north.   After crossing the Connecticut River it bends to the north again in the Pocumtuck
Hills.   This seems to indicate that an east-west fold of early

date, probably Jurassic, lifted the Amherst region at least two thousand feet.

Postglacial lakes.—The Connecticut Valley lowland was well developed by the end of the Miocene, was elevated in the Pliocene, and was then depressed under the load of the ice sheet. When the ice began to retreat, the lower end of the valley was the first part to be elevated; so that the lower end of the nearly flat valley was higher than the northern end. This resulted in the formation of a lake, which at its maximum extended from near Middletown, Connecticut, to above Greenfield, Massachusetts, where it was bordered by the ice sheet. It was partially divided by the Holyoke Range, the southern portion being named the Springfield Lake, the northern portion Hadley Lake. Its shore line is marked by beaches, and especially by deltas opposite the mouth of each entering stream. These deltas are freely used as a source of gravel. The bottom was covered with clay, laid down in annual films, or *varves*. These varves indicate that the lake was in existence some 4,000 years and from a study of these it is estimated that the retreat of the ice sheet began some 25,000 years ago. The clay is the basis of the brick-making industries throughout the valley and forms the impervious subsoil which holds the water table near the surface and adapts the valley floor to such rank-growing crops as tobacco and onions. In contrast, the porous sands and gravels of the beaches and deltas support the orchards around the margins of the valley.

When the ice sheet retreated far to the north, the upper valley also rose and the lake was drained. The Connecticut River was again re-established, but at first flowed over the clays of the lake bottom.

Similar lakes, with the south end blocked by uplifted land, and the north shore against the ice, were numerous in the province, including Lake Bascom near Williamstown, Massachusetts, Lake Housatonic near Pittsfield, Massachusetts, Lake Bouvé south of Boston Harbor, and Lakes Sudbury and Nashua near the towns of the same names, to mention but a few of them. All are indicated by beaches, deltas, and clay deposits.

Western Uplands.—The Uplands of New England generally represent the Schooley Peneplain surface. Near the coast this surface starts close to sea level, rises gradually to 2,000 feet in altitude in central New Hampshire and Vermont, holds this general level to the northern boundaries of these states, and then drops gently toward the St. Lawrence, being about 1,000 feet high at the edge of that valley. The southernmost portion of the New England Province is New York City. Here the Schooley Peneplain rises gradually from the Battery northward on the highly metamorphosed and contorted Fordham gneiss, while the lower levels of the city are on less resistant rocks, mostly limestone. The Hudson, East, and Harlem rivers all are drowned, their deep Pliocene gorges being filled with till and recent silts to a depth of several hundred feet (page 99).

The western margin of New England is made by the Taconic Mountains, which are separated from the rest of the western highland by a series of valleys made mostly in limestone. This western highland is known as the Berkshire Hills in Massachusetts, and in Vermont as the Green Mountains, where many peaks rise above the peneplain level as monadnocks. North of Vermont the upland bends toward the east following the St. Lawrence Valley. Here it becomes the Notre Dame Mountains, which were first formed as three anticlinal ridges in the Taconic disturbance, and later further distorted and metamorphosed by intrusions at the time of the Acadian disturbance. The peneplain has removed the tops of these anticlines and exposed the volcanic material intruded into them, and also the metamorphosed adjacent rocks. One of these anticlines, starting from Lake Memphremagog and running northeasterly, is known as the serpentine belt since the highly metamorphosed rocks carry quantities of serpentine, asbestos, talc, iron, chromium, and antimony. At present this region supplies 80 per cent of the asbestos of the world. As the Notre Dame upland extends into the Gaspé Peninsula, it is more and more made up of granites and intruded lavas, this part of the upland being known as the Schickschock Mountains.

Eastern Uplands.—East of the Connecticut Valley the upland through Connecticut and Massachusetts is termed the Eastern Upland, and is fairly uniform in its upper surface except for lesser monadnocks like Mt. Wachusett in Massachusetts, Mt. Monadnock in southern New Hampshire, and Mt. Bartlett in

New Hampshire.—In northern New Hampshire there are an increasing number of monadnocks, culminating in the White Mountains. This less-reduced belt probably represents the head of the early drainage systems. From northern New Hampshire the eastern highland swings easterly across Maine, where Mt. Katahdin is an outstanding monadnock, and across New Brunswick, which has but few monadnocks.

Drainage.—The drainage of New England has streams of two types: those which conform to the trend of the rocks, and those which flow across the strong and weak rocks indiscriminately. The first type have their valleys in the less resistant rocks, and

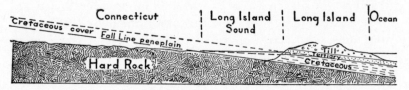

Fig. 62. Section from Long Island to Connecticut to show the relation of the Fall Line Peneplain and its Cretaceous covering to the present surface, or Schooley Peneplain.

have evidently adjusted themselves to the present courses in more recent times. They are such streams as Otter Creek in the marble belt of Vermont, the Housatonic River in the Stockbridge limestone of western Massachusetts and Connecticut, and the Connecticut River in the Triassic sandstones. But the lower Housatonic River suddenly leaves the limestones and flows southeast across the much stronger rocks to the sea. In like manner the Connecticut River leaves the sandstone lowland and flows southeast across the eastern highland. The Farmington, Westfield, Deerfield, West, Blackstone, Merrimac and Saco rivers flow southeast regardless of the varying strength of the rocks they cross. After a study of these phenomena, Johnson concludes that the southeast courses are the original ones and that these rivers acquired that direction as they began to flow on the Cretaceous Beds (see page 111), which covered the Fall Line Peneplain. As they cut down through the weak Cretaceous deposits they were let down, or superimposed, on the underlying strong rocks. Parts of these streams have maintained their initial courses, but in some cases the side

streams which were on weak rocks have developed faster and
have diverted parts, at least, of the older streams to new
courses.   The Farmington rose in the western highland, crossed
the Triassic weak rocks, and continued across the eastern highland.   A northern trib-
utary in the sandstone
enlarged its valley
faster than the Farm-
ington on strong rocks;
the tributary finally
reaching so far north
that it tapped the
Westfield River and
diverted the westerly
portion of it into the
Farmington. Similarly
a tributary of the West-
field captured the
westerly portion of the
Deerfield, and a tribu-
tary of the Deerfield
added the West River
to the group, so that
the Connecticut River
of today is a composite
of several younger trib-
utaries and the old
southern   southeast
portion.   Similarly the
Housatonic River is

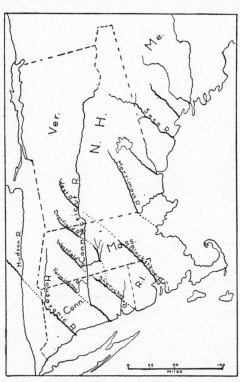

FIG. 63.   Development of the Connecticut
River.   (After D. W. Johnson, from *Stream
Sculpture on the Atlantic Slope*, by permission
of the Columbia University Press.)

composed of a younger upper portion and the older lower
southeast-flowing portion.   The rivers of Maine have not yet
been studied from this point of view, but they seem mostly
to be in their original courses.

   St. John's River.—The St. John's River has had an interesting history.   The upper portion flows northeast, conforming to
the strike of the rocks, and is apparently young, while the lower
portion cuts across the trend of the rocks, both weak and strong,
and is apparently superimposed like the old rivers of Massa-

chusetts. The lower portion of the St. John's River was buried under the glacial ice, which, when it retreated, left the channel irregularly filled with till. Through most of its course the till was soon cleared from the river channel; but near Grand Falls the channel was so choked that the river was forced out of its course, and for half a mile cut a new narrow gorge. In this half mile it has a waterfall of 60 feet and cascades down another 55 feet before it returns to the preglacial valley. The lower end of the river (86 miles) is drowned, this tidewater portion and the harbor representing the gorge cut during the Pliocene uplift.

BIBLIOGRAPHY

Antevs, E., *The Last Glaciation, with Special Reference to the Ice Retreat in Eastern North America*, American Geographical Society, Research Series, No. 17, 1928.

Barrel, J., *Central Connecticut in the Geological Past*, Conn. Geological and Natural History Survey, Bulletin 23, 1914.

Fairchild, H. L., "Postglacial Uplift of Northeastern America," *Bulletin of the Geological Society of America*, Vol. 29, p. 187, 1918.

Guidebook No. I of the Canadian Geological Survey, *Excursions in Quebec and the Maritime Provinces*, 1913.

Guidebook No. I of the International Geological Congress, XVI Session, *Eastern New York and Western New England*, 1933.

Johnson, D. W., *New England Acadian Shoreline*, 1925.

Johnson, D. W., *Stream Sculpture of the Atlantic Slope*, 1931.

La Forge, L., *Geology of the Boston Area*, U. S. Geological Survey, Bulletin 839, 1932.

Powers, S., "The Acadian Triassic," *Journal of Geology*, Vol. 24, pp. 1, 105, 245, 1916.

Raisz, E. J., "Scenery of Mt. Desert Island," *Annals of the New York Academy of Science*, Vol. XXXI, p. 121, 1929.

Twenhofel, W. H., "Physiography of Newfoundland," *American Journal of Science*, Vol. 33, pp. 1–24, 1922.

U. S. Geological Survey Folios: Holyoke, Mass., No. 50; Penobscot Bay, Me., No. 192.

U. S. Geological Survey, Topographic Maps: Casco Bay, Mt. Desert, Bar Harbor for Maine; Boston, Boston Bay,* Northampton, Provincetown* for Massachusetts; Middletown for Connecticut; Narragansett Bay for Rhode Island; and Harlem* for New York.

---

*The asterisk indicates maps described in the U. S. Geological Survey Professional Paper, No. 60. See Preface, p. v.

CHAPTER XII

THE GENESIS OF THE EASTERN PROVINCES: THE COASTAL PLAIN

The several provinces from the Coastal Plain on the east to the Central Lowland on the west are all the results of the same set of original large earth movements, so that they may be introduced together, and then described separately as their histories differ. All the stratified rocks of the eastern portion of the United States have as a foundation the Pre-Cambrian peneplain. At the beginning of the Cambrian the eastern margin was warped up to make the old land, Appalachia, while to the west a trough was warped down to make the Appalachian Trough. (See Fig. 8.) The highlands were later eroded, and the material was transported to the trough and deposited in it. Time after time as the rocks of the upper surface were eroded off, the highland rose, and time after time as the trough was overloaded by deposits, the trough sank. (See *isostacy*, p. 69.) The sediments in the trough are coarse on the eastern margin and become finer to the westward, indicating that they came mostly from the east.

The Filling of the Appalachian Trough.—In each of the periods of the Palaeozoic era, the Appalachian Trough was depressed below sea level and flooded. At the same time Appalachia was elevated, and its streams rejuvenated, so that again and again sediments from the highland accumulated on the lowlands, usually while they were flooded, though some of the sediments are continental in character. In the Cambrian, Ordovician, Silurian, Devonian, Mississippian, and Pennsylvanian, thick layers of sediment accumulated in the trough, each thinning out as it extended westward toward the Mississippi River region. In Pennsylvania the total depth of the deposits is over 30,000 feet, and somewhat less to the south.

These great accumulations are all of shallow-water character; and the waters teemed with life, as the remains of coral and shell fish testify.

Salt beds.—In the early part of the Silurian period Appalachia was raised before the trough was depressed, so that the coarse detritus brought down by the streams was deposited on the lowland above sea level. The lowland had an arid climate, with the result that several large saline lakes of the type of Great Salt Lake developed on it. These lakes were especially large in western New York, Ohio, and Michigan. As they dried up, owing to the arid climate, salt was deposited in beds that range in thickness from 10 to 250 feet. The thick beds are not composed entirely of

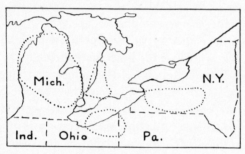

FIG. 64. The positions of the salt lakes which formed in the Silurian.

salt, for the salt layers are separated by water-borne layers of clay and sand, and (less often) of gypsum, indicating changes in climatic conditions.

The salt deposits were formed in the early Silurian, and were later buried under hundreds (or thousands) of feet of sediments, so that they were preserved. Now they are the principal source of the salt used in the United States.

Clinton iron ore.—Later in the Silurian Period, when the sea had flooded the Appalachian Trough, quantities of iron were brought in solution into the inland sea and there precipitated, apparently by bacterial action, thus making a layer of hematite iron extending from New York to Alabama. In the north the thickness of the layer is but one or two feet, but it increases in depth southward until in Alabama the layer is ten feet thick. It is the basis of the great iron industry centering at Birmingham. The iron in the water seems to have been injurious to the animal life of the sea, for all the fossils from the iron-bearing beds are dwarfs, one-half to one-quarter the size of those in the beds above and below this layer.

Petroleum.—The Devonian deposits are especially thick in Pennsylvania. These beds also testify to a great abundance of life in the inland Devonian sea for, in addition to myriads of shells of many types, they contain great quantities of petroleum. The petroleum originated as a result of the bacterial decomposition of organic matter, especially animal matter. Microscopic globules of oil from the decaying shellfish, worms, and crustacea, rising through the muddy waters, united with the particles of clay; and then both settled to the bottom to make bituminous shales. The increasing weight of later layers of sediment pressed out the imprisoned oil and it percolated to the more porous (sandy) layers, where it has been held through the succeeding periods to be released when a hole is bored into these early deposits.

Coal.—During the latter part of the Pennsylvanian Period the trough was a lowland just above sea level, and on it developed great swamps from Pennsylvania to Alabama and westward to Illinois and Missouri. The forests of the time were composed of trees which are now extinct, but are represented by such dwarfed descendants as the ferns, horsetails, and ground pine. As the trees, or their leaves, fell and were covered by the shallow water, masses of peaty vegetation accumulated to thicknesses of from one foot to one hundred feet. Then a depression permitted the sea to cover the peaty deposits with a layer of clay. With each slight elevation the swamps were developed again, only to be buried later. This happened time after time. In Pennsylvania there are 29 separate beds of coal, each covered by a layer of marine sediments. The coal layers vary from three inches to ten feet in thickness, averaging $3\frac{1}{4}$ feet.

Appalachian Revolution.—By the end of the Pennsylvanian Period sediments had accumulated in the trough to a depth of from 6,000 to 8,000 feet in Georgia, 30,000 feet in Pennsylvania, and lesser amounts to the westward. Then came the Appalachian Revolution, when these sediments were thrown into a series of north-south folds. In the south the folding was accompanied by both normal and overthrust faulting. By reason of the folding (and faulting) the distance across the beds was reduced by about half, or by from 20 to 50 miles. While this folding was going on, the whole eastern half of America as far west as Minnesota and Missouri was raised, a maximum where the eastern mountains now are, and less to the west. Since the Appalachian Revolution the whole region has been subjected to a series of uplifts and associated periods of erosion, whereas previously depressions and the deposition of sediments had prevailed.

Triassic basins.—During the Permian and the early Triassic periods erosion reduced the whole of eastern North America to a lowland, if not to a complete peneplain. Then about the middle of the Triassic great faults developed, especially over the section that had been Appalachia. Basins were made in the Bay of Fundy region and in the Connecticut Valley (page 10). But the greatest of all the basins was formed by a fault, starting at the Hudson River and extending across New Jersey, southeastern Pennsylvania, and Maryland into Virginia. Other basins were formed in southern Virginia and in North Carolina. In these fault basins the block on the northwest rose, while the one to the southeast sank. Conglomerates and sands were worn from the western block and filled in the depressions. At times lava welled up through the fault fissure and spread over the gravels of the basin. The Palisades of the Hudson and the Watchung Mountains of New Jersey are composed of lavas (trap) of Triassic age.

In Pennsylvania the total depth of Triassic deposits amounts to 20,000 feet. In Virginia and Maryland the fill is less in thickness and the sediments finer in texture. In the Jurassic there was another period of faulting of less extent than that of the Triassic, and the deposits were broken into smaller blocks and tilted slightly.

Fall Line Peneplain.—After the Jurassic the area became more stable, and erosion again reduced it to a peneplain, known as the Fall Line Peneplain. This was completed in the middle Cretaceous. Then the area was so warped that all the eastern portion was depressed below the sea and covered by marine marls and clays. The whole region was then raised in a low arch on which a consequent drainage was developed, to be later let down, or superimposed, on the strong rocks below the Cretaceous cover.

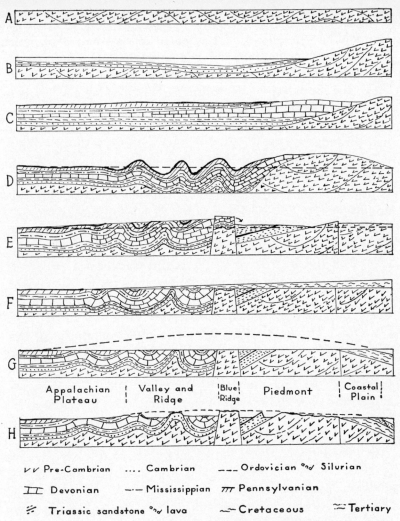

A   Appalachian   Valley and |Blue| Piedmont | Coastal|
      Plateau   Ridge |Ridge| Plain

ⱽⱽ Pre-Cambrian   .... Cambrian   ___ Ordovician ⁿ⋁ Silurian

ꚀꚀ Devonian   —·— Mississippian   ⫫⫫⫫ Pennsylvanian

⁑ Triassic sandstone °ⁿ⋁ lava   ⌒⌒ Cretaceous   ⌇⌇ Tertiary

Fɪɢ. 65. Sections to show the history of the Coastal Plain, Piedmont, Blue Ridge, Valley and Ridge Province, and the Appalachian Plateaus: A, the Pre-Cambrian Peneplain before warping. B, Silurian times, when old Appalachia was high, and deposition was taking place in the Appalachian Trough. C, the Appalachian Trough filled, with coal beds in black on the top. D, at the end of the Pennsylvanian, folding begun. Erosion followed, reducing the land to a peneplain, indicated by the broken line. E, faulting in the Triassic with filling of the Triassic valley from the upraised Blue Ridge block. F, erosion to the Fall Line Peneplain, and its covering by Cretaceous sediments, making the surface on which rivers were superimposed. G, the foregoing surface arched, then eroded to the Schooley Peneplain. H, warping of the Schooley Peneplain, shown by the broken line, and erosion to the Lowland Peneplain.

Schooley Peneplain.—This arching rejuvenated the streams, erosion became more active, and eventually, in late Cretaceous times, the great Schooley Peneplain was developed both on the strong granites and metamorphic rocks of Appalachia, and on the weaker sandstones and shales of the mountains and plains. As in New England, this peneplain is not perfect: for a few monadnocks still rise above it, mostly in the southern part of old Appalachia.

Lowland Peneplain.—In the early Eocene this whole area was again warped in a low arch. The axis of this last uplift is not quite parallel to the trend of the mountain folds, but starts in the south, on the east side of the folded mountains, while at the north end it is on the west side of these same folds. The maximum uplift (some 4,000 feet) was in West Virginia and North Carolina, and the doming was less to the north and south. The uplift rejuvenated the streams again.

It is at this time that the Coastal Plain, the Piedmont Belt, the Blue Ridge, the Valley and Ridge Province, the Appalachian Plateaus, and the Interior Plains became differentiated. During the warping the eastern portion of the Schooley Peneplain, originally a part of the oldland, Appalachia, was bent downward, was covered by marine deposits (see Fig. 65), and later was raised above sea level to form the present Coastal Plain. The central part of old Appalachia (including the parts on which Triassic continental deposits were laid down) was tilted, so that its eastern margin was about at sea level and the western margin about 1,000 feet high. This forms what will be described later as the Piedmont Province.

The western margin of the oldland was abruptly bent (partly faulted) upward and makes the Blue Ridge. The highly folded sedimentary rocks make the Valley and Ridge Province, and the gently folded sedimentary rocks farther west form the Appalachian Plateaus. West of the Plateaus the horizontal, or slightly arched, sediments extending beyond the Mississippi River make the Central Lowland in the north, and in the south the Interior Low Plateaus.

Coastal Plain.—The Coastal Plain is a zone of relatively recent marine sediments overlapping the Fall Line Peneplain. Coastal Plain deposits underlie a portion of Cape Cod and

Long Island (page 131) but the Plain begins in New Jersey and extends in a widening strip along the Atlantic coast to Florida, and thence around the Gulf of Mexico to Yucatan (Figure 1). Since the early Cretaceous this continental margin has several times been depressed below sea level, and layers of marine clays and sands deposited on it. The strata are still almost horizontal and but little consolidated. The continental margin has also at several times been higher than it is now, and during each period of elevation some of the marine deposits were removed by erosion. Were all the original deposits still intact, the top of the Coastal Plain would be some 400 feet higher at the old shore line.

The western margin of the Atlantic Coastal Plain is called the Fall Line, being the line at which the rivers from the Piedmont Province descend into the weak marine sediments, either by falls or by rapids. Several cities, from Trenton, New Jersey, in the north to Macon, Georgia, in the south, are situated along this line. Trenton, Philadelphia, Baltimore, Washington, and Richmond are also at the head of navigation as well as at the Fall Line. The Fall Line also marks the intersection of the Fall Line Peneplain and the Schooley Peneplain.

The Atlantic Plain.—That portion of New Jersey east of a line from Staten Island through Trenton to the head of Delaware Bay lies on the Coastal Plain. Most of it is flat and sandy, but in the northern portion the Navesink Highland rises to an elevation of 250 feet. The preservation of this highland is due to the fact that the beds are made up of coarse gravels which are well cemented, and at the same time so porous that the rain sinks through the gravel instead of forming surface streams, which promote erosion.

From Delaware to Alabama the Coastal Plain has the character of a sea bottom raised but little above sea level. The larger rivers cross it in deep valleys made in the Pliocene—valleys which are now largely filled. In the early Pleistocene a depression caused nearly all this southern plain to be submerged for a short time and to be covered by a mantle of reddish sand and clay, some 30 feet in thickness. This mantle, where preserved, gives the present top soil a characteristic red color from southern New Jersey to Louisiana.

Swamps—The time has been so short since the last elevation that complete drainage has not been developed and extensive areas between the rivers are often large swamps, as yet undrained. One of the best known is the Dismal Swamp on the boundary between Virginia and North Carolina. It is a great tract of poorly drained land from 12 to 22 feet above sea level,

Fig. 66.   Cypress trees and knees growing in Dismal Swamp. (After Darton, U. S. G. S.)

in the center of which is a clear lake, Lake Drummond, from six to ten feet deep (according to the rainfall), and with a sandy bottom. This lake is clear of vegetation, but around it there is a dense growth of hydrophytic trees and plants growing on from five to twelve feet of peat. Similar swamps occur as far south as Florida, and westerly across Louisiana. Many of the innumerable lakes in Florida are solution lakes formed in the easily soluble limestone.

Pliocene uplift.—During the Pliocene, when the land of the Coastal Plain was higher than at present, each of the major rivers cut deep channels across the Coastal Plain and the Continental Shelf (page 99). Since the Ice Age the land has sunk and the valleys have been drowned at their lower ends, thus forming deep bays. The Pleistocene depression took place in at least two stages; an earlier, larger, and a later, smaller movement. Between the two movements the major valleys were widened and the numerous tributary streams cut their valleys to grade. On the second movement both the major valleys and the secondary valleys were flooded, making such broad shallow bays or estuaries as Chesapeake and Delaware bays. In each case there is a deep median channel bordered on each side by shallow flats, from five to fifteen feet deep. Estuaries are characteristic features of the coast from New Jersey to Florida.

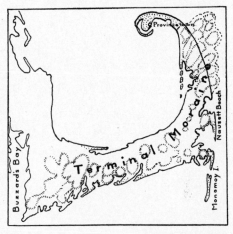

FIG. 67. Cape Cod, showing the terminal moraine and its modifications by wave action, also the position of the cuesta.

Cape Cod.—Cape Cod is composed of Coastal Plain deposits overlain by moraine, both unconsolidated material. This weak material was easily eroded by waves. These, striking the end of the moraine, established two currents—a northerly and a southerly one. The northerly current swept around the end of the mass of till and deposited sand to make the hook at Provincetown, while the southerly current cut off the headlands and made such bars as Nausett Beach and Monomoy Island. The eastern side of the Cape is being worn away at the rate of 3.2 feet a year. Coastal Plain deposits are exposed at the base of the Highlands.

Long Island.—That portion of the Coastal Plain which was east (and a little north) of New York City is now mostly submerged. In New Jersey the even surface of the plain is broken by a cuesta, the top of which conforms to the top of the Cretaceous deposits. As this cuesta extends northeast, it makes the north shore of Long Island, appears on Cape Cod, and is traced by Johnson across the Gulf of Maine to make the northern margin of the Georges Banks and the Grand Banks. From

New York east the Coastal Plain is entirely submerged, except for traces of it on Long Island, Cape Cod, Marthas Vineyard, and Nantucket. The farthest advance of the Continental

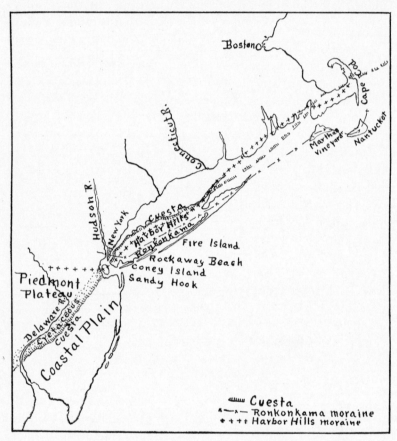

FIG. 68. The Long Island region, showing the terminal moraines of the glaciers, and the cuesta extending from New Jersey along Long Island, across Cape Cod, and out to sea.

Glacier deposited terminal moraines in these sections and thus brought their surfaces well above sea level.

Long Island has two diverging moraines which cause the fish-tail appearance of the east end of the island. These moraines make very irregular hills, composed of boulders and sand, and pitted by kettle holes. The more southerly moraine comes from under the other moraine near Brooklyn on Long

Island, and extends the length of the island as the Ronkonkoma Hills. This moraine also makes the higher portions of Marthas Vineyard and Nantucket. The second moraine runs along the north side of Long Island as the Harbor Hills, and then crosses to the south shore of Connecticut and Rhode Island, finally making the base of Cape Cod. (See Fig. 68.)

Some of the finer till has been washed out of the moraines and spread out as an outwash plain between the two moraines, and in other outwash plains south of the Ronkonkoma ridge. When the island became stabilized at its present level the south shore had a very irregular outline; but this has been greatly modified by the action of the waves and the alongshore currents. The headlands have been cut off, and the sandy debris has been strewn out in a series of bars and beaches pointing westerly, such as Fire Island, Long and Rockaway beaches, and Coney Island. Tidal marshes have developed in the shallow waters inside these beaches.

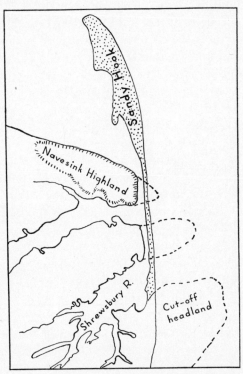

Barrier beaches.— While the irregularities of the coast from Long Island to Florida are primarily due to the submergence of a dissected land, wave and current action have considerably modified

FIG. 69. Sandy Hook and its formation by the cutting off of headlands, and the strewing of the sand in a bar and hook to the north.

the unconsolidated deposits. Storm waves have thrown up barrier beaches in about 25 feet of water, behind which is an almost continuous series of lagoons, often called sounds. Many

of the smaller lagoons have been partially or completely filled
with detritus and vegetation and form tidal marshes.   In many
places the beaches have been reshaped by the alongshore currents.   These tend to cut off the headlands and make spits,
some of which tie the barrier beaches to the mainland.   Two
striking spits are found at the entrance to New York Harbor:
one is Sandy Hook, which is a northerly extension of the barrier
bar off Navesink Highland, and the other is Coney Island, built
out from the Long Island shore.

Florida.—Florida occupies about half of a great projection
of the continental shelf which separates the deep waters of the
Gulf of Mexico from those of the Atlantic Ocean.   The trench
occupied by the Gulf Stream (an old river valley of the Pliocene) is the eastern and southern boundary of the Florida shelf.
This shelf extends to the west for 200 miles before reaching a
depth of 300 feet and then the depth increases abruptly to over
9,000 feet.   This submerged plateau has existed since ancient
times and appears to have been a part of old Appalachia.   It
was above sea level until it was submerged for the first time in
the Upper Cretaceous.   On this sunken platform some 3,700
feet of limestones and calcareous muds were deposited during
the late Cretaceous and early Eocene.   The topmost of these
deposits, and the only part now above sea level, is the white
Ocala limestone, some 300 feet in thickness.   The material for
this great depth of sediment was derived from the Appalachian
Highland; but, owing to the distance from the source, only the
finer clays reached the Florida area.   Much of the material
composing the strata is lime derived from the local animal and
plant life of the time.

Following the period of deposition the strata were slightly
arched just after the Eocene, lifting the Ocala limestone about
150 feet above sea level, and through the early Oligocene
Florida was above the sea.   In middle Oligocene time it was
again submerged.   Then rising in late Oligocene, it remained
above sea level until the middle of the Miocene, when it was
again submerged and some 200 feet of sandy limestone (Hawthorne) was deposited unconformably on top of the other beds.
Before the end of the Miocene the region again rose, and the
central part of Florida has been a land area since that time.

The low-lying east and west coasts were submerged again during the Pleistocene, when the Anastasia sands and limestones were deposited. This last formation is now about 25 feet above sea level at its inner margins, from which its surface slopes gradually to the sea.

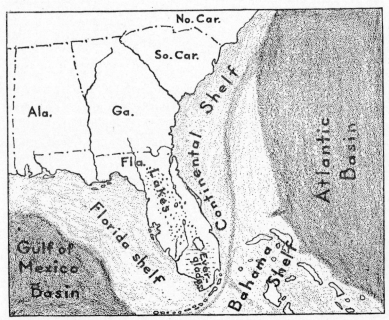

FIG. 70.   Florida, showing its relation to the continental shelf, and the distribution of lakes and the Everglades.

During the Pliocene and recent times, most of the sandy Hawthorne beds have been removed by erosion, but remaining patches form higher hills in the middle and northern parts of the state, where altitudes rise as high as 230 feet. There are areas in this formation where, in the process of erosion, the lime was dissolved and carried away, but the sands and the included phosphates and bones were left. Where the phosphates are concentrated, as they are especially west of the main axis of the state, phosphate mines occur.

Where the Ocala limestone is above sea level in the central part of the state, the rainwater has percolated into the limestone, and dissolved out underground passageways, through which most of the rainfall is now drained to the sea. Where large solution depressions have been formed, sink holes of all sizes dot the landscape. The hundreds of lakes of the "Lake Country" of central Florida are sink holes which have been filled with water. The water of the lakes is clear, as it has been filtered in passing through the rocks. Most of the lakes have no visible inlets or outlets, since they are fed and drained by underground streams. They rise and fall with changes in the underground water supply, and without regard to the immediate rainfall. In places, as at Silver Spring, an underground stream may come to the surface.

The flat east and west coasts and the Everglades are portions of the sea floor raised so recently that its slight irregularities are still unchanged. In the minor depressions shallow ponds and lakes have formed, usually with grass and water vegetation about their margins. In general the slope of the plain is so slight that during the rainy season (summer), water stands six or more inches deep over fully half of the surface. Grass grows up through the water, except where it is two or more feet deep. In recent years drainage canals have been dug across some of these flats, to make the land suitable for agriculture, and these drained areas make excellent sites for citrus fruit orchards and for the growing of vegetables for northern winter markets.

The Everglades are a great tract, some 5,000 square miles in extent, on which the water stands all the year around. Much of the Everglades is covered with a coarse grass growing through the water, and is underlain by an accumulation of six to eight feet of peat. Scattered through the area are hummocks (keys) of vegetable origin, on which bushes and even trees grow, while in other parts the water is deeper and open. In the northern part of the Everglades there are clumps of cypress trees.

Lake Okeechobee is the largest body of open water, being 35 miles across, and some 18 feet above sea level. This shallow depression, 15 feet deep in the middle, has been lowered three or four feet by means of drainage canals to the sea, and a large acreage has in this way been redeemed for farming. However, the grade is so slight and the flow so slow that the canals tend to become choked with growths of water hyacinths.

Along the Atlantic coast, from St. Augustine to Miami, barrier beaches of sand have been thrown up by the waves and

currents, forming a long narrow inner lagoon, known as the
Indian River.   The west coast also has its barrier beaches extending from Charlotte Harbor to Tampa Bay.   Southerly
from Miami there is a long line of keys.   The keys of the outer
part of the fringe, as far as Bahia Honda Channel, are parts of
an old coral reef, which grew up along the margin of the Gulf
Stream during the Pleistocene.   When the country was raised,
these were lifted above
sea level.   The other
keys are made up of the
same sort of rock as
the adjoining mainland
(Miami oölite).   On the
smaller keys and around
the south end of Florida,
the rocks are covered
with a growth of man-
groves to the water's
edge.

The East Gulf plain.
—The East Gulf coastal
plain rounds the south-
ern end of the Appala-
chian Highland and in-
creases in width across
Alabama and Mississippi
and the western parts of
Kentucky and Tennes-

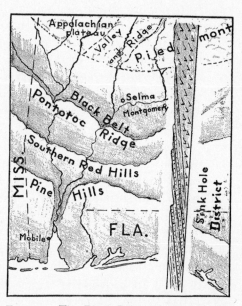

FIG. 71.   The Black Belt of Alabama, with
the cuestas around the south end of the Piedmont; also a section to show the structure.

see to the mouth of the Ohio River.   The surface rises from the
coast at the rate of from four to five feet per mile, but the sediments are tilted so as to rise from thirty to forty feet per mile,
and range from Cretaceous to early Pleistocene in age.   The
present slope of the surface is due to the beveling of the exposed
portions of the various formations.   (See Fig. 71.)

As the surface has been worn down, the weaker layers have
been more deeply eroded than the stronger layers.   Thus ridges
have been produced trending easterly and westerly with the
strike of the rocks (page 76).   Each ridge has a steep north-
facing bluff (cuesta) overlooking a broad interior lowland.

The northern cuesta is the best developed of the series.
It is from 600 to 800 feet above sea level, and the lowland to
the north is from one to two hundred feet lower. It starts
on the Mississippi River bluffs in western Kentucky, extends
southeastward across Tennessee, then eastward across Alabama, and finally dies out near Montgomery, Alabama. The
interior lowland is known in Alabama as the Black Belt, because the impure limestone (Selma Chalk) on which it is developed weathers to a black soil—the most fertile in the South.
The lowland is from 20 to 30 miles wide, its width being determined by the thickness of the Selma Chalk formation.

Two other less-developed cuestas occur between this one
and the Gulf of Mexico, but their interior lowlands have at-
tracted less attention, because they are less perfectly developed
and have less fertile soil. The lowland north of the Pine Hills
is on a weak limestone (Clayton) which in the eastern part of
the state contains so many solution cavities, or sink holes, that
it is called the "sink hole district."

The lower Mississippi Valley.—The Mississippi River crosses
the Coastal Plain in a lowland 50 to 70 miles wide, with bluffs
one to two hundred feet in height on both the east and west
sides. In the Pliocene the river occupied a much deeper valley,
which it carved out while the land was much higher than it is
at present. In post-glacial times this valley was depressed
and the waters of the
Gulf of Mexico flooded
it as far as Cairo at the
mouth of the Ohio
River. The Mississippi
River carried (and still
carries) tremendous

Fig. 72.   Section across the Mississippi Valley.

loads of sediment, enough each year to cover a square mile to
a depth of 268 feet.

Levees.—Gradually the submerged valley was filled to an
unknown depth as the river built its delta forward. Well
drillings have gone down 1,000 feet without reaching the bottom
of the river deposits. On top of the delta the river has laid
top-set beds of sufficient thickness to provide a grade to its
mouth of about six inches to the mile. Incidental to depositing

these top-set beds, the overflowing river has built natural levees on either side, so that the land immediately adjacent to the river became higher than that at the margins of the valley. In the early days these levees were the high ground on which the plantation houses were built. Frequently the river broke out of its restraining levees and made new courses over the delta top so that from Cairo to New Orleans this lowland is strewn with abandoned channels. The most recent of the deserted channels appear as oxbow lakes and swamps.

Before 1880 no attempt was made to prevent the river from overflowing much or all of the lowlands in time of flood, but since then, in order to hold the river in check, artificial levees have been built on top of the natural levees, not only on the main stream, but also up the tributary streams. From time to time breaks have occurred and larger or smaller areas have been flooded. In 1927, the most destructive flood of which there is any record occurred when unusually high water came at the same time from both the Missouri and the Ohio basin, and a large percentage of these artificial barriers gave way. This flood proved that there is a limit to the practicability of levees; for they tend to cause the river to deposit silt on the bottom of the channel, and ever higher and higher levees are required to hold the river in bounds. It may be that floods

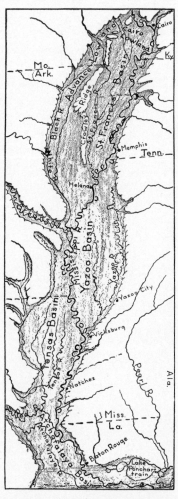

FIG. 73. The Mississippi River basin from Cairo, Illinois, south, to show the amount of excavation during the Pliocene uplift, and the fill since that time.

can best be controlled by building dams to tributary streams, thus holding some of the flood water back in reservoirs.

The history of the lower Mississippi River.—The northern part of the Mississippi lowland consists of two parts, the Advance Lowland and the Cairo Lowland, separated by a remnant of the upland termed Crowley's Ridge. The earlier

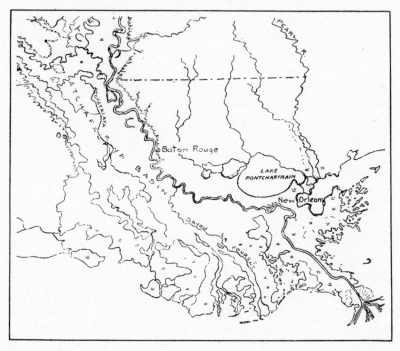

FIG. 74. The lower portion of the Mississippi River, showing the building out of the delta into the Gulf of Mexico. (After A. K. Lobeck, from *Physiographic Diagram of the United States*, courtesy of A. J. Nystrom & Co.)

course of the Mississippi River was through the Advance Lowland, by way of valleys now occupied by the Black River and the lower part of the White River. At that time the Mississippi united with the Ohio River at the point where it is now joined by the White River. In the meantime a small branch of the Ohio River worked back across Crowley's Ridge and tapped the Mississippi River, which then shifted its course approximately to that now followed by the St. Francis River, joining the Ohio about where Helena, Arkansas, now stands.

Later the great river found a cut-off across Crowley's Ridge farther upstream and shifted to its present course, joining the Ohio at Cairo. These shifts shortened the Ohio River by some 100 miles, and the two older courses of the Mississippi River are now occupied by smaller rivers. The Cairo and St. Francis basins were made by the Ohio River, and by it filled to approximately their present levels.

In 1811 and 1812 a series of earthquakes occurred in the western portion of Kentucky and Tennessee and in southeastern Missouri and northeastern Arkansas (known as the New Madrid earthquake). Some areas were elevated, and a large area was depressed; the latter is still known as the "sunken lands." The result of this disturbance in an already ill-drained country was to convert sluggish streams into lakes and bayous. The St. Francis River was in part depressed, and Big Lake, St. Francis River Overflow, and Little River Overflow are enduring reminders of the earthquakes. On the east side of the Basin, Reelfoot Lake has the same origin.

Between Memphis and Vicksburg, the Mississippi River is on the western side of its valley, the area between it and the eastern bluffs being known as the Yazoo Basin. The Yazoo River, flowing along the east side of the basin, not only gathers the waters coming from the eastern highlands, but also has several tributaries which rise on the eastern levees of the Mississippi River itself, and flow away from the big river.

At Vicksburg the Mississippi swings back to the eastern side of the basin. The lowland to the west of it is the Tensas Basin, drained by the river of the same name, which flows into the Red River. Below the Red River is the Atchafalaya Basin, drained by the Atchafalaya River. This stream gathers several large western tributaries and empties into the Gulf of Mexico without ever reaching the Mississippi. The major streams from the west cut deep valleys during the Pliocene, so that the bluff on the west side of the lowland is much dissected.

From Baton Rouge south, the Mississippi delta is built out into the Gulf of Mexico, and the mud-laden river is depositing silt opposite each of its many mouths. The frequent choking of these outlets by deposits causes shifting of the mouths from place to place on the delta, a navigable channel being kept open only by constant dredging.   In the irregular shiftings of the river's mouths some areas have been blocked off from the Gulf without being filled to the full height of the delta.   Such places are converted into shallow lakes, fresh rain water soon replacing the sea water.   Such was the origin of lakes like Pontchartrain, Salvador, Allemandes, and Grand.   The unconsolidated muds

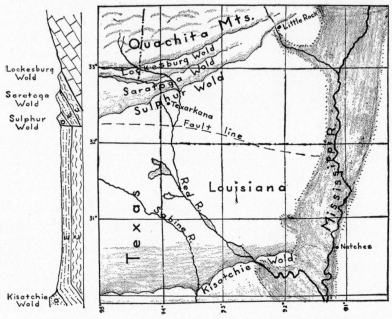

FIG. 75.   The wolds of Louisiana.   The structure section on the left shows their formation.

deposited by the river are easily acted on by the waves and currents, which have built barrier bars and islands eastward as far as Mobile Bay.

West Gulf Coastal Plain.—West of the Mississippi River the Coastal Plain occupies Louisiana, and extends into Arkansas to the Ouachita Mountains.   In Texas it becomes narrower, finally ending in Yucatan opposite the middle of Mexico.   This section of the plain was higher in the Pliocene than it is now, as was true on the Atlantic coast, and the rivers cut valleys well below the present sea level.   The mouths of all these river valleys are now drowned, and the old channels are partly filled,

making the rivers sluggish. The West Gulf plain has been
subjected to an erosional history similar to that already described for the eastern section. As a result the stronger layers
outcrop as cuestas, which locally are called "wolds." The
southernmost of these, the Kisatchie Wold, starts in Texas and

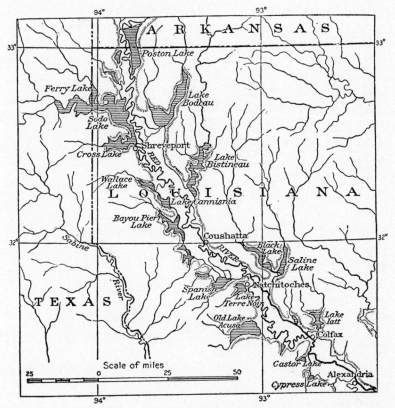

Fig. 76. The Red River, showing the overflows at their maximum. (After
Veatch, U. S. G. S.)

extends to the Mississippi Basin. North of this are three
others: the Sulphur, Saratoga, and Lockesburg wolds.

Instead of the uniform upward slope from the seacoast
generally characteristic of a coastal plain, the beds rise rather
steeply (35 to 100 feet to the mile) as far north as a line from
Angelina County, Texas, to Vicksburg, Mississippi. This line
makes the crest of a gentle fold, to the north of which the beds
are nearly horizontal, until they reach an east-west fault, which

has been traced from Dennison, Texas, to Alabama Landing, Louisiana. The displacement on this fault is about 600 feet, but as the weaker rocks have been worn off on both sides to about the same level there is no contrast in surface forms on opposite sides of the fault plane.

Red River rafts.—Something over 200 years ago the Red River was choked by the formation of a log jam of drifting tree trunks at a point about 160 miles below Alexandria, Louisiana. (See Figure 76.) The jam slowed up the flow of the water and caused the deposition of silt. Floating logs and other debris gradually piled up behind the dam, forming what is termed the "Great Raft." The water behind rose until it found an outlet some four or five miles above the jam. Other jams were successively formed and the raft, with some open sections, was gradually built up the river, until it reached Alexandria.

As debris filled the river, lakes were formed, mostly at the mouths of tributary streams, and new channels were made from lake to lake around the sections of the jam. When the logs at the lower end of the great raft decayed or became waterlogged and sank, the channel was again partly opened and the side lakes were slowly drained. The sinking of the raft proceeded at the rate of about a fifth of a mile a year while at the same time the jam continued to form above Alexandria. In 1873 the government began to break up the raft, since which time the river has returned to its original channel, and most of the lakes have been drained.

Mounds.—Rudely circular mounds three to five feet high, and 20 to 100 feet in diameter, occur by the hundreds on the top of the late Pleistocene (Port Hudson) deposits, forming the "pimple prairies." They also occur on other formations, but not on the recent flood plains. They are composed of fine loam, which, however, is coarser in texture than the clayey soil on which they rest and remains distinct from it. As yet they are unexplained, though numerous theories of their origin have been offered. It seems to the writer most likely that they are the remains of former termite hills. Desert sand hills, gas vents, and springs have also been suggested as possible origins.

Domes.—Domes are much larger structures, being a mile or more in diameter, and formed where the rock layers have been pushed up from 200 to 300 feet by cores of salt. Usually the tops of these domes have been eroded off, but they may even then be recognized by the circular ridges due to the varied strength of the rocks involved.

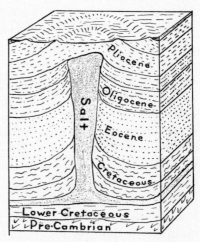

The salt-bearing bed is Lower Cretaceous in age, and overlain by a great depth of later rocks. The pressure exerted by the weight of the overlying rocks has evidently caused the salt to flow toward points of weakness where in some cases it has broken through the cover and in other cases lifted the overlying beds. What determined the points of yielding is not known. Many salt domes are found in Louisiana, the only region where they are known to occur in the United States.

FIG. 77. Structure of a salt dome.

These domes are of special interest not only on account of the salt, but also because they provide suitable points for the accumulation of petroleum. Many salt domes have become the sites of successful oil production. The oil wells are usually "gushers" when first brought in.

BIBLIOGRAPHY

Cooke, C. W., and Mossum, S., *Geology of Florida*, Florida Geological Survey, 20th Annual Report, 1928.

Fuller, M. L., *Geology of Long Island*, U. S. Geological Survey, Professional Paper, No. 82, 1914.

Johnson, D. W., *New England Acadian Shoreline*, 1925.

Veach, A. C., *Geology and Underground Water Resources of Louisiana*, U. S. Geological Survey, Professional Paper, No. 46, 1906.

U. S. Geological Folios: Norfolk, Va., No. 80; Choptank, Md., No. 182.

U. S. Geological Survey, Topographic Maps: Islip, Staten Island for New York; Sandy Hook* for New Jersey; Ocean City* for Maryland; Washington and Vicinity for District of Columbia; Norfolk* for Virginia; Ocala for Florida; Bayou Sara for Louisiana.

CHAPTER XIII

THE PIEDMONT PROVINCE

That portion of old Appalachia which lies west of the Coastal Plain and east of the sharp upturn which makes the Blue Ridge is the Piedmont Province or Belt. It extends southward from the Hudson River until it disappears under the Coastal Plain in Alabama. In the north it is about 50 miles wide, but it broadens southward until in South Carolina it is 125 miles in width. Here above sea level at its contact with the Coastal Plain it is about 400 feet, and it rises 20 feet to the mile until on the western side it is 1,000 to 1,200 feet in altitude. In general the rock surface consists of highly folded and metamorphosed Pre-Cambrian rocks. On the west side there are bits of infolded Cambrian and Silurian sedimentary rocks, and in the north to middle portions are large insets of Triassic sandstone and lava. Generally the top surface of the whole belt is the Schooley Peneplain, the Lowland Peneplain being developed only on the weak rocks of the Triassic inset and on the infolded bits of Cambrian or Silurian rocks.

Drainage.—The rivers mostly have a southeast course, the result of their development on the Fall Line Peneplain and of being superimposed on this region. They cross the Piedmont without regard to the trend or strength of the rocks. On the lowlands developed on the Triassic area, there has, however, been some diversion of streams by pirating; but as these streams cross several provinces, their history will be considered later.

Triassic Lowland.—The most interesting portion of the Piedmont is the lowland developed on the Triassic sandstones, whose origin is described on page 10. The Triassic lowland is confluent with the Coastal Plain from Staten Island to the Delaware River; and with the Valley and Ridge Province from Reading, Pennsylvania, to beyond the Susquehanna River, thus making a deep bay of lowlands reaching to Culpeper,

Virginia. The Triassic deposits include no lava flows which extended over the whole area, but in places there are one,

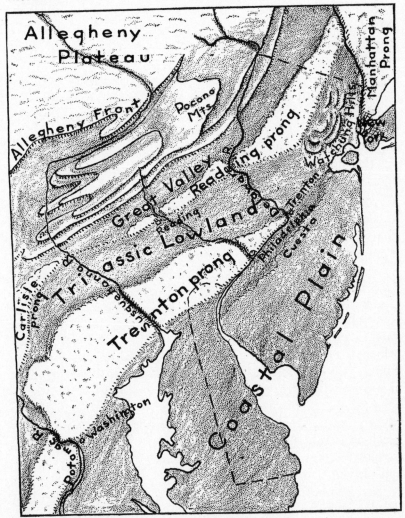

FIG. 78. Northern portion of the Piedmont Province, showing the inset Triassic area and the surrounding "prongs."

two, or three sheets of lava, and on the northern border there is an intrusion, which spread between the layers to make an extensive sill. Where the sandstone has been eroded to make the lowland, the lava sheets and the sill stand out in relief.

Prongs.—The lowland area is surrounded by a series of tapering highlands which Davis has described as "prongs," giving each the name of the city near its point. There is the Manhattan prong on the east, the Reading prong on the north, the Trenton prong on the south, and the Carlisle prong on the southwest.

The Reading prong extends along the Hudson River from Stony Point to Newburgh, and thence across southern New York and northern New Jersey to a point near Reading, Pennsylvania. It is a highland with the hills from 900 to 1,000 feet in altitude. In New Jersey the heights are ridges on the more resistant rocks, while the intervening valleys are mostly on infolded limestones.

FIG. 79. Section from New York City across the Watchung Hills, to show the relation of the Schooley and Lowland Peneplains.

The Carlisle prong is more elevated than the others and merges into the eastern border of the Blue Ridge Province, which is separated from the Piedmont Belt by the Triassic fault. At the north end the prong is about 1,000 feet high, but it rises rapidly to the south and in Maryland reaches an altitude of 2,100 feet. The eastern portion of the prong is a hill-and-valley country composed of folded crystalline rocks which slope gradually down to an abrupt margin with the lowland.

The Trenton prong, while a highland on hard rocks, ranges only from 400 to 600 feet in elevation.

The Manhattan prong is the southwest corner of the New England Province and consists of highly metamorphosed and contorted rocks.

The northern Piedmont.—The Hudson River follows the contact line between Triassic rocks and the older rocks of the New England Province. This portion of the Hudson apparently has a subsequent course, owing to the work of a small stream which developed between the strong rocks of New England and the sill now known as the Palisades, and which tapped the older Hudson and diverted it to its present course, sometime before the Pliocene. Its older course was through the Sparkill gap across the Watchung Hills to the Raritan River. (See Fig. 80.)

Palisades.—The intrusion of lava which now forms the Palisades cooled slowly, and as a result developed a columnar structure. As the Hudson River cut under the lava, some of

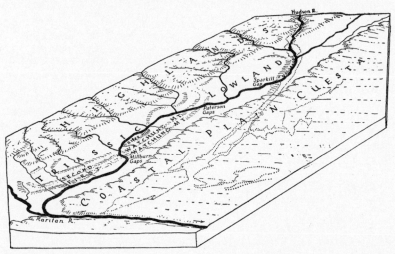

FIG. 80. Block diagram of the Hudson River in the Miocene when it flowed through the Watchung Hills. (After Johnson, from *Stream Sculpture on the Atlantic Slope*, by permission of the Columbia University Press.)

the columns fell, leaving the cliffs known as the Palisades. The top of the Palisades sill forms a ridge which rises from the sea south of Jersey City, reaches a height of about 100 feet at Hoboken, and then rises to approximately 300 feet farther north. The top surface of the Palisades is the Schooley Peneplain.

The wharves and docks of Hoboken are on the Lowland Peneplain, and all but one of the railroads extending south or west tunnel through this sill. To the west of the Palisades the roads come out again onto the Lowland Peneplain in the Hackensack Meadows. On this surface, which rises gradually toward the west, are situated Newark, Elizabeth, and Passaic.

A little farther to the west are three crescent-shaped ridges, the Watchung Hills, some 300 feet high. They are the outcrops of three sheets of lava separated by Triassic sedimentary rocks. On these ridges in the lowland are located Orange, Paterson, and Plainfield. A few other lesser ridges of lava occur in the lowland.

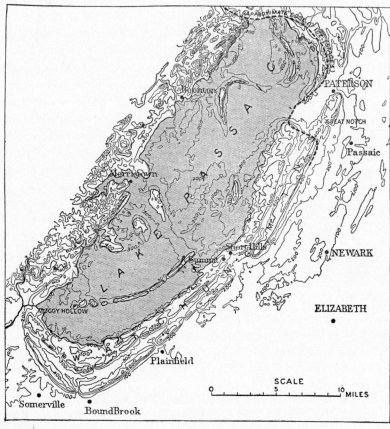

FIG. 81. Lake Passaic at its maximum development. (After Darton, U. S. G. S.)

Passaic Lake.—The Ice Sheet covered a corner of the Piedmont Belt, the terminal moraine extending from Staten Island nearly to Paterson, New Jersey, and thence on through Morristown, New Jersey. With the changes in elevation and in the position of the ice front associated with the advance and recession of the Continental Glacier, the Passaic River was blocked and flooded the basin between the Watchung Hills and the Morristown highlands, to make a large lake (now extinct) known as Lake Passaic.   At the time of its maximum development (see Fig. 79), it was drained by a stream at the south end going out through Moggy Hollow.   The postglacial uplift and retreat of the ice drained the lake and restored the preglacial drainage conditions.

The southern Piedmont.—The southern portion of the Piedmont Province is on the strong crystalline rocks of the old land, Appalachia.   The amount of material removed from this region in the past has been great, and today the roots of an old mountain system are here exposed, as they are in portions of New England.   During the development of the Schooley Peneplain the Piedmont was nearly leveled except for a few monadnocks of which Stone Mountain, near Atlanta, Georgia, is the most conspicuous.   Since the upwarping of the Schooley Peneplain, valleys have been cut into the strong rocks, but nowhere has any extensive area of lowlands been developed.   The Piedmont here is a hill-and-valley country with the peneplain level shown by the even sky line and the uniform height of the hilltops. The section is far south of the glaciated region, and the deep soil cover is entirely residual.

BIBLIOGRAPHY

Johnson, D. W., *Stream Sculpture on the Atlantic Slope*, 1931.
U. S. Geological Survey Folios: New York City and the Adjacent Country, No. 83; Passaic, N. J., No. 157; Raritan, N. J., No. 191; Fairfield and Gettysburg, Pa., No. 225.
U. S. Geological Survey Topographic maps: Paterson for New Jersey; Philadelphia for Pennsylvania; Antietam for Maryland; King's Mountain, Mount Mitchell, Pisgah for North Carolina; Ellijay, Rome for Georgia.

CHAPTER XIV

THE BLUE RIDGE, THE VALLEY AND RIDGE PROVINCE, AND THE APPALACHIAN PLATEAUS

The three provinces, the Blue Ridge, the Valley and Ridge Province, and the Appalachian Plateaus, have had a unified physiographic history in spite of the differences in rock character and strength. For this reason it is unfortunate that the Blue Ridge is often termed the Older Appalachians, and the Valley and Ridge Province the Newer Appalachians. These are geologic terms and refer to the relative ages of the rocks. They suggest that the present differences in physiographic expression were developed at different periods, when as a matter of fact they result from the uplift of the Schooley Peneplain which had been developed in late Cretaceous or early Tertiary times, over all the Appalachian Highland. The central axis of the arch of the uplift does not follow the structural lines of the mountain ranges, which were formed during the Appalachian Revolution, for the southern end of the axis lies on the crystalline rocks of the Blue Ridge, while the northern end is on the west side of the Valley and Ridge Province (see p. 128).

The Fall Line Peneplain received a thin cover of Coastal Plain deposits, on which consequent streams were developed as the land rose and the sea receded. During subsequent periods of elevation these consequent streams became superimposed on the underlying strong rocks, while their tributaries gradually developed courses adjusted to the strength of the rock layers. Therefore, today the Valley and Ridge Province is drained by streams that have the trellis arrangement characteristic of adjusted streams.

Following the uplift of the Schooley Peneplain, the Lowland Peneplain (generally called the Harrisburg Peneplain in this region) was developed on the weaker layers of rock, particularly in the Valley and Ridge Province. The Lowland Peneplain was again elevated and the Somerville Peneplain was developed on the weakest rocks. Finally, during or just before the Ice Age, both peneplains were raised approximately to their present height, and the rivers are now cutting shallow trenches into the latest, or Somerville, peneplain. Thus the physiographic history of these three provinces represents several stands of the land in reference to the sea, and during each stand landscape features were developed which are still extant.

The Blue Ridge.—The Blue Ridge is composed of the same types of rocks as is the Piedmont Province; but it is higher than the Piedmont because at the time of the first uplift of the Schooley Peneplain a sharp upward flexure developed along its eastern margin. In places, especially in the north, faulting took place along the line of flexure.

The Blue Ridge begins at the Hudson River, as the "Highlands of New York," and narrows to a point near Reading, Pennsylvania, forming the Reading prong already described (page 148). Here the Blue Ridge is interrupted by a gap some 50 miles in width where the Triassic Lowland (page 146) meets the Great Valley. The Blue Ridge then reappears at South Mountain near Carlisle, Pennsylvania, where it is narrow and only about 1,000 feet in height. Southward the altitude steadily increases until about thirty miles south of the Potomac River the Ridge is 2,000 feet high. Beyond this point there are some mountain peaks—Marshall (3,374 feet), Stony Man (4,031 feet), Hawks Bill (4,066 feet)—which represent the first of a series of monadnocks rising above the Schooley Peneplain.

In North Carolina the Blue Ridge Province begins to widen, and becomes a tangled mass of minor ranges. The eastern border of the mountain belt, known locally as the Blue Ridge Mountains, is the divide between the rivers flowing to the east and those flowing to the west. The western margin of the Blue Ridge Province comprises several short ranges, the most outstanding being the Unaka, the Great Smoky, the Iron, the Bald, and the Stony, together with several smaller ranges at various angles to these, such as Cow Bell, Sassafras, and Frog.

An early peneplain of uncertain age is represented in places by the even crest lines of many peaks, but it was incomplete,

and many single or clustered peaks rise above it.   On the eastern so-called Blue Ridge Mountains the highest monadnock is
Grandfather Mountain (5,964 feet); but on the broader interior
highland there are still higher peaks, especially in the Black
Mountain Range of North Carolina. Mt. Mitchell (6,711 feet)
is the highest peak in the United States east of the Mississippi

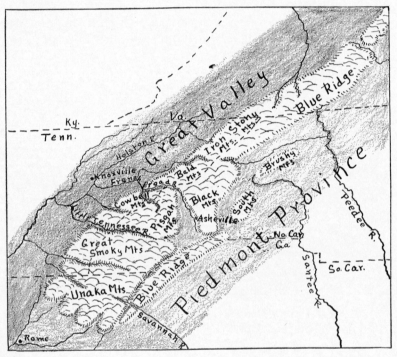

FIG. 82.   The southern portion of the Blue Ridge.

River. The clusters of peaks rising above the peneplain level
are termed *unakas*, named from the Unaka Mountain Range.
Because of the resistant character of the rocks the Schooley
Peneplain is only locally developed in the Blue Ridge Province,
where it corresponds with the broad valley floors near the
headwaters of the streams at an altitude of about 2,000 feet.
The French Broad at Asheville is an instance. From the
strong rock uplands there is an abrupt drop on the west side
to the Lowland Peneplain of the Great Valley, forming what is
termed the "eastern front."

The Valley and Ridge Province.—The Valley and Ridge Province is composed of a series of valleys on the Lowland Peneplain level, alternating with ridges which in general rise to the level of the Schooley Peneplain. The western margin of the province is made by an abrupt wall rising from the lowland to the edge of the Appalachian Plateaus, and termed the "Allegheny Front." This escarpment is due to a great bed of strong sandstones and conglomerates which underlie the surface of the Plateaus and which have been left in relief as the

FIG. 83. Pisgah Mountains from Eagle's Nest near Waynesville, N. C., to show the character of the southern portion of the Blue Ridge. (After Keith, U. S. G. S.)

surrounding lowlands have been developed by erosion. In the north the Front begins at the Catskill Mountains, and extends southwestward at an altitude of about 2,000 feet into Pennsylvania, where it is termed the Pocono Mountains. The altitude rises slowly to 3,327 feet at the Pinnacles in West Virginia, then to 4,400 feet at Roaring Plains. From that point the altitude decreases, being about 2,400 feet at Cumberland Gap, and only about 900 feet where it meets the Coastal Plain in Alabama.

The Valley Ridges: Great Valley.—The rocks which underlie the Valley and Ridge Province are highly folded sedimentary rocks of early Palaeozoic age. The ridges are the stronger sandstone layers which have been beveled off to the level of the Schooley Peneplain, while the intervening shale and limestone layers have been eroded down to the level of the Lowland Peneplain and are now being again dissected. In the north the ridges are largely confined to the western side of the province, while the eastern portion is a continuous lowland, called the Great Valley, and contiguous in Pennsylvania with the Triassic Lowland (page 146). The Great Valley is known as

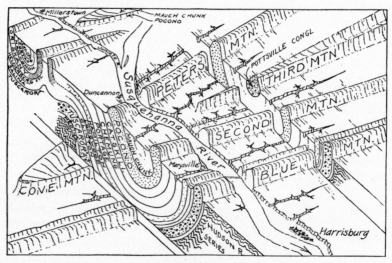

FIG. 84. Structure section and block diagram of the region near Harrisburg, Pennsylvania, to show how the ridges are dominantly on the sandstone layers, while the valleys are on the shales and limestones. (Courtesy of A. K. Lobeck, from *Atlas of American Geology.*)

the Lebanon Valley in Pennsylvania, the Shenandoah Valley in Virginia, and the Hagerstown Valley in Maryland. In the south the ridges are most prominent on the eastern side of the Valley and Ridge Province, while the Tennessee River occupies the broad lowland on the west.

The floor of the Great Valley south of the Catskills is about 300 feet above sea level, but it rises slowly southward until it is 2,000 feet above sea level in southern Virginia. From this point southward it then drops slowly until in Alabama it is less than 500 feet high where it abuts on the Coastal Plain. The warping of both the floor of the valley and the fronts, since the latest peneplain was formed, took place just after the Pliocene or in the Ice Age. The heights of the ridges above the valley lowland represent the interval between the Schooley and the Lowland Peneplain levels.

In the southern portion of the Valley and Ridge Province, owing to greater uplift, the tops of the folds were eroded off in the development of the Schooley Peneplain so that the strong sandstone layers form more or less parallel ridges. In Pennsylvania the uplift was less, and the tops of the folds have not been entirely removed by erosion. As a result, a strong rock layer may be traced continuously about adjoining anti-clinal and synclinal folds. Such curves in the ridges are described as "zigzags," and are particularly well shown in the region from which most of the anthracite coal comes (Fig. 84). Similar structures are seen in the foothills of the Catskills and mark the dying out of the Appalachian folds.

Drainage development following the uplift of the Schooley Peneplain.—The original drainage of the Valley and Ridge Province and of the Blue Ridge Province was established on the Cretaceous deposits which were laid down on the top of the Fall Line Peneplain during the development of the Schooley Peneplain. With the up-arching of the Fall Line Peneplain, drainage was developed in opposite directions from the axis of the uplift. On the easterly side of the axis the general direction of the drainage was to the southeast, which is still the course of the rivers in the southern section—such as the Roanoke, the Peedee, the Santee, and the Savannah. These rivers rise on the Blue Ridge, and have been superimposed on strong rocks, with but slight diversion from their original courses.

North of the Roanoke the axis of the greatest elevation of the Fall Line Peneplain was on the west side of the Valley and Ridge Province and formed the drainage divide. While the lower portions of the streams often still have the original south-east courses, the upper reaches have in most cases been more or less diverted from their original courses by the piracy of younger streams developed on the weak sedimentary rocks of the Valley and Ridge Province. Their present courses are thus composite in character, being in part superimposed and in part subsequent in origin (page 75).

The Delaware River.—The Delaware River of today is such a composite stream. The upper branches of the river drain the south and west sides of the Catskill Mountains and flow to the southeast, but their courses suggest that preceding the development of the Schooley Peneplain and even after it began to be uplifted, they rose on the Adirondack Mountains. They were later diverted by the subsequent Mohawk River which worked its way westward from the Hudson and captured them. The escarpment forming the northern margin of the Plateau has developed as the Mohawk has deepened its valley.

At Port Jervis the Delaware turns abruptly to the southwest and for a short distance follows the weak rock valley north of the Kittatinny Ridge. Then as suddenly it reverts to the southeast again, passes through the famous Delaware Water Gap which it has cut through the Kittatinny Ridge, and continues in the same direction to the edge of the Coastal Plain, whence it follows a subsequent southwesterly course to the head of Delaware Bay.

The portion of the Delaware River flowing southeast represents parts of ancient streams. The portion of the river north of the Kittatinny Ridge is younger in date and represents a pirate stream which was a tributary of the North Branch of the Susquehanna River (Fig. 85). As this young subsequent stream elongated toward the northeast, it diverted the upper Delaware River and also several other smaller streams which were crossing the Kittatinny Ridge. The original courses of these smaller streams are indicated by wind gaps in the ridge, such as Culver's Gap, and the one near Buskill, N. J. The original lower Delaware River must have flowed southeasterly across the Coastal Plain (as indicated by the dotted line) but, along with the Schuylkill River, its present lower portion has been diverted to the southwest by a subsequent stream which developed along the outcrop of the Cretaceous beds.

The Susquehanna River.—The Susquehanna River is also a composite stream, which has in addition suffered decapitation by changes during the Ice Age. Before that time the Susquehanna drained all of central and southern New York State. During the retreat of the Ice Sheet, a large moraine was deposited east and west across the state. The Susquehanna tribu-

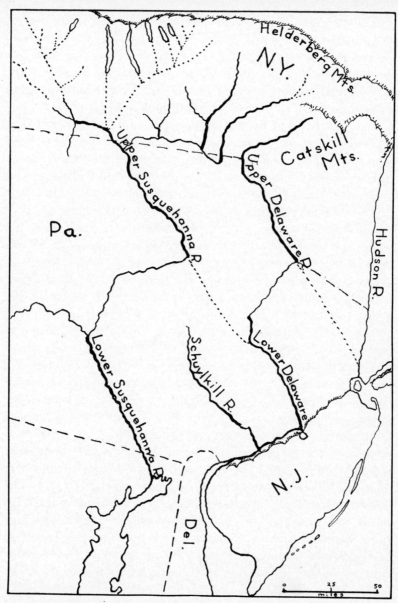

FIG. 85. The Susquehanna and Delaware rivers, with dotted lines to show
their original superimposed courses. (After D. W. Johnson, from *Stream
Sculpture on the Atlantic Slope*, by permission of the Columbia University
Press.)

taries to the north of the moraine backed up against this barrier and made the so-called Finger Lakes (Canandaigua, Keuka, Seneca, and Cayuga). These lakes overflowed toward the north before they reached an outlet over the moraine and thus robbed the Susquehanna River of more than a dozen of its tributaries, as indicated on Figure 85.

That portion of the river marked Upper Susquehanna is an old course antedating the Schooley Peneplain. Where the river crossed the Appalachian folds to make the lower Delaware it was tapped by a branch from the lower Susquehanna, and its waters diverted to that stream and carried to the head of Chesapeake Bay, under which there is a submerged channel extending to the edge of the continental shelf.

The Potomac and James rivers.—The Potomac is a superimposed river, which rises on the east side of the Appalachian Plateaus, crosses the transverse ridges of the Valley and Ridge Province, and cuts through the Blue Ridge in the water gap at Harper's Ferry. Several smaller streams to the south ran parallel to the Potomac. With the uplift of the Schooley Peneplain, the Shenandoah, a tributary to the Potomac, began to develop on the limestone belt of the Valley and Ridge Province, and progressively beheaded several of the smaller streams, whose former courses are now indicated by wind gaps. The first was Beaverdam Creek, which was making slow work of cutting a channel across the Blue Ridge. Its course was through the wind gap known as Snicker's Gap. Eventually the Shenandoah reached its base level (the Lowland Peneplain) and gradually made the mature valley in the floor of which it is now inset. The James River is the most southern of the rivers which rise on the west of the Blue Ridge and follow a course across it.

The drainage on the westerly side of the arch.—The drainage which developed on the westerly side of the Appalachian arch flowed normally toward the northwest. The New-Kanawha, rising near the eastern front of the Blue Ridge and crossing the Valley and Ridge Province and the Appalachian Plateaus on its way to the Ohio River, is the only stream which maintains a northwest direction throughout its course. The headwaters of a large number of these northwest-flowing streams are

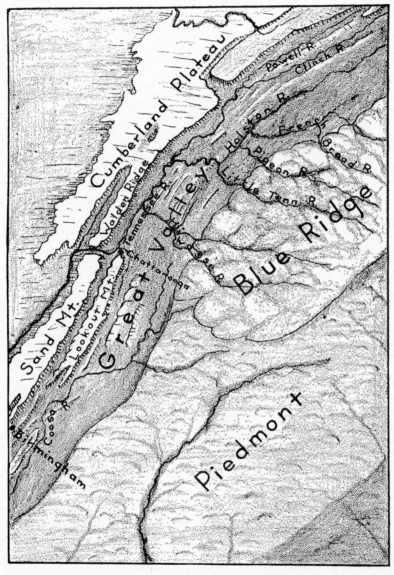

FIG. 86. The southern portion of the Appalachian Mountains, and the modified drainage resulting from the piracy of such streams as the Holston and Tennessee rivers.

now represented by the French Broad, the Pigeon, the Little
Tennessee, and the Hiwassee, each rising on the Blue Ridge
and flowing westerly. All these streams, except the New-
Kanawha, have been intercepted by the Holston, Clinch,
Powell, or Upper Tennessee rivers in the process of becoming
adjusted to the limestone valleys between the sandstone ridges
of the Valley and Ridge Province, and now flow southwest
after leaving the Blue Ridge Province.

The Cumberland River was a large river which left the
Valley and Ridge Province at Cumberland Gap. It had eroded
at least half way down to the level of the Lowland Peneplain
before it was tapped and beheaded by some subsequent stream
like the Powell River. Cumberland Gap is now one of several
wind gaps along the Allegheny Front. It was through this gap
that the "Wilderness Road" of the early pioneers passed from
the Valley and Ridge Province onto the Plateau.

The southern end of the Valley and Ridge Province is drained
by the Coosa River, which is very little altered from its original
superimposed position. The Coosa River has developed a
recent peneplain at an altitude of approximately 600 feet,
through which it is now following a meandering course cut well
below the valley level. Its course has evidently been inherited
from the previous cycle when the river had old-age features.

Plateau outliers in the Valley and Ridge Province.—From
Chattanooga southward several isolated uplands which are
usually considered as belonging to the Appalachian Plateaus
seem to the writer to belong to the Valley and Ridge Province.
Sand, or Raccoon, Mountain, whose surface layers are strong
sandstones, is a flat-topped remnant of the Schooley Peneplain.
It was isolated from the Appalachian Plateau because anticlines on either side, owing to the weak rocks underlying the
sandstones, have been weathered down to the Lowland Peneplain level. Lookout Mountain is a similar remnant on sandstone, which has been made famous as the site of the Battle
of Lookout Mountain. Walden Ridge is another similar
feature, but it is only partially separated from the Appalachian
Plateau by the anticlinal valley now followed by the Sequatchie
River.

Birmingham is situated near the south end of Sand Mountain,

where a ten-foot red hematite iron layer of Silurian age outcrops. Close by are two coal fields, and the floor of the valley is underlain by limestone. Thus all the raw materials requisite for producing steel are found close together.

Appalachian Plateaus.—Westward from the Allegheny Front is a broad belt of land, known as the Appalachian Plateaus, where the little-folded top layers are mostly sandstone and conglomerate, and over which the Schooley Peneplain was well developed. In the south only a few minor monadnocks rise above this level, and these are due not so much to the resistant character of the rocks as to location between opposing streams. When the Schooley Peneplain was raised in the Eocene, little shale, or limestone, was exposed on this surface, and hence the Lowland Peneplain has not been developed.

The border of the Appalachian Plateaus begins just north of the Catskill Mountains and runs west across New York State as far as Cleveland, Ohio. There it extends southward through Ohio, Kentucky, and Tennessee, meeting the Coastal Plain in north central Alabama (Fig. 1). The resistant Helderberg Limestone makes a strong escarpment, called the Helderberg Mountains, which faces the Mohawk Valley and forms the northern border of the plateaus in New York State. From the middle of the state westward, the Helderberg formation becomes thinner and the escarpment is not so marked.

Catskill Mountains.—The so-called Catskill Mountains, on the east end of the Plateaus, are composed of nearly horizontal layers of sandstone, shale, and limestone, neither folded nor metamorphosed. They are residuals or monadnocks left standing above the Schooley Peneplain owing to the resistance of the top layers. The relief is made more prominent because the Hudson Valley on the east and the Kittatinny Valley on the south have been eroded to the Lowland Peneplain level. From these valleys, which are only about a hundred feet above sea level, the Catskills rise abruptly to elevations above 4,000 feet (Slide Mountain 4,205 feet, Hunter Mountain 4,025 feet, Black Dome 3,990 feet). To the north and west the drop to the Schooley Peneplain level is only about 2,000 feet.

On the east, streams have carved deep ravines (known as coves) into this residual mass, forming two clusters of peaks

separated by Esopus Creek. It is this creek that New York
City has dammed at Gilboa to supplement its water supply.
Two of these streams now dissecting the escarpment have
beheaded Schoharie Creek, which flows northwest.

The Genesee River.—The Genesee River in western New York
has had a complicated history.

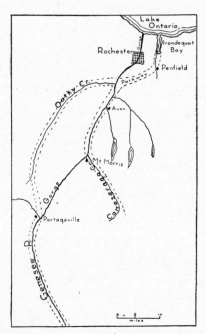

Before the Ice Age it flowed
northerly into Lake Ontario, or
rather into the Ontario River,
and had developed a mature
valley, as indicated in Figure
87. The ice sheet buried or
obstructed the old pre-glacial
valley, and the post-glacial
Genesee River left its former
course at Portageville. It
carved a deep gorge along a
new path to Mt. Morris and
then followed the mature valley of Caneseraga Creek nearly
to Rochester. Here it again
left its old valley and has cut
a gorge to Lake Ontario, near
the head of which are three
waterfalls: the upper one, in
the middle of Rochester, 98
feet high; the second but 20
feet high; and the third, on the
north side of the city, 102 feet
high. The old abandoned val-

Fig. 87. Shifting of the Genesee
River as a result of blocking during
the Ice Age. The dotted lines are
the preglacial course; the solid lines
represent the present course. (After
Grabau.)

ley (now a parkway) may be followed around the city to the
east to Irondequoit Bay.

The central portion of the Plateaus.—The Plateaus attain their
greatest height in West Virginia and Kentucky, reaching a
maximum altitude in one section of 4,000 feet. This portion
of the Plateaus is often popularly styled the Allegheny Mountains because young valleys have been cut to depths of from
1,000 to 1,500 feet below the upland level of the Schooley
Peneplain. The digitate streams are so numerous and their

valleys are so deep that the relief is very strong. In consequence it has been difficult to build roads and, though the region was early occupied, it has developed slowly, except where coal-mining has become established. Extensive beds of bituminous coal are interbedded between the upper layers of sediments, and have been exposed on the sides of many of the valleys.

As the rocks are nearly horizontal, mining is relatively easy, and today Pennsylvania and West Virginia are the leading coal-producing states in the United States. Petroleum occurs in the lower strata; it was in Pennsylvania that the first oil well in the country was opened. The largest city on the Plateaus is Pittsburgh, at the head of navigation on the Ohio River, in the midst of the coal fields, near to iron deposits, and on an easy route across the region.

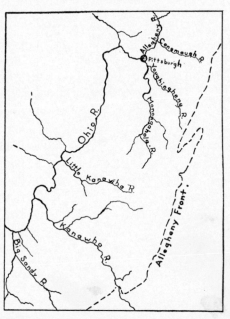

FIG. 88. The drainage of the Appalachian Plateau, showing the original streams and their relation to the Ohio River, formed in the Glacial Period.

Drainage.—The pre-glacial drainage of the central portion of the Plateaus was northward from the Allegheny Front into the Erie basin. The Conemaugh, the Youghiogheny, the Monongahela, the Little Kanawha, the Kanawha, the Big Sandy, and the Licking represent the upper portions of these early streams. The farthest advance of the Ice Sheet was approximately to the present position of the Allegheny and Ohio rivers. Hence streams flowing from the plateau came against the ice, moved along the ice front, and developed a course which is that of the present Ohio River. The drainage formerly entering the Erie basin has in this way been diverted to the Mississippi River. Farther south the Cumberland

River, though it has been beheaded, represents the original drainage. The lower Tennessee River, which has gathered the heads of streams from the Blue Ridge, follows approximately the old course established as a result of the up-warping of the Schooley Peneplain.

The southern portion of the Plateaus.—From the Cumberland River southward, the Appalachian Plateaus slope downward and narrow to a point a little south of the Tennessee River, which in its lower portion closely parallels the edge of the Plateau. This portion of the Plateau is often called the Cumberland Plateau. It differs from the northern and central portions of the province in that it has been but slightly dissected by streams. As a result the upland surface of the Schooley Peneplain is well preserved over extensive areas, and the underlying coal deposits are available only at a few points. Tributaries of the Tennessee have in places cut back into the edge of the Plateau and undermined the strong rock cover, and have formed lowlands on the weak rocks, thus giving the plateau a fretted front.

About ten miles west of the Allegheny Front there is a last sharp fold, which brought limestone beds to the surface of the Schooley Peneplain, and their erosion made the narrow Sequatchie Valley. This valley is partly occupied by the Sequatchie River and partly by the Tennessee River, and it serves to isolate Sand Mountain and the Walden Ridge.

BIBLIOGRAPHY

Fairchild, H. L., *The Susquehanna River in New York*, N. Y. State Museum Bulletin, No. 256, 1925.

Johnson, D. W., *Stream Sculpture on the Atlantic Slope*, 1931.

Shaw, E. H., "High Terraces and Abandoned Valleys in Western Pennsylvania," *Journal of Geology*, Vol. 19, p. 140, 1911.

U. S. Geological Survey Folios: Chattanooga, Tenn., No. 6; Sewanee, Tenn., No. 8; Richmond, Ky., No. 46; Greenville, Tenn., No. 118; Watkins Glen–Catatonk, N. Y., No. 169; Mercersburg, Pa., No. 170; Bessemer, Ala., No. 221.

U. S. Geological Survey Topographic Maps: Harrisburg,* Kittanning, Pittsburgh, Warren, for Pennsylvania; Chattanooga,* Loudon, Greenville, Murfreesboro, for Tennessee; Bessemer, Birmingham, Muscle Shoals, for Alabama; Binghamton, Ithaca, Slide Mountain, Watkins,* for New York.

CHAPTER XV

THE CENTRAL LOWLAND

Extent and recent history.—Extending southward from the Canadian Shield and Superior Upland to the Gulf Coastal Plain, and westward from the Appalachian Plateaus to the Great Plains, is a large area of low-lying country, forming the Central Lowland Province. This province extends to the St. Lawrence River Valley and to the Mohawk Valley on the east. It includes the narrow lowland bordering Lake Erie and Lake Ontario and a maturely dissected area in Kentucky and Tennessee, known as the Interior Low Plateaus. The western border of the province is not always clearly defined, but in places it is marked by a low escarpment or by a hilly region. The boundary is the line of the contact between the nearly horizontal Palaeozoic limestones and shales and the over-lapping Cretaceous marine shales and sandstones. On both sorts of rocks lowland peneplains have been developed, but, while the peneplain on the Palaeozoic rocks is approximately horizontal, that on the Cretaceous beds slopes gently up toward the Rocky Mountains. This border extends through the middle of the Dakotas, Nebraska, Kansas, and Oklahoma into western Texas.

With but few exceptions the surface of the Central Lowland is that of the Lowland Peneplain, which in the Pliocene was slightly raised and warped, so that the eastern margin is about 800 feet above sea level, the central portion 500 feet, and the western margin about 1,000 feet. The northern portion of this province, approximately to the Ohio and Missouri rivers, was covered largely by ground moraine deposited at different stages of the continental glaciation, and the preglacial drainage was extensively modified by the ice invasion. As a result of the Pliocene uplift the larger rivers have since cut valleys from

167

one to two hundred feet in depth, but the upland surface is in general monotonously level.

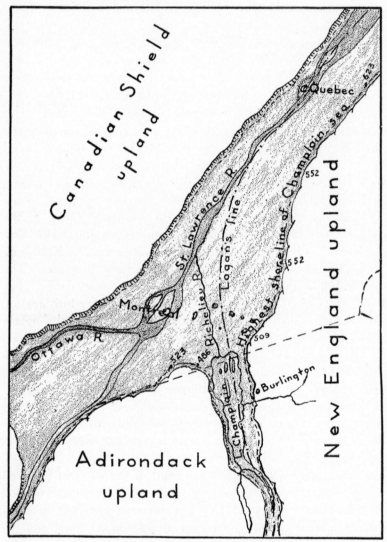

FIG. 89.   Orientation map of the St. Lawrence Lowland.

St. Lawrence Lowland.—The St. Lawrence Lowland lies between the Superior Upland on the north and the Adirondacks and the New England Province on the south, and its development is intimately related to that of the bordering provinces.

The valley is continuous with the Champlain Valley, which connects on the south with the Hudson Valley and the Mohawk Valley of New York State. The valley surface is that of the Lowland Peneplain underlain by shales, while the surface of the adjacent uplands is that of the Schooley Peneplain on crystalline and metamorphic rocks. The shales to the south and east of Logan's Line (Fig. 89) are folded and crumpled as a result of the disturbance at the end of the Ordovician (page 106), the margin of the overthrust being marked by this line. The

FIG. 90.   The Micmac shore line as seen at Bic, Quebec.   (Courtesy of the Canadian Geological Survey.)

beds of shale north and west of Logan's Line are almost horizontal, never having been greatly disturbed. As a result, the Lowland Peneplain developed in the valley from west of Montreal to far out under the St. Lawrence Gulf. During the Pliocene uplift this area was lifted high above its present level, and the St. Lawrence River and its tributaries carved deep gorge-like valleys. During the Ice Age the surface was depressed to more than 600 feet below its present level. Immediately after the recession of the ice sheet the valley was flooded by the sea, forming a large estuary. Salt (or at least brackish) waters extended into the Lake Ontario lowland, and through the Champlain and Hudson valleys. Thus for a time New England was an island. During this period of depression, beaches, with shells of marine and brackish-water animals in them, were formed all around the estuary and its tributaries (see Fig. 89).

Micmac shore line.—The St. Lawrence Lowland has been

raised, on an average, some 600 feet from its maximum depression. The uplift brought the Montreal region well above sea level, but eastward the peneplain surface slopes down until a little east of Quebec it dips beneath the sea and makes the floor of the Gulf of St. Lawrence. The uplift did not take place all at once, but by stages, some of which are indicated by raised beaches, one of which makes a bench in places half a mile wide. This is the Micmac shore line which for 300 miles easterly from Quebec stands at the level of 300 feet above the Gulf of St. Lawrence.

St. Lawrence River.—The combined Ottawa and St. Lawrence rivers are an ancient stream which has a gorge-like channel cut deep below the present sea level; but the portion of the St. Lawrence between Lake Ontario and Montreal is only of post-glacial age and has a shallow valley. The city of Quebec with its Plains of Abraham is on a small outlier of the Lowland Peneplain.

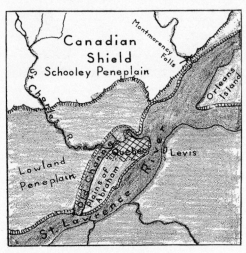

FIG. 91. Modifications of the St. Lawrence River Channel at Quebec and at Orleans Island.

The St. Lawrence flows south of the city in a narrow channel, while to the north of the city there is an old abandoned channel, now partly occupied by the St. Charles River. This abandoned channel was the preglacial course of the St. Lawrence River, but just how the river was diverted from the old channel to the new cannot be definitely determined. The new channel was apparently largely cut by a tributary stream, and the main river was forced into it during the disturbances associated with the retreat of the ice sheet. The Island of Orleans below Quebec is also evidently the result of a postglacial shift of the channel.

Montreal Region.—During the development of the lowland near Montreal several strong volcanic masses were left in relief as the weaker shales were eroded. These now rise above the plain as striking features and are known as the Monteregian Hills. They are in part necks, and in part laccoliths formed by volcanic activity in late Devonian times. Five of them range in height from 1,400 to 1,755 feet, and their tops approximate the level of the Schooley Peneplain. Mt. Royal, Mt. St. Bruno, and Mt. Johnson are but 700 to 800 feet high, being

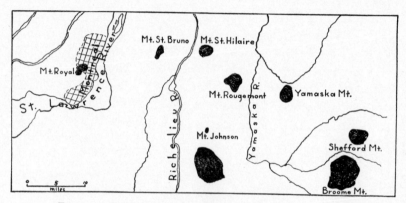

Fig. 92. The Monteregian Hills. (After F. D. Adams.)

small and having lost a portion of their tops by erosion. The largest of the group of eight summits which extends easterly from Montreal for about 50 miles is Mt. Broome with an area of nearly 30 square miles. It is a laccolith.

Great Lakes.—While the surface of the Central Lowland is generally the Lowland Peneplain, there are a few stronger layers which were not completely reduced to this level. The most striking residual is the Niagara Escarpment formed by a layer of strong dolomitic limestone. This escarpment makes a north-facing cuesta which first appears near Rochester, N. Y. It crosses into Ontario just below Niagara Falls, extends northwesterly to make the Indian Peninsula and Manitoulin Island separating Georgian Bay from Lake Huron, turns around the upper end of Lake Michigan, separates Green Bay from Lake Michigan, and disappears under glacial drift south of Lake Superior. (See scalloped line on Fig. 93A.)

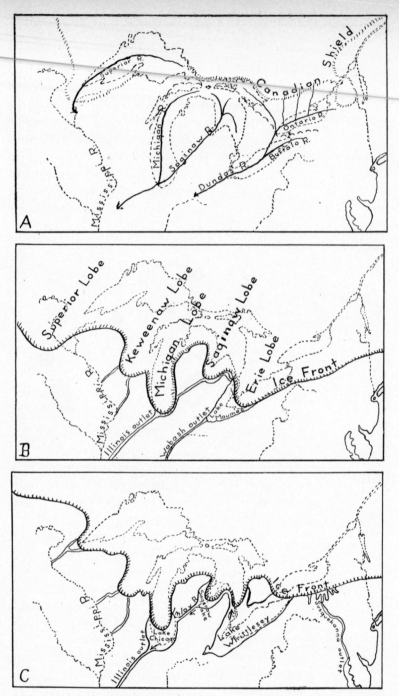

FIG. 93. Evolution of the Great Lakes: A, preglacial drainage and formation of the basins. B, the ice front in retreat, as it begins to uncover the Erie basin and Lake Maumee appears. C, a further retreat of the ice front, which uncovers the Michigan basin and causes Lake Chicago to appear. D, the

172

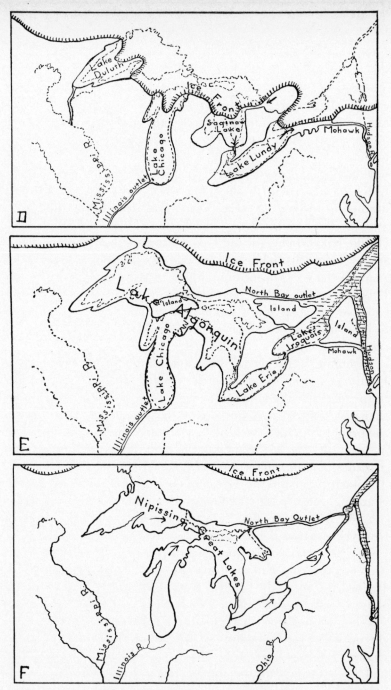

Superior basin uncovered, and the appearance of Lake Duluth. At this time the Mohawk River becomes the outlet of the lakes. E, maximum development of the lakes, and flooding of the St. Lawrence Valley. F, a late stage when the Ottawa River is still the outlet for the lakes. (After Leverett, U. S. G. S.)

On the portion of the Central Lowland covered by the ice sheet are numerous looped moraines, drumlins, eskers, and other glacial formations, and in places well borings have indicated a rugged preglacial surface covered to a depth of several hundred feet by ground moraine. The most important effects of the continental glacier were the drainage changes and the formation of the Great Lakes. Before the Pleistocene there were no Great Lakes. Their basins were mature river valleys which had been cut in the weak Palaeozoic shales, and which drained to the southwest into the Mississippi River and thence into the Gulf of Mexico. The basins of Lake Superior, Lake Huron, Lake Michigan, and Lake Ontario are today partly below sea level and must have been excavated when the land was higher than it is now. This presumably occurred during and after the Pliocene uplift. It is possible that the ancient valleys were widened by ice action. Lake Superior and Lake Ontario seem to have been subjected to some warping at the end of the Ice Age.

Assuming a preglacial drainage somewhat as depicted in Figure 93A, the formation of the Great Lakes was due, in part, to the fact that the land under the ice sheet was depressed more than the land to the south. As the glacier began to recede, the preglacial valleys were uncovered and the water impounded in front of the ice to make the first lakes. Moraines also played a part in the forming of Lake Michigan and Lake Erie. The history of all the Great Lakes involves a succession of changing outlines, of changing outlets, and of changing levels.

Lake Erie.—The first lake to appear was Lake Maumee, which was a small lake at the southwest end of the present Lake Erie. Lake Maumee stood at a higher level than the present lake, and had an outlet by way of the Wabash River. Its beaches may be traced from Cleveland, Ohio, to Fort Wayne, Indiana, and thence north nearly to Imlay, Michigan.

When the ice sheet had receded a little farther to the north, the outlet of this lake shifted to Saginaw Bay, and the Imlay channel was developed across Michigan to Lake Chicago, which had been formed at the upper end of Lake Michigan. The enlarged lake, known as Lake Whittlesey, was at a somewhat lower level than that of Lake Maumee. Still later an enlarged lake, known as Lake Lundy, found an outlet to the east by way of the Mohawk Valley, and the Niagara River came into existence, but without its waterfall, for the earlier Lake Ontario stood 150 feet higher than it does now. The final stage in the development of Lake Erie occurred when Lake Ontario found a lower outlet and the Niagara River developed its falls. Detroit and Toledo are built on the beaches and floors of Lakes Maumee and Whittlesey.

Lake Michigan.—The second lake to come into existence was Lake Chicago, which had an outlet to the Illinois River. The early stages of Lake Chicago are marked by a series of three beaches, still well preserved on the flats south of the present Lake Michigan. The earliest lake built the Glenwood beach, about 60 feet above the present lake. This beach may be traced around the south end of Lake Michigan at a distance of from two to

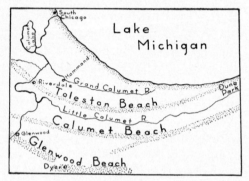

Fig. 94. The beaches at the south end of Lake Michigan, showing the levels of the various stages of the earlier lakes. (After Leverett, U. S. G. S.)

twelve miles from the lake. The second, or Calumet, beach lies at 40 feet; and the third, or Toleston, beach at 20 feet above Lake Michigan. Were Lake Chicago still in existence, Chicago and South Chicago in Illinois, Hammond and Gary in Indiana, and Grand Rapids in Michigan would be under water. When the level of the lake was so lowered that the Illinois River was no longer an outlet, Lake Michigan came into existence. With the lowering of the water level the exposed sands of the abandoned beaches were drifted into sand dunes by the action of the wind. Some of the dunes in the vicinity of Miller and Dune Park (25 miles southeast of Chicago) rise to 150 feet in height. Between Michigan City, Indiana, and St. Joseph, Michigan, there are even bigger dunes, rising to 200, 300, and one to 390 feet in height. The dunes, ever in motion, have in some places buried forests, whose dead tree trunks are now to be seen on the windward sides of the dunes.

Lake Huron and Lake Superior.—The beginning of the present Lake Huron was in the region of Saginaw Bay. Saginaw Lake first appeared. Its outlet was across Michigan, forming the valley which is now mostly occupied by the Grand River. As the ice retreated, the lake expanded to the north, in its later stages covering much of the land immediately to the north of the present lake. It then had an outlet through the basin of the present Lake Nipissing and the Ottawa River Valley into the St. Lawrence River. This outlet lasted until very recent times.

Lake Superior was the last of the Great Lakes to come into existence, its first beginning being termed Lake Duluth. For a time its outlet was through the St. Croix River Valley to the Mississippi River, but it soon became connected with the other Great Lakes.

Lake Ontario.—Lake Ontario first appeared as a series of small basins in the region of the "Finger Lakes" (Fig. 93 C), at so high a level that they drained to the Susquehanna River. When the ice sheet receded so that the Mohawk Valley was opened, it became the outlet not only for the early Lake Ontario but also for Lake Erie. While the lake was at this level the beach on which the Ridge Road (from Lewiston to Rochester, N. Y.) is now situated was formed. The Niagara River had come into existence, but there were no falls. As the lake gradually enlarged with the recession of the ice sheet, it extended far beyond the present northern border of Lake Ontario. At this stage Lake Iroquois existed. In the next stage the St. Lawrence Valley outlet was uncovered, and the sea reached so far inland that salt, or at least brackish water, invaded the east end of the lake. This same flooding invaded the Champlain, Hudson, and Mohawk valleys, so that New England and the Adirondacks were islands. At this stage the lakes Superior, Huron, and Ontario were much expanded to the north and all emptied by way of the Ottawa River into the St. Lawrence Valley. This maximum expansion of the lakes was called Lake Algonquin. After the ice had receded still farther north the region was raised to the north and depressed to the south, and the northern shore lines then approximated their present position. Lakes Erie and Michigan were but little affected by this movement, but it shifted the outlet of all the lakes to the present St. Lawrence, which at this time first appeared as a river from the lakes to Montreal.

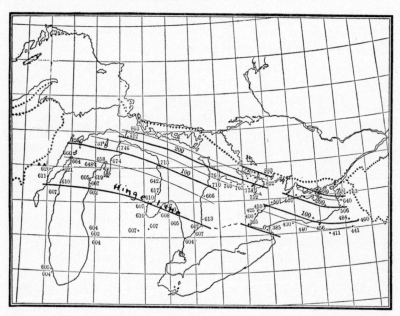

Fig. 95. The Great Lakes, showing how much the northern portions have been raised relative to the southern land—i. e., south of the "hinge line." (After Goldthwaite.)

Niagara Falls.—At the time of this last stage Lake Ontario got its present relatively low level, and the Niagara River first had a waterfall. This waterfall began at Lewiston, where the river first dropped into the Ontario basin. The falls are today seven miles south of Lewiston and are migrating slowly toward Lake Erie. The fall is over a bed of Niagara limestone, which is more resistant than the underlying weak shales and sandstones. The limestone layer dips gently (35 feet to the mile) to the south, so that the falls have less height as they retreat to the south. When they have retreated about two miles farther, the falls (now 160 feet) will be only about 100 feet high and entirely in the limestone, so that they will change their character and become rapids.

As the Niagara River leaves Lake Erie, the water is clear and without any scouring material, so that the river channel is very

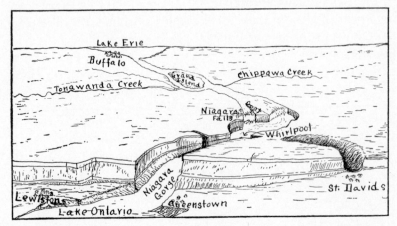

FIG. 96.   Bird's-eye view of the Niagara River.   (After Gilbert.)

shallow.   The recession of the edge of the falls is due to the action of the water which wears away the soft shales under the falls, and causes the limestone to drop down in blocks.   The retreat of the falls is at present at the rate of about four feet a year.   The time since the falls began cannot be ascertained by dividing the present distance (7 miles) by this four feet per year; for the height of the falls at the beginning was greater than now, and at one point there is a buried river gorge across the course of the river.   This old gorge was filled with glacial till which would be removed quickly.   The

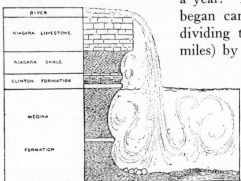

FIG. 97.   Niagara Falls, showing the under-cutting action of the water.

Whirlpool is situated at the point where the buried channel crossed the river.   Further, it is known that the volume of water flowing through the river has varied, for at least twice in its history the Niagara River has drained only the basin of Lake Erie.

After many allowances for these conditions are made, a figure
is reached of about 25,000 years, or somewhat less, for the age
of the Falls. This estimate coincides reasonably well with the
figure which was obtained for the length of time since the glacial
period by counting the varved clay layers of the postglacial
lakes.

Red River Basin.—Northwest of Lake Superior are Rainy
Lake, Lake of the Woods, and Lake Winnipeg, the remnants of

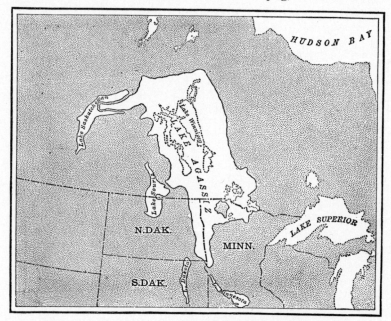

Fig. 98. Glacial Lake Agassiz. (After Upham, U. S. G. S.)

a greater postglacial lake, called Lake Agassiz. Today the
drainage of this basin is to the north by way of the Red River
into Lake Winnipeg and thence by the Nelson River into
Hudson Bay, as it was before the ice sheet covered the region.
In that time probably other rivers, such as the Missouri, also
flowed to the northeast. At the time of the farthest advance
of the ice sheet, the Missouri and other streams from the northern Rocky Mountains had to find a route to the south of the
ice barrier. At that time the present course of the Missouri
River was established.

As the icefront moved north and uncovered the Red River

basin, the water ponded back and formed Lake Agassiz between the ice and a divide to the south over which it overflowed. The river which drained Lake Agassiz is called Warren River. It carried all the water from this section of the melting ice sheet. The channel then made can still be seen as a valley a mile or more in width, and 100 to 220 feet deep, beginning where Lake Traverse now is and extending 250 miles to Fort Snelling on the Mississippi River. Its course, except for the last 25 miles, was through a flat plain underlain by glacial till and is therefore a conspicuous landscape feature. Stony Lake is in the upper end of this old valley which is now occupied by the lower portion of the Minnesota River.

As the ice sheet retreated, Lake Agassiz increased in size until it covered the area indicated in Figure 98. There were also some smaller adjacent temporary lakes. The highest beaches of Lake Agassiz, including deltas and sand and gravel bars, are about at the 1,065-foot level. The bottom of the lake, covered with fine clays, has become the wheat-growing area of the Red River Valley lying in the United States and Canada. The present Red River of the North is flowing in the lake clays in a newly made channel only 20 to 40 feet deep.

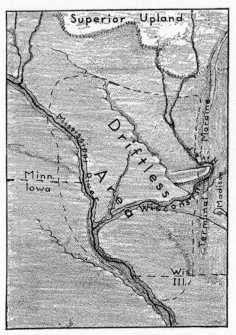

Fig. 99.   The Driftless Area.

The sides of the valley slope so gently (2 to 4 feet to the mile) that the region appears to be level.

Driftless Area.—In southern Wisconsin, and extending slightly into Minnesota, Iowa, and Illinois, is a tract of about 10,000 square miles, termed the Driftless Area, which, though well within the glaciated region, was never covered by ice. Within this area there are no glacial scratches, no till, no glacial lakes. The residual soil is deep, and river valleys have been cut from 200 to 300 feet into the underlying rocks. The profiles everywhere are characteristic of unglaciated regions. The failure of the continental glacier to occupy this area was due, not to its elevation (just under 1,200 feet above sea level), but to the fact that it was protected by the highland of the Lake Superior Upland which rises to 1,600 and 1,700 feet. This highland acted as a wedge to force the ice sheet to either side so that one lobe of the sheet followed Lake Superior and one followed Green Bay. These lobes finally surrounded the Driftless Area, but failed to cover it.

Recently Kay has discovered evidences that the earliest glacial advance covered nearly a third of the region. Here there are decayed boulders, and the soil is an old till. The term Driftless Area may be strictly applied to the inner portion of the area; and all the area shown in Fig. 99 was untouched by the last advance of the ice sheet.

Interior Low Plateaus.—A section of the Central Lowland, including parts of Kentucky, Tennessee, and southern Ohio, is marked by a slight doming of the beds and by mature dissection of

Fig. 100.   The Blue Grass Basin.

the upland surface. This area is known as the Interior Low Plateaus (Fig. 1), and has two low domes, the Cincinnati Dome and the Nashville Dome. In both cases the tops of the domes have been eroded off and the stronger upper layers now remain as rims surrounding basins which have developed on the weaker and older rocks in the centers of the domes. In the case of the Cincinnati Dome the uplifted beds were not equally resistant, and two basins have been formed on the broad anticlinal arch.

The outer and larger basin is the Blue Grass region, and the inner one the Lexington Plain, both famous for stock raising.

FIG. 101.   The Nashville Basin.

The surrounding rims are but little, if any, above the level of the Lowland Peneplain, but they make distinct boundaries.

Nashville Basin.— The rim surrounding the Nashville Basin, known as the Highland Rim, is composed of a more resistant sandstone. It rises to an elevation between that of the Lowland Peneplain and that of the Schooley Peneplain. On the eastern side this rim broadens out to make a low plateau which is deeply dissected by young stream valleys. The contrast between the barren sandy soils on the Rim and the rich soils of the Basin is indicated by the agricultural development in the two areas. The Nashville Basin, however, is not so famous for its agriculture as is the larger Blue Grass section.

FIG. 102.   Mammoth Cave, showing sink holes and solution passages. (Courtesy of A. K. Lobeck, from *Atlas of American Geology*.)

Limestone caverns.—Well-drained limestone regions are often characterized by numerous caves and underground passages, which have been developed as water, percolating through the crevices, has dissolved and removed the lime content of the rocks.   The surface in such regions is characterized by sinks, and lacks the usual digitate arrangement of surface streams. The most famous cavern section of this province lies in midwestern Kentucky, and includes Mammoth Cave. This cavern contains miles of underground passages on three levels. Each level represents a stage when, in the development of the cave, the top of the ground water was approximately at the level of the passages, and determined the level to which the limestone could be dissolved.

BIBLIOGRAPHY

Gilbert, G. K., "Niagara Falls," *Physiography of the United States*, pp. 203–236, 1896.

Kay, G. F., "Classification and Duration of the Pleistocene," *Bulletin of the Geological Society of America*, Vol. 42, pp. 425–466, 1931.

Leverett, F. and Taylor, F. B., *History of the Great Lakes*, U. S. Geological Survey, Monograph LIII, 1915.

Taylor, F. B. "Niagara Falls," *Bulletin of the Geological Society of America*, Vol. IX, pp. 59–84, 1898.

Upham, W., *Glacial Lake Agassiz*, U. S. Geological Survey, Monograph 25, 1895.

U. S. Geological Survey Folios: Chicago, Ill., No. 81; Detroit, Mich., No. 205.

U. S. Geological Survey Topographic Maps; Rochester,* Niagara,* for New York; Napoleon for Ohio; Milan for Illinois; Ann Arbor for Michigan; Bowling Green, Mammoth Cave, for Kentucky; Reelfoot Lake for Tennessee; Mineral Point for Wisconsin.

CHAPTER XVI

THE OUACHITA PROVINCE AND OZARK PLATEAUS

The unified history of the provinces.—In Missouri south of the Missouri River, in Arkansas west of the Mississippi Alluvial Plain, and extending into eastern Oklahoma, the Ouachita Province and Ozark Plateaus interrupt the continuity of the Central Lowland. Whereas in the Central Lowland the underlying rocks are nearly horizontal beds of marine shales and limestones, the Ouachita Province has developed on coarser sedimentary rocks of Cambrian to Pennsylvanian age, which were deposited in shallow waters to a depth of some 25,000 feet, forming a Palaeozoic geosyncline. The Ozark Plateaus are composed of the same beds but of less thickness and of a character indicating deposition farther offshore. At the end of the Pennsylvanian period the rocks of the Ouachita Province were highly folded and faulted, whereas the rocks of the Ozarks were elevated with only slight folding. The whole region has been peneplained several times. The Schooley Peneplain is repre-

FIG. 103. The Ouachita and Ozark provinces. (From Lobeck's *Physiographic Diagram of the United States*, courtesy of A. J. Nystrom & Co.)

184

sented by the summit levels, and the Lowland Peneplain by the lowlands on the shale and limestone layers, where exposed.

The plateaus to the north are separated from the mountains to the south by the valley of the Arkansas, which is underlain by gently folded weak rocks. The relationship of the several areas is the same as for the Appalachian Plateaus and the Valley and Ridge Province: sedimentary deposits are of the same types and ages, and the periods when peneplains were developed are the same. Hence these two provinces are regarded as an extension of the Appalachian forms and structures, the connecting section being buried under the Coastal Plain from Alabama to Arkansas. This relationship was first suggested by a study of surface features and has been checked by various oil companies which have drilled down through the Coastal Plains deposits well to the east of the Ouachita Mountains and found the Ouachita structures still continuing.

Ouachita Mountains.—The Ouachita Mountains are some 250 miles long with altitudes running up to 2,850 feet. At the east they rise from under the Coastal Plain as rather simple folds, but westward faulting increases. In the middle portion there are not only numerous faults, as seen in Figure 104, but there are many overthrusts of the southern masses over those to the north, some of these overthrusts amounting to more than 20 miles. At the west end, the Ouachita Mountains are cut off by a

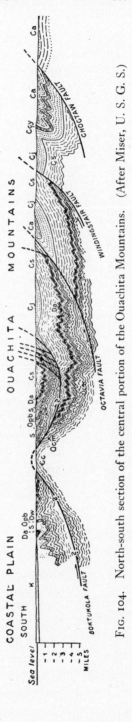

Fig. 104. North-south section of the central portion of the Ouachita Mountains. (After Miser, U. S. G. S.)

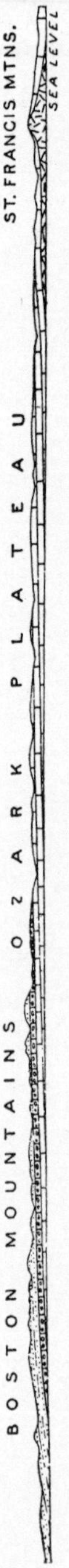

FIG. 105.   Northeast to south-southwest section across the Ozark Mountains to show the structure.   (After Purdue, U. S. G. S.)

fault; then after a gap their structure is seen again in the Arbuckle Mountains. These latter mountains, however, are composed only of the coarser sandstones, and are less folded. The source of the sediments of both these mountain groups was the oldland on the south, termed Llanoria. Llanoria extended through Texas into Mexico and existed as a highland until Comanchean time.

There is one formation in the Ouachita Mountains, the Caney shale (Pennsylvanian), which is almost unique. This comparatively fine marine shale contains scattered boulders of all ages before the Pennsylvanian, ranging in size from a few inches up to 300 feet in diameter. Such boulders could come to rest in a shale formed in deep water only if transported by icebergs. This suggests that glaciers existed on the oldland of Llanoria during the Pennsylvanian period.

Ozark Plateaus.—The Ozark Plateaus represent the less folded, deeper-water deposits of the same age as those of the Ouachita Mountains. They form a low dome with a rather sharp rise on the southern margin, where the folded, more coherent sandstones of Pennsylvanian age were not entirely leveled off by the Schooley Peneplain. This upland with its monadnocks makes the Boston Mountains. The Lowland Peneplain is not developed in this section, but the rivers have cut deep valleys and made it a hill-and-valley region, not unlike portions of the Appalachian Plateaus. North of the Boston Mountains, where the strata are almost horizontal, a fairly level plateau has been developed at an elevation intermediate between those of the Schooley and Lowland peneplains. The western portion is called the Springfield Plateau, and the eastern the Salem Plateau. In the northeast portion of the Ozark region, granites of the Pre-Cambrian floor come to the surface and rise to an elevation of 1,500 feet, forming St. Francis Mountain.

The whole Ozark region is more or less isolated by valleys: the Osage on the north, the Arkansas on the south, the Black on the east, and the Neosho on the west.

BIBLIOGRAPHY

Miser, H. D., *Structure of the Ouachita Mountains*, Oklahoma Geological Survey, Bulletin No. 50, 1929.

U. S. Geological Survey Folio: Winslow, Arkansas, No. 154.

U. S. Geological Survey Topographic Maps: Winslow, Eureka Springs, for Arkansas; Atoka, Tishomingo, Winding Stair, for Oklahoma.

CHAPTER XVII

THE CANADIAN SHIELD; THE ADIRONDACKS; THE SUPERIOR UPLAND

THE CANADIAN SHIELD

The greatest single physiographic unit of North America is the Canadian Shield, an area of more than a million square

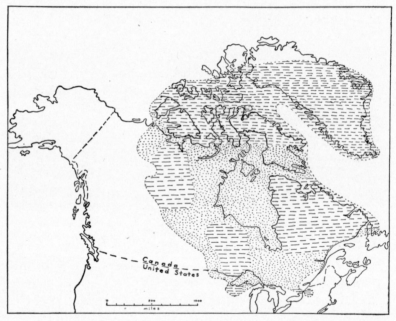

FIG. 106. The Canadian Shield. The dotted portions are those which were covered by the sea in the Palaeozoic; the hatched areas are those which were land areas continuously from before the Cambrian until after glacial times.

miles, composed of igneous and metamorphic rocks of Pre-Cambrian age. It extends from the St. Lawrence River and the Great Lakes to the Arctic Ocean, and from the Atlantic Ocean to a line running through Winnipeg, Great Slave, and Great Bear lakes.

The larger surface features.—The most striking feature of this great tract is its generally level aspect. Standing anywhere on it, one looks across long distances of slightly undulating country to a level sky line on all sides. Elevations of 50 or 100 feet stand out prominently. The level character is not due to structural conformity of the underlying rocks, for they make differing angles with the surface, and are of varying strength. All (or nearly all) of the rocks are of igneous or metamorphic

Fig. 107. View across the Canadian Shield to show level character. (Courtesy of the Canadian Geological Survey.)

origin, and indicate that the region at one time was a great mountain system, long ago worn down to its roots. A peneplain extends from the margins of the area under the over-lapping Palaeozoic sediments on the south and west, and also under the patches of Palaeozoic sediments around St. James Bay. Inasmuch as the peneplain underlies other equally old sediments far from the present Shield, it must be Pre-Cambrian in age, and the mountain-building period was even earlier.

Since this Pre-Cambrian Peneplain was formed, some hundreds of millions of years ago, only a small portion of the Shield has been submerged at any time. Even though not highly elevated, an exposed peneplain could not preserve its surface

intact through all that time.   The present surface as seen on
the ridges and higher elevations should be attributed to the
Schooley Peneplain.   The lowlands are the Lowland Peneplain,
so imperfectly developed that it is scarcely recognizable.   The
Shield is sometimes referred to as the Laurentian Plateau, but
it is in reality a shallow basin, the western and southern margins
being 1,500 to 1,700 feet in height.   From the margin the
surface of the Shield slopes toward Hudson Bay at a grade of
from one to two feet to the mile.   The Bay is very shallow,
deepening slowly from the west and south sides to about 70
fathoms on the east side.

Southeasterly from Hudson Bay the land rises slowly to
about 1,000 feet at the "Height of Land," and then slopes
gently toward the St. Lawrence Valley, at the edge of which
it makes an escarpment about 800 feet in height, called the
Laurentian Mountains.   Seen from the valley, this escarpment
looks mountainous; but from the top of the escarpment, it is
seen to be the edge of the plateau which slopes up to the Height
of Land.

The east side of Hudson Bay is precipitous, rising abruptly
from the water to about 1,000 feet (on a relatively recent fault),
and then sloping up gently to an altitude of about 2,000 feet
on the Labrador Coast.   Toward the north this eastern margin
increases in height and forms a mountain range, 2,000 miles
long, which ends at Cape Sabin in Ellesmere Land.   Along
the range there are peaks rising to 6,000 feet in altitude.

The basin character of the Shield seems to have originated in
early geologic time, for in both the Silurian and Devonian
periods the sea flooded the interior portion of the basin and
deposited thin beds of marine sediments, remnants of which
are still found around James Bay, and in certain rocky gorges.
After this early flooding, the sea did not invade any parts of the
Shield until after the Glacial Period, when Hudson Bay came
into existence.   The present basin seems to have been formed
by postglacial warping, which is still going on.

Postglacial movements.—The evidences of postglacial movements are widely distributed, especially in the northeast portion
of the area.   To the east and south of James Bay raised shore
lines, with layers of stratified clay filled with marine shells, occur

to heights of 400 to 500 feet above the present sea.   On the
Labrador Coast raised beaches are found up to 1,500 feet above
sea level.   The raised beaches of the St. Lawrence Valley have
already been referred to (page 169).

Immature drainage.—The continental glacier scraped off
the residual soil which had been formed during the long ex-
posure of the peneplain surface to subaerial erosion.   It scoured
and polished the rocks, and left a thin veneer of till over the
surface of the shield.   This till cover disrupted the preglacial

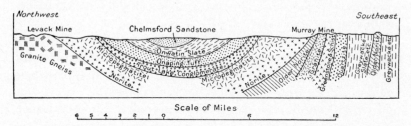

Fig. 108.   Section in the Sudbury Region to show the complicated foldings
and intrusions of the rocks of the Canadian Shield.   (After Coleman.)

drainage and dammed the sluggish streams, forming thousands
of lakes.   The recession of the ice sheet has been so recent
that the streams have made but little progress in clearing their
channels, and fully 20 per cent of the surface is covered by
lakes—a proportion equaled only in Finland, where the retreat
of the ice was also recent.

Canyons.—A puzzling feature of the Canadian Shield is the
number of deep gorges, or canyons, which radiate from the
central portion toward the south and east.   The canyon of
the Saguenay River, reaching from Ha Ha Bay to the St.
Lawrence River, is typical of these.   Cliffs of granite and
gneiss here rise precipitously on either side of the river to the
level of the upland, 1,000 feet above.   At Cape Eternity the
cliffs are 1,500 feet high, and soundings show the water to be
876 feet deep, making a canyon 2,376 feet deep.   The Hamilton
River on the east side of Labrador enters the Atlantic Ocean by
way of a similar canyon.

Lake Temiscaming is in a rock-bound gorge, the walls of
which rise 800 to 1,000 feet.   From the lake to Mattawa the
Ottawa River is in a continuation of the gorge.   Above the

lake the gorge is occupied by Wabi Creek, near the head of which it is nearly filled with marine sediments of Silurian age. These typical conditions exist in several other gorges.

The occurrence of Silurian beds in the Wabi Creek gorge (and at other places) indicates that the gorges were made very early and not during the Pliocene uplift. Their steep walls also indicate that they have not been exposed to prolonged weathering. It would therefore seem that the gorges were made by the beginning of the Silurian, then filled, and were recently re-excavated, following the rise of the land just before the Pleistocene.

The physiographic history of the Shield is not known in detail, except for small areas, because a large part of the area is not easily accessible and can be traversed only during the short summer.

Mineral wealth.—As would be expected in an area which has been subjected to great distortion and metamorphism, the rocks of the Canadian Shield contain many mineral deposits of economic importance, especially gold, silver, copper, nickel, cobalt, and hematite iron.

THE ADIRONDACK PROVINCE

The southern apex of the Shield extends across the St. Lawrence River at the Thousand Islands and forms the Adirondack Province with an area of some 11,000 square miles. This area is similar to the Shield in that it is composed of metamorphic rocks which have been intruded by masses of granite. Like the Shield, the Adirondack region has been raised and depressed at various times, and its margins have been overlapped by marine sediments, burying the Pre-Cambrian Peneplain.

The Adirondack Mountains have been a land mass continuously since the beginning of the Palaeozoic. During the Mesozoic, the region was stable, and the Schooley Peneplain was developed over it, except in the eastern portion, where a number of monadnocks rise. In the western Adirondacks the Schooley Peneplain has been raised some 2,000 feet and has been so dissected by streams that the peneplain surface is apparent only when viewed from the upland levels.

The present rugged outlines in the eastern Adirondacks are due primarily to faulting which took place just after the Schooley Peneplain (Eocene in age) was completed, and to the presence of monadnocks. A system of major faults, generally about 20 miles in length and running north-northeast, is intersected by lesser faults at approximately right angles. These faults break the area into a mosaic of rectangular blocks, some of them elevated, some of them depressed by from 500 to 2,000 feet. The individual blocks have been so worn down by atmospheric and ice erosion that they appear rounded. The outlines of the blocks have been generally preserved and are indicated by the pattern of the adjusted streams.

Effects of the continental glacier: *Lakes.*— Before the ice sheet covered most, if not all, of the

Fig. 109. The Adirondack Mountains, showing the block-fault character of the eastern portion.

province, the area was well drained. The ice sheet removed the mantle rock down to bare rock, rounded the surface features, and deepened the valleys, but did not materially alter the outlines of the region. During the recession of the ice sheet the surface was generally covered with a thin deposit of till, and moraines blocked the streams in a host of places, forming alternate lakes and rapids, with many cascades and waterfalls where streams were thrown out of their courses. Though many of the smaller lakes have been recently filled with vegetation, and others have been lowered or drained by the cutting down of their outlets, the Adirondack Province is still a region of lakes. The stories of a few lakes which typify the whole region are here presented.

Raquette Lake, with its 100 miles of shore line and its spider-like shape, occupies portions of several converging valleys, and is held in its present position by a morainic dam across its northeast arm, which was the preglacial valley of the Raquette River. Forket and Long lakes are also held up by morainic dams across the old Raquette River, the gravel beaches at the lower (east) ends of the lakes being but little altered. Long Lake is a stretch of a preglacial stream where it followed one of the above-mentioned fault lines.

The Fulton Chain of lakes is due to eight morainal obstructions across a single continuous valley. Lakes Saranac, Tupper, Cranberry, and Placid would all disappear if the moraines which block the valleys were removed. Lake George, with its low beaches at either end and high-walled narrows in the middle, has had an interesting history. Before the ice invasion two streams rising near each other but flowing in opposite directions existed. Later these were dammed by glacial debris. The lakes thus formed rose high enough to unite across the divide before either found an outlet over the moraines.

Glacial Lake Pottersville is an example of lakes which were formerly of greater size. Its former shore line was about 75 feet above Lakes Schroon and Brant, which are present-day remnants of the larger lake. The highway past Schroon Lake is on the old beach, a series of deltas and beaches making a good level bed for the road. This former lake has been drained because its outlet through the blockading moraine has been lowered by erosion. The proposed Schroon Lake reservoir to furnish water for Albany would restore almost exactly the postglacial Lake Pottersville.

Diverted streams.—Many streams were diverted from their earlier courses as a result of the ice invasion. For instance, the Hudson River has a fairly wide mature valley of preglacial age to the point where it is joined by the Schroon River. Here it turns into a narrow gorge which continues beyond Corinth, and follows a course established while the ice was blocking the Lake George region. At Glens Falls the Hudson returns into its old valley, and the old, wide preglacial valley from the Schroon River to Glens Falls still remains unused. In preglacial times the Sacandaga River flowed south into the Mohawk River, but it now turns abruptly to the northeast and enters the Hudson near Corinth, the lower part of its course being almost in reverse direction to that before the Ice Age. Figure 110 shows some of these changes in the drainage.

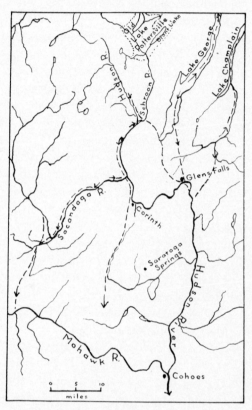

Entering the Adirondacks on the highway from Utica, after crossing the Black River at Forestport, one comes upon several miles of sand and gravel flats. Their presence is due to the fact that the ice sheet melted from the central Adirondacks earlier than it did from the adjacent lowlands to the southwest of the mountains. On leaving the mountains the Black River then found its

FIG. 110. Map to indicate the changes in the drainage of the Hudson and its tributary streams as a result of the Ice Age. (After Miller, N. Y. State Museum.)

valley blocked by ice so that it, with its tributary streams, was ponded back and formed a large lake in the Forestport region. All the streams entering this lake rapidly formed deltas until the lake was practically filled. Finally the ice blockade melted away, and the Black River first flowed across the gravel flats, but, has since cut a deep channel through them.

SUPERIOR UPLAND

From the Thousand Islands region the south margin of the
Canadian Shield strikes westward to Georgian Bay on Lake
Huron, and then crosses Lake Superior into the United States

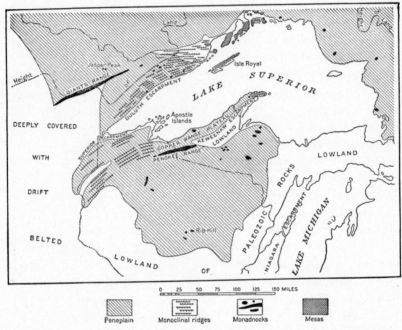

FIG. 111.   The Lake Superior lobe of the Canadian Shield.   (After Van Hise,
U. S. G. S.)

to make the Superior Upland of northern Michigan, Wisconsin,
and Minnesota. (See Fig. 111.) The surface of the Upland,
developed on crystalline rocks and standing 1,350 to 1,600 feet
above sea level, with occasional monadnocks on it rising to
2,300 feet, is that of the Schooley Peneplain made in the early
Eocene. About the west end of Lake Superior the surface of
the Upland is broken by a group of faults. The Duluth fault
on the north side of Lake Superior and the Superior fault on
the south side have permitted the block between them to drop
a thousand feet, thus making the basin for the west end of Lake
Superior. The escarpment along the south side of Keweenaw

Peninsula also represents a fault line, a block having dropped to the south of it.

The irregularities of this upland surface are due to the unequal strength of the rocks. The underlying rocks are highly folded, their beveled edges coming to the surface on northeast-southwest lines. Here the weaker layers make valleys with a relief of from 100 to 200 feet and the stronger ones ridges, or "ranges," as they are termed. These ranges have an especial interest, because a shaly layer which carries a large amount of hematite iron ore occurs under some of them. This layer is so rich in iron that this region has become the premier iron-mining section of the world. The Masabi (or Giant's) Range is some 80 miles long and yields half of the iron supply for the United States each year. Other ranges, especially the Penokee Range south of Lake Superior, bring the production of iron for the region to more than three-fourths of the annual production for the country.

North of Lake Superior is a section in which the layers of rock are almost horizontal. Here the strong layer is a lava beneath which a soft schist is exposed along stream courses. The schist weathers readily and the remnants of the lava cap make tables and mesas along the north shore of the lake. The valleys between the mesas have in some cases been flooded by the lake and make such bays as Thunder, Black, and Nipigon, while the mesas stand above the water with sheer walls to make such striking features as Thunder Cape, Pie Island, and Mt. McKay.

The Keweenaw Peninsula has a unique structure, being made of alternate layers of lava and coarse conglomerate. In the spaces between the pebbles and in the steam holes in the lava, native copper was deposited in such great quantities that through the second half of the nineteenth century this was the great copper-producing region of the world. Deposits which can be mined more cheaply have since been found in other sections and, though copper mining is still carried on, the region has lost its supremacy.

Over this region the ice sheet left an unusually thick layer of till (amounting in many places to over 100 feet), drainage was deranged, and lakes and swamps abound.

Bibliography

Adams, F. D. and Coleman, A. P., *Problems of American Geology*, 1915.

Bell, R., "Proofs of the Rising of the Land about Hudson Bay," *American Journal of Science*, Vol. 151, p. 219, 1896.

Butler, B. S. and Burbank, W. S., *Copper Deposits of Michigan*, U. S. Geological Survey, Professional Paper, No. 144, 1929.

Miller, W. J., *The Adirondack Mountains*, New York State Museum Bulletin, No. 193, 1917.

Van Hise, C. R. and Leith, C. K., *Geology of the Lake Superior Region*, U. S. Geological Survey, Monograph No. 52, 1911.

Wilson, A. W. G., "The Laurentian Peneplain," *Journal of Geology*, Vol. II, p. 615, 1903.

U. S. Geological Survey Topographic Maps: Bolton, Cranberry Lake, for New York; Calumet, Crystal Falls, Menominee Iron Ranges, for Michigan.

CHAPTER XVIII

THE RELATED GEOLOGIC HISTORY OF THE GREAT PLAINS PROVINCE AND THE SEVERAL PROVINCES OF THE CORDILLERAN HIGHLAND

The several physiographic provinces comprising the Great Plains, the Rocky Mountain System, the Colorado Plateaus, the Basin and Range Province, and the Columbia Plateaus are related to one another in their geologic history. The earlier sedimentary accumulations were common to all these provinces and in later periods they were all affected, but to different degrees, by the same disturbances, which involved folding, faulting, and volcanic eruptions, and which reached their acme in the Rocky Mountains. The several provinces are expressions of the varied amount by which each participated in the common history.

History.—The basement under the whole region is the Pre-Cambrian Peneplain which developed on the earlier granites and metamorphic rocks. This peneplain was warped along the west coast at the beginning of the Cambrian so as to make the Cordilleran upland with the comparatively deep Cordilleran trough to the east of the upland—i.e., through Nevada, Oregon, and Washington—and a less depressed basin eastward to the edge of the Central Lowland. From time to time the trough and the basin were submerged beneath wide but shallow seas and received sediments, especially from the uplands of the west and south. The marine invasions generally started in the north and spread toward the south, so that the deposits are thicker in the north. The first marine invasion was that of the Cambrian. This spread over most of the area, leaving from 200 to 300 feet of deposits in the south, but over 5,000 feet in the northern Rocky Mountain section. In the Ordovician epoch the trough portion received some 3,000 feet of deposits in Nevada, and over 4,000 feet in the Mackenzie

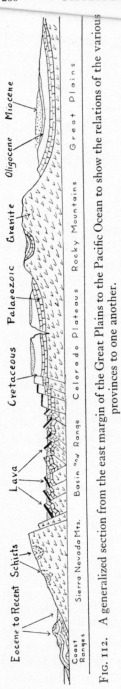

FIG. 112. A generalized section from the east margin of the Great Plains to the Pacific Ocean to show the relations of the various provinces to one another.

River region, but to the eastward the deposits were much thinner or entirely absent. Through all of the Silurian and the Devonian periods this broad area was either at or just above sea level, receiving no deposits and at the same time suffering little or no erosion. In the Mississippian and Pennsylvanian periods the sea spread widely over the area, and thick beds of limestone were laid down. The deposits were thin in the south, about 1,600 feet deep in the Northern Rocky Mountains, and 2,300 feet deep in Alberta.

Shortly after the Pennsylvanian a long series of mountains was formed in the present Basin and Range Province and in the Columbia Plateaus. These ranges corresponded in type and in extent with those of the Appalachian Highland in the east, but are usually less discussed, for they were entirely obliterated by a series of mountains later formed in the same regions by faulting.

During the Triassic and Jurassic the southern part of this region was a desert basin into which infrequent but violent storms washed sands and gravels. Temporary lakes of the playa type were formed. Some of these lakes lasted for a long time but finally dried up and left deposits of salt and gypsum which are now interbedded in the sandstone layers. The desert winds picked up the sands and drifted them into shifting dunes. These arid land deposits form the extensive "red beds" of western Texas, New Mexico, Arizona, and southern Utah. These beds, ranging from 200 to 2,000 feet in thickness, are today striking landscape features on account of their red, buff, and gray colors, their cross bedding, and their tendency to form cliffs. While these desert deposits were being accumulated in the southwest, the region now comprising Nevada, Idaho, and Oregon was below sea level and received deposits of limestones.

Colorado Sea.—In late Jurassic time the center of mountain-building activity was transferred to the West, and the Cascade and Sierra Nevada Mountains were elevated for the first time. As they rose, the region to the east sank to make a broad basin. Into this basin ocean waters slowly advanced from the north and from the Gulf of Mexico until they met, and a broad sea then reached from the Gulf to the Arctic Ocean. This sea, termed the Colorado Sea, reached its maximum extent in the Cretaceous, its greatest depths being where the Rocky Mountains now are found. All through the Comanchean and Cretaceous epochs, sands and muds were washed into this sea, especially from the young Cascade–Sierra Nevada Mountains, until the basin was almost filled. These deposits are only 200 feet in depth on the eastern edge of the Great Plains, but they thicken toward the west until there are 10,000 feet of shales and sandstones in the Rocky Mountain sections of Wyoming and Montana. Toward the end of the Cretaceous, semicontinental deposits, including flood plains, swamps, and deltas, were deposited on top of the marine beds. The swamps were luxuriant and beds of coal were formed from their peat. In some places twenty successive beds of coal are now found interbedded with other deposits. This repetition of coal beds seems to suggest cyclic changes of climate and rainfall during the time the swamps were formed.

Laramide Revolution.—At the end of the Cretaceous the Laramide Revolution began and the central part of the basin from New Mexico to Alaska was folded into high mountains. The region to the east was so little elevated during the revolution that the streams from the new mountains had precipitous courses down the mountain sides, and gentle courses across the lowlands to the Mississippi River on the east, or to a stream which followed approximately the present Colorado River on the west. In times of high water the major streams, heavily laden with sediments from the mountains, overflowed their

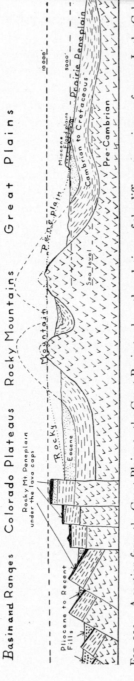

FIG. 113. A section from the Great Plains to the Great Basin to show the relations of the different erosion surfaces. In the Colorado Plateaus and the Great Basin the Rocky Mountain Peneplain is broken by faults. On the eastern part of the Great Plains the Prairie Peneplain is warped down.

banks, and deposited a part of their sediments as flood plains on the lowlands. In this way aprons of flood-plain deposits were built up on either side of the mountains, especially during the Eocene. As the mountains were worn down and the plains built up, the contrast in the slope of river courses in the mountains and across the lowlands was reduced, and fine deposits were laid down in flood plains. These flood-plain deposits are in many places over 1,000 feet thick adjacent to the mountains and thin out to the east and west.

Rocky Mountain Peneplain.—By the end of the Oligocene the Rocky Mountains were reduced to a peneplain (except for a few monadnocks) which cut across the tops of the folds of sedimentary rocks, generally exposing the underlying granites and metamorphic rocks. During the development of the peneplain, portions of the sedimentary rocks and of the Eocene aprons on the lowlands were removed. Over 10,000 feet of sedimentary beds were removed from the mountains, and in Wyoming and Montana as much as 2,000 to 3,000 feet of the beds adjacent to the mountains. Wherever there were warps or domes they too were reduced to this peneplain level. In this text this peneplain will be referred to as the Rocky Mountain Peneplain, though several different names have been applied to it in different localities.

The Miocene period opened with a second period of uplift, which formed a broad arch with its axis following the general direction of the Rocky Mountains. Along the axis the uplift amounted to from 4,000 to 5,000 feet, but was not uniform. Some sections were raised higher, and some, especially in the north, not so high as the average uplift.

The result of the uplift was a rejuvenation of the streams so that they again were overloaded with sediment from the highlands. Again they deposited sediments on the lower-lying plains. The contrast between the river profiles in the mountains and on the plains was not so great as in the earlier period of uplift, and the sediments are therefore not so thick. These flood-plain deposits laid down on top of the Rocky Mountain Peneplain extend for some 500 miles east of the mountains themselves, and form what is termed the High Plains on top of the Great Plains.

While the uplift was taking place in the Rocky Mountains and Great Plains, the sections to the west of the mountains— the Colorado Plateaus, the Basin and Range Province, and the Columbia Plateaus region—yielded to the strain and broke into a mosaic of blocks. In the Colorado Plateaus the blocks were not tilted, but were raised or dropped without changing the horizontal position of the layers of rock. In the Columbia Plateaus and the Basin and Range Province, however, the blocks were tilted to make a region of great complexity of rock structure.

In the last two regions mentioned above there was (as at present) but little rainfall, and detritus from the mountains could be carried only to the foot of each mountain, there to be deposited by the action of wind and water, gradually burying the bases of the mountain blocks.

In the Columbia River section volcanic activity, which began early in the Miocene, poured out very fluid lava from time to time, until not only were the valleys filled, but even the mountain ranges themselves were buried, making a broad plateau of lava over the whole region. A similar broad lava plateau connecting with that of the Columbia River region was built in the Snake River region.

Prairie Peneplain.—After the Miocene uplift erosion again set in and a new and lower peneplain, the Prairie Peneplain, was developed on the weaker rocks, but not on the strong rocks. This later peneplain is some 4,000 feet below the Rocky Mountain Peneplain near the mountains, but in the east the difference in height between the two peneplains is much less. The Prairie Peneplain forms the present surface of the Great Plains on those areas where the High Plains are not developed.

West of the Rocky Mountains, where the rainfall is light, the Prairie Peneplain is developed only over small areas, the weaker rocks being reduced below the level of the Rocky Mountain Peneplain but not down to that of the Prairie Peneplain. In the early Pliocene the present Rocky Mountains were about 5,000 feet high, and the Great Plains but little above sea level. The Colorado Plateaus and the Wyoming Basin were at intermediate levels.

In the middle or late Pliocene another uplift occurred, again in the nature of a warp. This lifted the central portion of the Rocky Mountains by another 5,000 feet and approximately to its present height. The Plains east of the Rocky Mountains were raised from a few hundred feet to over 5,000 feet. They slope down to an eastern margin of some 1,500 feet, this difference in height representing approximately the uplift on the east side of the upwarp.

This uplift again rejuvenated the streams and many of them are still cutting down through the deposits they made in the Miocene. Generally the rivers have formed deep narrow valleys in the higher portions of the uplifted region, but they have not yet cut down to base level in any part of the area.

Volcanic activity: Glaciation.—Volcanic activity in the Cordilleran Highland has been very great. It started in the Miocene and has continued up to the present. The volcanic deposits include wide flows of lava in all the periods since the Miocene, and also tremendous quantities of volcanic ash, found sometimes in beds and sometimes in deposits carried to a distance from the original places of accumulation by stream action. The thickness of the combined flows and ash beds in the Columbia Plateau region is over a half a mile. On the La Plata Mountains in Colorado there is a cap of ash and lava flows of from 3,000 to 5,000 feet in thickness. In the Yellowstone Park region the flows and ash have buried the north end of the Absaroka Mountains, and have filled the Yellowstone Basin with lavas so young that the confined heat still warms the waters of the hot springs and geysers.

Only a small portion of the area thus briefly described was covered by the ice sheet which extended from Alberta into Montana, Idaho, and Washington. Local glaciers formed on the higher mountains during the Ice Age carved them into alpine forms, and changed the V-shaped valleys into characteristic U-shaped valleys.

The foregoing are the major events which affected this great area as a whole and which form the background against which the detail of the various smaller units in the region will be taken up in the succeeding chapters.

CHAPTER XIX

THE GREAT PLAINS

The Great Plains extend from the Rocky Mountains to the Canadian Shield in Canada and to the Central Lowland in the United States. They slope eastward from an elevation of close to 6,000 feet adjacent to the Rocky Mountains in Colorado to an altitude of 1,500 feet where they meet the Central Lowland, with an average inclination of about ten feet to the mile. In the extreme south the Great Plains have a short contact with the Coastal Plain and the Basin and Range Province. The area as a whole appears as a wide, almost flat surface, crossed by the relatively deep valleys of many east-flowing streams. In places its generally level character is broken by domed uplifts, by mesas, by volcanic intrusions, and by "bad lands."

The Missouri Plateau.—The northern portion of the Great Plains (i.e., north of the Pine Ridge—see Fig. 114) may be termed the Missouri Plateau, as its drainage is dominated by the Missouri River. Its surface is that of the Prairie Peneplain, and it is broadly level, except for several residual elevations, which represent local upwarps that have brought stronger rocks above the level of the peneplain. In places the surface of the peneplain seems to be in accord with the marine shales on which it is mostly developed, but wherever these shales have been folded, even slightly, the peneplain surface is continued across the beveled edges of the rock layers.

When the Rocky Mountains were formed, lesser folds and domes like the Big Horn Mountains, the Black Hills, the Little Rocky Mountains, and the Bearpaw Mountains developed to the east of the main folding. In the making of the lower Prairie Peneplain these rocks were not reduced, and the stronger masses rise above the Prairie Peneplain to the level of the older peneplain. On the weaker rocks the Prairie Peneplain is generally well developed.

Near the Canadian boundary on the eastern margin of the Great Plains is the west shore of glacial Lake Agassiz, and there is an abrupt rise of 200 feet from the lake bottom to the Plains. This rise, or escarpment, is called the Coteau de Prairie in its southern portion, and the Manitoba Escarpment in Canada. The south end of this escarpment is but 200 feet (often less) in height, but as it approaches the northern boundary of Montana it is higher and forms the Pembina Mountains.   After a break

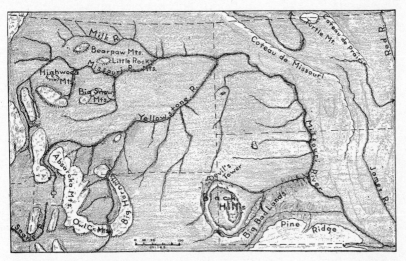

Fig. 114.   Orientation map for the northern portion of the Great Plains.

in the ridge it reappears in Manitoba as the Riding and the Duck Mountains, followed by the Porcupine Hills, and finally by the Pasquia Mountains, these last rising from 700 to 1,000 feet above the Lake Agassiz level.   On the west side this escarpment has a gentle downward slope, so that it is a typical cuesta.   Some 200 miles west of the Coteau de Prairie there is a second similar escarpment, the Coteau de Missouri, which is about 500 feet high.   Beyond the Coteau de Missouri the plain slopes uniformly up to the Rocky Mountains, at a grade of some 5 feet to the mile, the altitude of the plain being about 4,000 feet at the base of the mountains at the international boundary.

While the surface is generally level between the rivers, each stream has sunk its valley some 400 feet deep since the Pliocene uplift.   The soft shales have been greatly dissected for several miles back from the streams, forming highly complicated "bad lands."   During the development of the Prairie Peneplain from three to five thousand feet of shales were removed adjacent to the mountains, and less easterly, down to about 800 feet on the eastern margin.   Layers which were more resistant, of which the two escarpments described above are examples, were not reduced completely to the peneplain level.   Turtle Mountain, Cypress Hills, and White Hills are other remnants protected by a stronger layer which have not been completely leveled off.

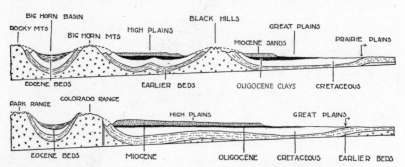

Fig. 115. Two diagrammatic sections of the Great Plains. The upper section crosses the Black Hills dome. The lower section crosses the middle of Nebraska.

Missouri River.—The Pleistocene ice sheet covered the whole of the Canadian Great Plains, and reached into the United States as far as the Missouri River.   In its greatest extension it covered the Little Rocky Mountains and the Highwood Mountains, and surrounded, but did not cover, the Sweetgrass Hills.   In eastern Montana the ice sheet left looped moraines, but not many lakes.   Its most striking effects are the changes caused in the course of the Missouri River.   Near the site of the city of Great Falls the ice blocked the Missouri River, which set back and made the Great Falls Lake.   The outlet of the lake was across the north end of the Highwood Mountains, where it made a channel nearly a mile wide and 500 feet deep.   Today this channel is abandoned and is known as the Shonkin Sag (b in Fig. 116).   Before the Glacial Period, the course of the Missouri River was west of the Bearpaw Mountains, where it made the valley now occupied by the Milk River.

At the time of the maximum advance of the ice its course was
through the Shonkin Sag across the present Judith River to the
Musselshell River.   The present course of the river is neither
the preglacial course nor the one used during the maximum
advance of the ice.   (See Fig. 116.)

From the mouth of the Musselshell River eastward the
Missouri is partly in and partly out of the preglacial channel,
until it joins the Yellowstone River.   From some point just

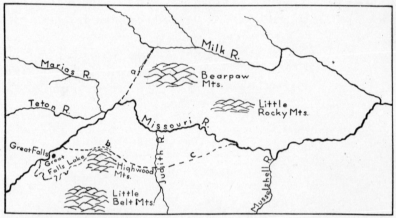

FIG. 116.   The Missouri River of today, and some of its shifts resulting from
the advance of the Ice Sheet: a, its course before the ice advance; b, Shonkin
Sag; b–c, the course of the river at the time of the maximum advance of the
ice.   (After Calhoun, U. S. G. S.)

beyond this junction the Missouri flowed to Hudson Bay in preglacial times; but the present course follows closely that established along the front of the ice sheet.   As the river crosses
North and South Dakota it is in the anomalous position of
flowing on a highland, just below the escarpment of the Coteau
de Missouri.

Black Hills.—On the line between Wyoming and South
Dakota the level surface of the Plains is broken by the Black
Hills, which are about 100 miles long from north to south and
50 miles wide from east to west.   The Black Hills are a dome
formed at the same time as the Rocky Mountains—that is,
at the end of the Cretaceous.   The top of the dome was beveled
in the formation of the Rocky Mountain Peneplain.   All the
sediments over the central portion were removed and the under-

lying pre-Cambrian granites and schists were exposed, some of the granites making monadnocks.   The dome was raised again at the beginning of the Miocene, and also in the Pliocene.

The Prairie Peneplain is not complete anywhere inside the Black Hills; but ever since the Miocene the weaker layers have

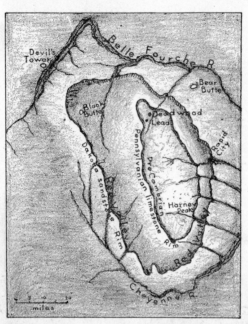

been eroded, causing the stronger layers to stand up above the valleys. Two of these layers, the Dakota sandstone of Cretaceous age, and the Pennsylvanian limestone, rich in chert, form cuestas which encircle the Black Hills. The Dakota sandstone makes the outer wall and is underlain by friable red sandstones and shale (Triassic and Jurassic). As a result there is a high inward-facing wall all around the hills, with the "red valley" likewise cir-

Fig. 117. The Black Hills, showing their character as a dome with the top eroded off.

cling the region. An inner, less perfect, wall and an inner valley, this last encircling the Pre-Cambrian granites and schists, have been formed on the Pennsylvania limestone and underlying weak rocks. The granites are exposed toward the south end of the inner oval, and while most of this section is reduced to the Rocky Mountain Peneplain level, a cluster of monadnocks, the Harney Peaks, rises to 7,216 feet in height. The northern part of this inner area is made of schists which have become famous as the source of the gold of the Homestake Mines at Lead and Deadwood, mines which have been operated continuously for over 50 years.

Laccoliths.—Clustered around the north end of the Black Hills is a group of volcanic intrusions of unusual character.

Sometime in the Eocene masses of lava rose from deep sources
and pushed their way toward the surface until they found
levels where they could spread out between the sedimentary

FIG. 118. The Devil's Tower. (After Darton, U. S. G. S.)

layers. A score and more of these masses have pushed
up the overlying layers and formed typical laccoliths. Sometimes they are intruded between the Pre-Cambrian and the
overlying sediments, sometimes between any two of the later
sedimentary beds, while a few masses came to the surface as
volcanoes. Wherever the lava was intruded, the overlying

beds were arched over it. In the erosion that made the peneplains, the tops of these arches were beveled off, sometimes exposing and cutting off the tops of the lava masses, sometimes
merely exposing them, and sometimes merely removing a part
of the cover. Those masses which made volcanoes have been
eroded away except for the necks. These strong masses,
whether necks or laccoliths, now stand up prominently as
monadnocks. Bear Butte is the most easterly of these monadnocks, the remnant of a laccolith, which towers 1,400 feet above
the surrounding country. It is a narrow mass, which lifted
the upper part of the Pennsylvanian limestone, and all the
overlying layers, so sharply that they faulted on the east and

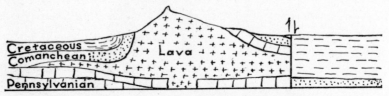

FIG. 119.   Structure section of Bear Butte.   (After Darton, U. S. G. S.)

south sides. (See Fig. 119.) The Devil's Tower (or Mato
Tepee) is a very unusual remnant of a laccolith. The original
hemispherical mass spread out between the Jurassic and the
Cretaceous beds. In cooling it developed a columnar structure
to a high degree. The outer portions of the mass have all been
worn away, leaving only the central mass standing. Its base
rests on the Jurassic shales, and the lava towers 626 feet above
it, mostly in unbroken columns, which are over 500 feet long.
Here we get a good idea of the amount of erosion which has
taken place, for the top of the Tower is 1,000 feet above the
Belle Fourche River near by, and something over 2,500 feet of
Cretaceous shales have been eroded from above the Tower.
Other laccoliths in this region include Bear Lodge Mountain,
Black Buttes, Inyan Kara Hills, and Sundance Hills, which
have been uncovered, but have not been worn away to any great
extent. Nigger Hill, on the other hand, was a volcano, of
which only the neck still remains.

In western Montana there occur several domes, similar in
character to the Black Hills, but of less extent. The Little

Rocky Mountains form a dome, where the Pre-Cambrian granites have been lifted so high as to be uncovered by the Rocky Mountain Peneplain, and now stand some 3,000 feet above the surrounding country, which is reduced to the Prairie Peneplain level. The Little Belt and the Big Snowy Mountain groups are also domes, but they were less elevated and the Rocky Mountain Peneplain cut down only to the Pennsylvanian rocks, which were so resistant that they still stand well above the Prairie Peneplain. The Highwood, Sweetgrass, and Bearpaw Mountain clusters are formed of lavas which flowed to or toward the surface with associated dikes and sheets extending outward from the central neck. In each case the lavas themselves have resisted erosion, and have also protected the adjacent shales, so that the mass is not reduced to the Prairie Peneplain level.

Oligocene Bad Lands.—To the east, south, and west of the Black Hills, the Cretaceous beds are (or were) covered by a layer of white, buff, or pink clays, from 100 to 400 feet in thickness. These are the flood-plain deposits of sluggish streams coming from the Black Hills dome as it was reaching its final stage of reduction to the Rocky Mountain Peneplain. They are Oligocene in age and over a broad belt around the Black Hills make the top of the Plains. In the Pliocene these poorly consolidated beds were raised to a fairly high altitude (about 4,000 feet). Since that time, though in a region of small rainfall, they have been eroded into a complex of sharp ridges, pinnacles, and buttes, termed "bad lands." The name comes from the difficulty experienced by early travelers in crossing these regions by wagon. Where the original surface is protected by grass, it makes table lands, like Sheep Mountain, the White River Table, and Tuba Table. The rivers, however, have cut deep valleys into these flat deposits, and from the margins of each of the tables radiate complexes of sharp ridges and valleys such as are shown in Figure 122. The largest area lies between the White and Cheyenne rivers, and is known as "the Big Bad Lands," being 100 miles long by 25 to 40 miles wide. These beds are famous, because they contain the richest collection of fossil turtles, camels, horses, rhinoceroses, cats, dogs, and other animals to be found anywhere in the world.

Southern Plains.—The southern half of the Great Plains is peculiar in having two surfaces, the lower one being the Prairie Peneplain and the upper one the top of a great mass of flood-plain deposits, laid down on the Rocky Mountain Peneplain. These flood-plain deposits are sands, gravels, and clays, irregular in composition and often cross-bedded, which were formed

Miocene sandstone

Oligocene clay

North Platte River

FIG. 120. Scott's Bluff to show the High Plains. The broken line marks the Rocky Mountain Peneplain.

during the Miocene and early Pliocene, a time when erosion was going on in the northern and southern parts of the Great Plains. These deposits are from 100 to 400 feet thick, and make what is known as the High Plains. They begin in the north with the Pine Ridge and extend southward to the Llano Estacado in Texas. The boundaries of the High Plains are indicated on Figure 121. Since the deposition of these sandstones, the region has been raised (in the Pliocene) from 2,000 to 4,000 feet, the lesser amount in the east, the larger amount on the west side; so that the rivers which formerly deposited these beds are now cutting down through them. The result is a rolling surface between the rivers; for these sandstones do not erode into the sharp ridges characteristic of the Oligocene. However, where the rivers have cut down through the sand-

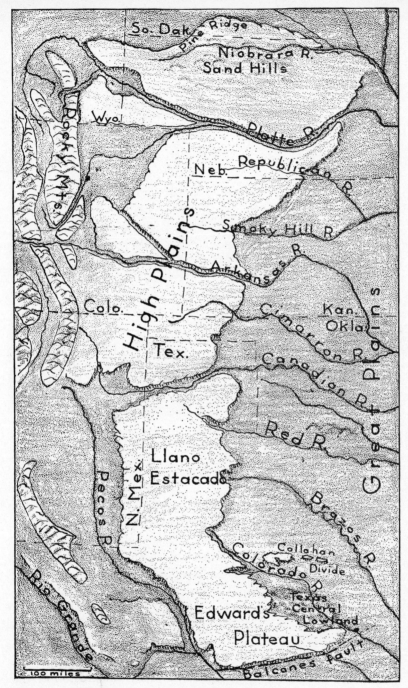

Fig. 121. Orientation map of the southern portion of the Great Plains.

215

stones, the underlying clays are cut faster, undermining the sandstones, and causing vertical walls to form. This action is aided by the fact that the rain which falls on the sandstone sinks to the top of the clay, and follows the line of contact until it comes to the river valleys. Across western Nebraska the

FIG. 122. Bad Lands near Scenic, South Dakota.

Platte River has a valley bounded on either side by such vertical walls. The tributary streams cut notches back from the main valley so that a series of promontories project into the valley. Then later secondary tributaries cut behind these promontories and they may become isolated, making such buttes as Scott's Bluff, Chimney Rock, and Jail Rock. On the boundary between Wyoming and Nebraska the North Platte has widened its valley into a basin 20 or 30 miles wide. This basin, surrounded by vertical walls, is known as Goshen Hole.

The northern boundary of the High Plains is the Pine Ridge, a sandstone mass which drops suddenly on the north side to the level of the Prairie Peneplain developed on the weak black Cretaceous shales. This drop makes a striking escarpment, starting near Douglas, Wyoming, and extending eastward for some 300 miles. The abrupt drop is due to the fact that the sandstones, which must have graded off gently to the north, have been eroded to the peneplain level by the erosion of the White and Cheyenne rivers.

From the Pine Ridge to the Platte River the High Plains are comparatively level, except for the valleys of secondary streams and the sandhills. In northern and central Nebraska there is an area of some 24,000 square miles where the wind has picked up sand from farther west and deposited it in great dunes. Some of the dunes are still moving, but most of them have been covered with grass and have become fixed. The location of these sand dunes indicates that the winds diminished to such an extent that the sand was dropped here, while the finer material was carried still farther east to make loess deposits, often over 100 feet in thickness, in eastern Nebraska, Kansas, and Iowa.

Staked Plains.—From the Platte River to the Canadian River the High Plains have a remarkably level surface, broken only by the valley carved across them by the Arkansas River. On the eastern margin they drop down to the level of the Great Plains proper, along a line of hills termed the "breaks of the plain," which is a strip of broken country three to four miles wide, and generally having no especial name, except that in Kansas the breaks are known as the Blue Hills escarpment. That portion of the High Plains south of the Canadian River is more distinctly marked off than elsewhere, and is known as the Llano Estacado, or "Staked Plains." The sandstones tend to get thinner and disappear nearly opposite the head of the Colorado River, the rest of the upland being coincident with the Rocky Mountain Peneplain, which is developed on the resistant Edwards limestone of Comanchean age. This southern part of the High Plains is then called the Edwards Plateau. The Staked Plains and the Edwards Plateau make a great upland of some 60,000 square miles. No streams have cut deeply into its surface, for the slight rainfall sinks into the sandy ground, and finally comes to the surface around the borders of the plain. This portion of the High Plains is bounded on the east by striking "breaks," on the west by the deep Pecos River valley, and on the south by the Balcones Fault, a young fault which, starting near Austin, Texas, with an escarpment 300 feet high, extends to Del Rio on the Rio Grande, where it is a thousand feet high. This escarpment is rather maturely dissected, so that it appears like a range of wooded hills, and is known locally as "the mountains."

East of the High Plains the Prairie Peneplain is well developed, making a level surface on the nearly horizontal Cretaceous shales in the north. However, south of Kansas this peneplain was formed on the Permian red beds, and the soil is red, instead of black, as it is in the north. In Texas there is a small area where the top of an early dome was removed in the formation of the Prairie Peneplain, so that Cambrian and Pre-Cambrian rocks were brought to the surface. This is the Texas Central Lowland. The Prairie Peneplain is being pushed westward continuously by the eating away of the eastern margin of the High Plains, especially in Texas. Thus remnants of the High Plains are to be found standing as tablelands and buttes to the east of the High Plains, such as those making the Callahan Divide between the Colorado and Brazos rivers.

Bibliography

Calhoun, F. H. H., *Montana Lobe of the Kewatin Ice Sheet*, U. S. Geological Survey, Professional Paper, No. 50, 1906.

Hill, R. T., *Physical Geography of the Texas Region*, U. S. Geological Survey, Topographic Atlas, Folio 3, 1900.

O'Hara, C. C., *The White River Bad Lands*, South Dakota School of Mines, Bulletin, No. 13, 1920.

U. S. Geological Survey Folios: Fort Benton, Mont., No. 55; Little Belt Mountains, Mont., No. 56; Scott's Bluff, Neb., No. 88; Devil's Tower, Wyo., No. 150; Llano-Burnet, Tex., No. 183; Central Black Hills, So. Dak., No. 219.

U. S. Geological Survey Topographic Maps: Big Snowy Mountains, Little Belt Mountains, Great Falls, for Montana; Devil's Tower, Sundance, for Wyoming; Harney Peaks for South Dakota; Goshen Hole, Gothenburg, Scott's Bluff, for Nebraska; Austin, Llano, for Texas.

CHAPTER XX

THE ROCKY MOUNTAIN SYSTEM AND ITS PROVINCES

The Rocky Mountain System stretches from northern Alaska across Canada and the United States to just over the northern boundary of New Mexico, where it is bounded by the eastern extension of the Basin and Range Province. The system includes, in the United States, the Northern, Middle, and Southern Rocky Mountain Provinces, and the Wyoming Basin. It comprises all that complex of ranges and uplands between the Great Plains on the east and the Columbia Plateaus on the west. The mountain complex which gives its name to the system includes hundreds of ranges. Some of the mountains are anticlinal folds, some are due to block faulting, and some are dissected uplands. A range may run a hundred miles and then end, the uplift being taken up and continued by other ranges.

Within the Rocky Mountain region several areas have been set aside as national parks, partly for the purpose of making them more accessible to the public, and partly to illustrate outstanding physiographic features. The Yellowstone Park in Wyoming is a region where subsurface volcanic activity is going on. The Glacier National Park in Montana is a region typical of those which have recently come out from under a covering of ice, as is also Jasper National Park in Canada. The Rocky Mountain National Park in Colorado illustrates the advanced dissection of an uplifted peneplain.

THE NORTHERN ROCKY MOUNTAIN PROVINCE

The Northern Rocky Mountain Province is a complex of many ranges that have been revealed by the dissection of a peneplain which can be traced across the whole area. This peneplain was later elevated to about 9,000 feet, and folded and faulted in places.

The Trenches.—The Province may be most easily studied if it is divided into four districts along three structural lines termed *trenches* (Fig. 123).   The term *trench*, as applied to this region, denotes a major structural depression which may be occupied by more than one river.   The trenches apparently had their origin as faults, the fault lines being used by rivers until they were widened into valleys, these valleys in turn being further changed to U-shaped cross sections by the action of valley glaciers large

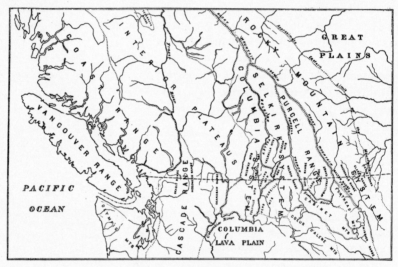

FIG. 123.   Diagram to show the subdivision of the Northern Rocky Mountains into groups by the trenches.   (After R. A. Daly.)

enough to cut out the divides between the various streams. Besides the three trenches here used to divide the Northern Rocky Mountains into districts, there are eight other trenches of lesser width, some of them hardly more than gorges.

The Rocky Mountain Trench starts at the south end of Flathead Lake and extends north some 900 miles to the Liard River in British Columbia, and is occupied for varying distances by the upper portions of the Flathead, Kootenai, Columbia, Canoe, Frazier, Parsnip, Finley, and Kachika rivers.   Daly would confine the Northern Rocky Mountains to the ranges between this trench and the Great Plains, but this use is not generally accepted.   The second trench to the west is the Purcell Trench, which begins near Bonner's Ferry, Idaho, and extends to the Rocky Mountain Trench near Donald, B. C., a distance of some 200 miles.   This trench is occupied by a part of the Kootenai River, Kootenai Lake, the Duncan River, and the Beaver River.   The mountains between it and the Rocky Mountain Trench form the Purcell Mountain system.   The third trench to the west is the Selkirk Trench, which begins at the junction of the Spokane and Columbia rivers and extends to the Rocky Mountain Trench, joining it at about the 52nd parallel.   The mountains between this trench and the Purcell Trench are the Selkirks, while those to the west of the trench are the Columbia group of mountains.

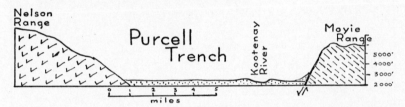

FIG. 124.   A cross section of the Purcell Trench on the international boundary line to show the character of a trench.   (After R. A. Daly.)

There has not been as much geological work done in these northern mountains as might be wished, but when the international boundary was surveyed, Daly carried a section all the way from the Great Plains to the Pacific Ocean, and on this we depend for much of our knowledge of the structure of these mountains.   In the Northern Rocky Mountains, those ranges east of the Rocky Mountain Trench are composed of moderately folded and faulted sedimentary rocks of late Pre-Cambrian age.   In contrast to this, the rocks of the Purcell, Selkirk, and Columbia mountains are highly metamorphosed, complexly folded, and intruded by batholiths of Cretaceous age, as well as by lavas of the Tertiary.

The whole mass of the Northern Rocky Mountains was first distorted at the end of the Cretaceous, by simple folding in the east, and by the intrusion of the batholiths with complex folding in the west.   This greatly disturbed area was then eroded to a peneplain, the Rocky Mountain Peneplain, which was completed by the end of the Oligocene.   During this period of erosion there was volcanic activity, especially in the Eocene, but whatever material was added to the irregularity of the surface was removed by erosion. At the beginning of the Miocene this peneplain was raised on the average to a height

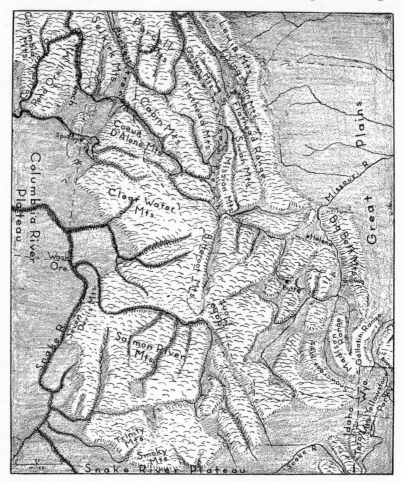

FIG. 125. Orientation map of that part of the Northern Rocky Mountains which is in the United States.

of some 5,000 feet; but the uplift was not uniform, the southern portions being raised somewhat higher than the northern ones.

Rivers had established courses on the peneplain which were not adjusted to the rock structure. When the peneplain was raised, the streams began the cutting of the valleys which now separate the various ranges from one another, but the rocks

were so resistant that the streams did not succeed in developing the Prairie Peneplain on enough of this area to make it
recognizable.

In the Pliocene the whole area was again raised approximately to the levels at which it now stands, and the streams
were again rejuvenated.   During the succeeding Ice Age the
continental glacier did not cover the Northern Rocky Mountains, at least in the United States, but local glaciers formed
all through the mountains.   Their snow fields carved out great
and deep cirques, while the glaciers deepened the river valleys
and carved them to U-shaped cross sections.   At the foot of
the mountains these mountain glaciers coalesced into broad
piedmont glaciers before they were melted.   Glaciers now
occur only in the highest mountains; but the disappearance of
the ice is so recent in date that the glacial character of these
mountains has scarcely been modified by later erosion.

Lewis Range.—The easternmost range of the Northern
Rocky Mountains in Montana is the Lewis Range, which rises

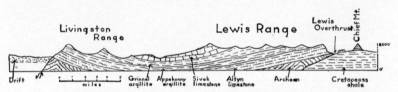

Fig. 126.   Section across the Lewis and Livingston Ranges, showing the
Lewis Overthrust at the right.   (After R. A. Daly.)

abruptly from the Great Plains with slopes of from 30 to 80
degrees along a line known as the Lewis Fault.   The Lewis
Range has been raised 3,400 feet along the fault plane, and
thrust-faulted so that the Pre-Cambrian rocks of the Range
have been moved eastward at least fifteen miles.   These ancient
rocks now rest on top of the much younger Cretaceous rocks,
as may be seen at the foot of Chief Mountain, which is one of
the more advanced lobes of the Lewis Range.   There is a
similar outlier in Crow's Nest Mountain, in Canada.   The
overthrust material faces the Great Plains as a wall often having
precipices 1,000 feet high.   Erosion and glaciation since the
faulting have made the Range so extremely irregular in outline
that it is famed for its scenic features.

Glacier National Park.—Glacier National Park, extending 45 miles south from the Canadian border, includes the most picturesque features of the Lewis Range. The Continental Divide runs through it, at altitudes of from 7,000 to 9,000 feet, the streams to the east descending to the Great Plains, those to the west joining either the Middle or the North Fork of Flathead River. Before the Ice Age these rivers had cut fairly deep V-shaped valleys (2,000 to 3,000 feet deep). During the

Fig. 127. A view in Glacier National Park, showing the glaciated character of the mountains. (After Stanton, U. S. G. S.)

Ice Age, snow fields formed on the heights and glaciers flowed down the valleys, often deepening them more than a thousand feet, and giving them the characteristic U-shaped cross section. The present glaciers are but remnants of the great glaciers of the past to which most of the carving of the Range is to be attributed. The snow fields developed deep cirques with precipitous walls rising one or even two thousand feet. The bottoms of the cirques are now occupied by picturesque lakes whose nearly vertical walls reveal the sedimentary layers of which the mountains are made. Isabel, Grinnel, Sue, Evangeline, Avalanche, Ellen, and Wilson are cirque lakes. In places overdeepened depressions in the valley floors are occupied by lakes, such as McDonald, Logging, Quartz, Bowman, St. Mary, and Two Medicine lakes.

The Canadian government has established Jasper National Park on the Athabaska River, 275 miles north of Glacier National Park. Its features are very similar to those of Glacier National Park. The Banff region, with Lake Louise, is likewise a portion of the glaciated Northern Rocky Mountains.

Other ranges of the Northern Rocky Mountains.—The Clark, Livingston, Swan, Mission, McDonald, and Galton ranges have much the same character as the Lewis Range— they are made of sedimentary rocks, have been folded, and have

FIG. 128. Looking across the Salmon River Mountains. Note that the peaks all rise to the level of the Rocky Mountain Peneplain. (After Lindgren, U. S. G. S.)

been highly glaciated—but they differ from the Lewis Range in that they have not been overthrust.

The mountain ranges west of the Rocky Mountain Trench are developed on strong metamorphic or igneous rocks, and occur in groups divided by rivers. The summit levels represent the Rocky Mountain Peneplain, and everywhere the skyline is approximately level. (See Fig. 128.) The highest part of this uplifted peneplain is in southeastern Idaho, where the peaks rise to 10,500 feet. From there the altitudes decrease to 9,000 feet in the Sawtooth Mountains, to 8,500 feet in the northern Salmon River Mountains, to 7,000 feet in the Clearwater Mountains, and to 6,000 feet in the Columbia Mountains. The broad surface of the peneplain was later broken by faults, along which trenches have developed dividing it into blocks. Each of these blocks was later dissected by streams, and eroded by glaciers, forming groups, like the Purcell group, the Selkirk group, and the Salmon River group.

To describe each of these groups is unnecessary because their histories are similar. The Bitterroot Mountains, however, stand out as a distinct range. Their formation is due to a fault on the east side, along which the Bitterroot River Valley has been dropped. The eastern face of the mountain range, with slopes from 18° to 26°, seems to be the fault plane. It is so young that it is as yet but little eroded. Movement on this fault took place as late as 1898.

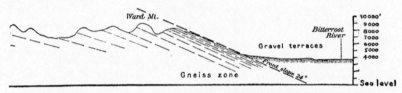

FIG. 129. Section of the Bitterroot Mountains, the front slope marking the fault face, and the tops of the mountains marking the Rocky Mountain Peneplain. (After Lindgren, U. S. G. S.)

The Northern Rocky Mountains are but sparsely inhabited, except in the few localities where grazing, lumbering, or mining is carried on. The mining districts are at Coeur d'Alene on the west side of the area, where silver and lead are mined, and at Butte, Montana, a copper-producing center.

The Tertiary Basins.—About the southeast margin of the Northern Rocky Mountains occurs a group of some twenty basins—the "Tertiary Basins"—whose origin is still undetermined. These basins, whose floors are between 3,000 and 5,000 feet above sea level, are located in mountains which rise to about 7,000 feet. The basins range in width to a maximum of 15 miles and in length to a maximum of 100 miles. Each basin is partly filled with Tertiary sediments, sometimes beginning with Oligocene beds at the bottom and ending with Pliocene sandstone near the top. Most of the beds are, however, Miocene sandstone.

Some of the basins originated as fault valleys, but most of them seem to be downwarped troughs of the Rocky Mountain

Peneplain. Most of the filling occurred just after the uplift of the Rocky Mountain Peneplain, and part of it has been removed by erosion since the Pliocene uplift.

In the Missoula basin several rivers unite to make Clark Fork River. During the Ice Age glaciers pushed down until they crossed the Clark Fork River and dammed back a large star-shaped lake, which reached a depth of 1,000 feet and which is known as Lake Missoula. These filled basins and valleys, such as the Bitterroot Valley, the Flathead basin and river valley, the Deerlodge River valley, the Smith River valley, and the Madison River valley, form the chief agricultural centers of the northern Rocky Mountain region.

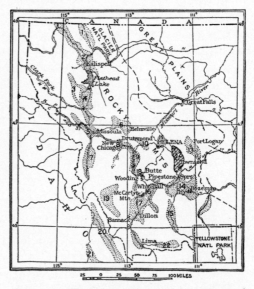

Fig. 130. The Tertiary Basins: 1, Flathead Valley; 2, Kalispell Valley; 3, Little Bitterroot Valley; 4, Mission Valley; 5, Missoula Valley; 6, Blackfoot Valley; 7, Bitterroot Valley; 8, Flint Creek Valley; 9, Deer Lodge Valley; 10, Avon Valley; 11, Prickly Pear Valley; 12, Townsend Valley; 13, Smith River Valley; 14, Gallatin Valley; 15, Madison Valley; 16, Jefferson Valley; 17, Beaverhead Valley; 18, Silver Bow Valley; 19, Big Hole Valley; 20, Lemhi Valley; 21, Pahsimeroi Valley; 22, Centennial Valley. (After Pardee, U. S. G. S.)

MIDDLE ROCKY MOUNTAINS

The Columbia, Selkirk, and Purcell systems end to the south where they come in contact with the Snake River lava plain, but the structure of the Northern Rocky Mountains on the east is continued through the Middle Rocky Mountains. The exact boundary between the Northern and the Middle Rocky Mountains is more or less arbitrary. The southeast portion of the Northern Rocky Mountains is a peneplained tableland with a granite top which has been cut into mountain groups by the headwaters of the Gallatin and Yellowstone rivers. The Madison Mountains lie between the Madison and the Gallatin rivers, and the Gallatin Mountains between the Gallatin and Yellowstone rivers. The boundary between the Northern and Middle Rocky Mountains may be drawn along

FIG. 131. Orientation map of the Middle Rocky Mountains.

any one of these three rivers; but the Yellowstone is generally considered the preferable boundary. The mountains east and south of this river are considered as belonging to the Middle Rocky Mountains.

While the Middle Rocky Mountain structure is a continuation of that of the folded Northern Rocky Mountains, the mountain trend in the Middle Rockies is sharply offset to the east. The result is a region of great irregularity in directional trends, some of the ranges running north-south, others even east-west. In the basins between the ranges continental deposition took place, especially during the Eocene, and the basins were filled as the tops of the folds were being eroded off in the formation of the Rocky Mountain Peneplain. (See Fig. 140.) The same uplifts occurred here as in other parts of the mountains, and also the same periods of erosion, but in the Middle Rockies a large percentage of the area does not have the Rocky Mountain Peneplain for its top. The weaker intermediate layers between the mountain ranges are two to three thousand feet below the mountain tops, but have not been worn down to the Prairie Peneplain level.

Big Horn Mountains.—The first range to the east of the Yellowstone River is the Beartooth Range. This is a broad

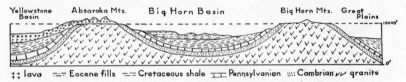

FIG. 132. Section from the Great Plains across the Big Horn Mountains, the Big Horn Basin, the Absaroka Mountains, and the Yellowstone Basin.

tableland whose top is the Rocky Mountain Peneplain. Streams have cut back notches into the rim of this tableland and subdivided it into lobes known as East Boulder Plateau, West Boulder Plateau, and Lake Plateau. When the Range was first folded the uplift was so sharp that the folds broke along the northeast and southwest sides, and faults now bound the tableland. On all sides the rise to the top of the tableland is sharp, but along the fault faces it is abrupt.

At the north end this tableland is about 10,500 feet in altitude, and represents the Rocky Mountain Peneplain. Farther south it is buried under comparatively recent lava flows, and the top is equal to, or above, that of the Beartooth platform. The portion covered by lava, called the Absaroka Range, makes the eastern boundary of Yellowstone Park. South of the Park the Range emerges from under the lava flows and is called the Shoshone Range. The mountain fold then turns to the east and becomes first the Owl Creek Mountains, and farther east the Bridger Mountains. Finally it bends around to the north and forms the Big Horn Mountains.

The lavas of the Absaroka Range are both flows and tuffs, the latter predominating, and represent eruptions beginning in the late Miocene and lasting into the Pliocene. The Range was deeply dissected following the late Pliocene uplift and was given an alpine ruggedness during the Ice Age, so that it is a region of very striking scenery.

Where the Range emerges from under the lava cover it is a rather narrow anticlinal fold (Shoshone, Owl Creek, and Bridger Mountains) rising only to 9,000 feet to the level of the Rocky Mountain Peneplain which was formed across the younger sedimentary beds. When the Range turns to the north, its peneplained top rises higher as the Big Horn Range. The top is about 10,000 feet high, with monadnocks which rise higher. In the median portion of this range all the sedimentary rocks have been stripped off, and the granite exposed. During the Ice Age the northern part of the Range supported an

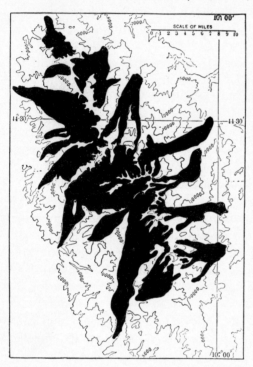

Fig. 133. Diagram to show the extent of the glaciation on the Big Horn Mountains. (After Atwood, U. S. G. S.)

extensive snow field, and in the Cloud Peak region glaciers descended the valleys both to the east and to the west, to an altitude of about 7,000 feet. The snow field carved many fine cirques. The one at Ten Sleep, Wyoming, is followed by the highway to the top of the range.

Big Horn Basin.—Lying between the Big Horn Mountains and the Absaroka Range is the Big Horn Basin, a structural syncline, established at the end of the Cretaceous Period, when the two ranges were first folded. The center of the basin was below the level of the Rocky Mountain Peneplain, and it was filled with Eocene continental sediments. After the Miocene uplift the basin was partly excavated, but not enough to lower it to the level of the Prairie Peneplain. Remnants of the Eocene fill left in the Basin were later carved into "bad lands," especially in the neighborhood of the Greybull River. These "bad lands" have become famous as the deposits from which the remains of a great number of Eocene animals have been recovered.

Big Horn River.—The Big Horn River has evidently had an interesting history. The river rises in the Wind River Mountains, crosses the basin between them and the Owl Creek Mountains, and cuts directly through the latter. It then flows across the basin and leaves it by a gap through the north end of the Big Horn Mountains. Such a course could have been established only when the Rocky Mountain Peneplain was near its completion, and at a time when the basin did not exist. Then after the Miocene uplift it began to cut down and was superimposed on the mountain ranges. It could not remove the weak rocks in the basin faster than it could cut the granites encountered in crossing the mountain folds. As a result the basin was not lowered to the level of the Prairie Peneplain; in fact the drainage inside of the basin did not even develop to maturity.

Yellowstone Park.—The Yellowstone National Park is a basin just to the west of the Absaroka Range, its floor being some 2,000 feet lower than the surrounding uplands. Originally it was a synclinal basin, formed at the end of the Cretaceous when the surrounding ranges were raised. The original surface of the basin is now buried by some 2,000 feet of tuffs and lavas, so that its present floor is between 7,500 and 8,500 feet above sea level. The lava outpourings began in the Eocene and practically filled the original basin.

After the Miocene uplift the flows in the basin were largely removed, but from late Miocene to recent times lavas and tuffs have again almost refilled the basin. During the Ice Age glaciers entered the basin from the north and the east, blocked the Yellowstone River, and formed a Yellowstone Lake, much larger than the present lake of that name. The glacial Yellowstone Lake stood 160 feet higher than the present lake and drained to the south by way of the Snake River. After the recession of the ice sheet the Yellowstone River cleared its

FIG. 134. The Yellowstone Basin, showing the distribution of the geysers and hot springs. (Courtesy of A. K. Lobeck, from *Atlas of American Geology*.)

channel of glacial debris, and of some lava flows which had choked it. It extended its headwaters southward until it tapped the glacial Yellowstone Lake and rapidly lowered the water to its present level.

The Yellowstone River seems to have begun to cut its canyon just after the Pliocene uplift, and to have developed it almost · to its present extent before the Ice Age. Since the Ice Age the river has had to remove obstructions formed of glacial de-

posits or by lava flows, and it is only recently that the river
has begun to cut its canyon deeper. The present gorge is a
thousand feet deep and is entirely in rhyolite lavas. The
waterfalls occur where the river has encountered dense beds
of lava. The vivid colors of the rocks on the sides of the
canyon are due to sulphur compounds which have been brought
to the surface by steam escaping through the lavas.

Geysers.—Outstanding features of the Yellowstone Park are
the hundred or more geysers and the four thousand hot springs.

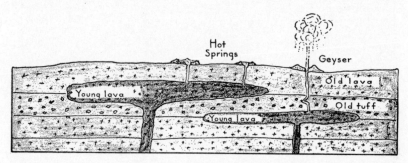

F IG . 135. Diagram showing the relation between intrusive lavas and the
geysers and hot springs.

All are found in the rhyolite lavas which are thought to be intrusives of very recent age. Geysers and hot springs wax and
wane, but the field facts indicate that geysers and hot springs
have been active in this region since before the Ice Age. Bodies
of hot lava under the surface heat the water of both geysers
and springs and the steam and vapors rising from the geysers
and hot springs are, in part at least, volcanic steam. This
new water (from the earth's interior) makes up at least 15% of
the steam and vapor emitted. The remainder seems to be
rainfall, which has sunk into the ground deep enough to be
heated by the lava.

The steam and waters from the lava may make geysers or
hot springs, depending largely on the nature of the underground
passages. If the passage is open and free, the flow of steam
(or water) will be continuous and make a spring; if the passage
is irregular, a water stopper may hold back the steam pressure
until enough force accumulates to blow out the water explo-
sively as a geyser. This explains why geysers are intermittent.

Hot waters carry minerals in solution, and on cooling at the surface the minerals are deposited. Silica is the most common mineral; it is this mineral which composes most of the geyser rims and cones. The Mammoth Hot Springs, which carry mostly lime, have built up great terraces. Each spring usually has some particular mineral in solution which accounts for the peculiar color of its deposits. Some springs have high colors, especially reds and greens, due to algae which live in the hot waters. Others bring up water with sulphur and arsenic compounds in solution. The sulphur causes a black color, the arsenic yellows and oranges. The mud geysers (or springs) owe their character to the fact that their passageways are through tuffs, or through glacial deposits, and volcanic ash or clay is ejected with the steam and water.

Teton Mountains.—After a gap on the southwest side of the Yellowstone Park the ranges begin again as a series of sharp anticlinal folds. The first of these folds makes the Teton Range, running north to south, and about 40 miles long. This range differs in type from the Northern Rocky Mountains in being an asymmetrical anticlinal fold, with its steep side toward the east and a gradual slope down to the west. Over the central portion the sedimentary beds have all been stripped off, exposing the granites. The two outstanding peaks, Mt. Hayden (13,700 feet) and Grand Teton (13,747 feet), are monadnocks on the top of the Rocky Mountain Peneplain.

The steep eastern side offered but little opportunity for snow fields to accumulate during the Ice Age, but a few small glaciers made short U-shaped valleys, and scooped out hollows at the foot of the mountains, in which lie such lakes as Jenny, Bradley, and Taggart. On the west side of the Range the glaciers were larger, but they did not extend down to the foot of the mountains. This range has recently been set aside as the Teton National Park.

To the south and west of the Teton Mountains are several lesser ranges, each with a southeast-northwest trend, such as Snake, Salt, and Caribou. Each of these is an anticlinal fold, but not high enough to have had the sedimentary rocks stripped down to the granite cores when the Rocky Mountain Peneplain was formed.

To the south and east of the Teton Range the major uplifts are the Gros Ventre Mountains and the Wind River Mountains. These reach to the southeast into the Wyoming Basin.   Both ranges are anticlinal folds sufficiently high to have the granite cores exposed on the Rocky Mountain Peneplain surface.

Wasatch Mountains.—The western margin of the Middle Rocky Mountain Province is made by the Wasatch Mountains, which, together with the Bear Mountains, make a continuous wall over 200 miles long.   On the west side the range has been faulted, as are the mountain blocks in the adjoining Basin and Range Province, while on the east side it is folded, as is characteristic of many ranges in the Rocky Mountains.   The Wasatch

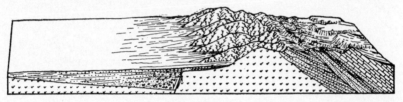

FIG. 136.   Structure section across the Wasatch Mountains.   (After G. W. Bain.)

Range was folded at the end of the Cretaceous and then eroded to the Rocky Mountain Peneplain level.   The crest of the range is generally at an altitude of 10,000 feet, but there are a considerable number of monadnocks which rise above this, several to 11,000 feet—at Mt. Timpanogos to 11,957 feet.   In late Miocene, or at a later period, a large block dropped on the west of the fault.   Erosion, especially in the Pliocene, dissected the mountains and produced the larger landscape features to be seen today.   From Salt Lake City northward the Range was extensively glaciated.   The larger glaciers on the west side were in some cases nearly ten miles long, and descended to the 6,000-foot level.   Some of the stream valleys are glacial troughs, at least in their upper reaches, with lateral and terminal moraines.   The American Fork River, for instance, has a wide, steep-walled upper valley, and a narrow V-shaped canyon in its lower portion.

Uinta Mountains.—The Uinta Mountains, which make the southwest boundary of the Middle Rocky Mountains, are an asymmetrical anticline extending east and west.   They were

folded at the end of the Cretaceous Period, and by the beginning
of the Miocene the Rocky Mountain Peneplain was well developed over them.   Approximately 18,000 feet of material
was removed from the top of the fold and deposited to a depth
of eight or nine thousand feet in the synclinal depressions north
and south of the mountains.   During the folding a large fault
was developed on the north side of the Uinta Mountains (see
Fig. 137), and part of the material eroded from the top
of the Uinta Mountain fold was deposited in a great lake which
had been formed to the north.   These deposits are fine white
shales, in which skeletons of fresh-water fishes of the Eocene

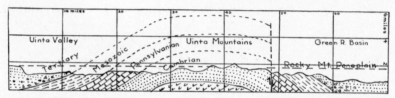

FIG. 137.   Section across the Uinta Mountains, showing the structure of the
range, the amount of the erosion, and the fills (Tertiary) to the north and the
south of the range.   (Adapted from Powell.)

are beautifully preserved.   In other places the debris accumulated as flood-plain deposits, in which many fossils of Eocene
land animals are now found.   The debris carried to the south
was deposited as flood plains on the upper portion of the
Colorado Plateaus.   The Miocene and Pliocene uplifts so
raised this mountain belt that the Rocky Mountain Peneplain
is now at altitudes approximating 10,000 feet.   At the end of
the Oligocene, the basins north and south of the present mountains must have been filled level with the mountains.

The Green River seems to have acquired its course on the
Rocky Mountain Peneplain.   It rises in the Wind River Mountains, flows across the Green River Basin at a level of about
7,000 feet above the sea, then enters the Uinta Mountains by
way of the Flaming Gorge, turns back in the Horseshoe Canyon,
and flows again for a short distance in the basin.   It again
enters the Uinta Mountains at the Gate of Lodore, but 60
miles within the mountains it turns east and flows an equal
distance along the axis of the range, then finally turns south
and leaves the mountains.   In all this distance it flows in a

canyon 2,500 feet deep and follows a meandering course, such
as would be followed by an old stream on a lowland plain.   It
is believed that the Green River followed a meandering course
on the Rocky Mountain Peneplain at the end of the Oligocene.

Fig. 138.   The Green River entering the Uinta Mountains at the Gate of
Lodore.   (After Powell.)

As the region was uplifted the river became superimposed and
entrenched itself along its old course.   It excavated the Green
River Basin, and carried the detritus through the mountains
to the muddy Colorado River.   The Green River and its tributaries have also excavated the Uinta Basin, on the south side of
the mountains.

During the Ice Age the Uinta Mountains were extensively
eroded by over 100 local glaciers, each more than a mile long.
Nowhere is there a finer development of cirques, with narrow
divides between them, and in places peaks of the Matterhorn

FIG. 139.   The crest of the Uinta Mountains, showing the cirques developed
on either side.   (After Atwood, U. S. G. S.)

type.   The glaciers of the south side were longer, ranging up
to twenty miles in length, and descended to the 7,000-foot level.
Those of the north side were shorter and stopped some 500 feet
higher up.

WYOMING BASIN PROVINCE

Between the Uinta Mountains on the south, the Big Horn
Mountains on the north, the Wasatch Mountains on the west,
and the Laramie Mountains on the east lies the Wyoming
Basin Province, with its floor mostly above the 7,000-foot level.
This floor does not represent the Prairie Peneplain, but rather
a stage of reduction reached when the rivers were limited in
their down-cutting by mountain barriers which were local base
levels and through which they have cut canyons.   The history
of the basin, as worked out by S. R. Knight, is shown in Fig.
140.

The Wyoming Basin is a structural basin, originating as a
syncline, or as several synclines, at the time of the Post-
Cretaceous Laramide Revolution.   Erosion removed the tops
of the folds and eventually cut them down to their granite cores.
The debris collected in the basins, filling them nearly to the

mountain tops, the depth in places ranging from 13,000 to 20,000 feet. Some of the deposits near the mountains are

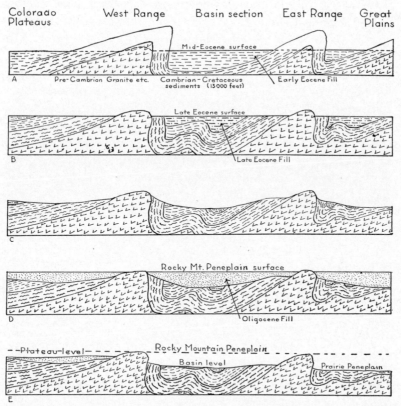

FIG. 140. The development of the Southern Rocky Mountains and Wyoming Basin: A, after the folding at the end of the Cretaceous and the first filling of the basins; B, after the second folding in middle Eocene time, and erosion and filling of basins a second time; C, excavation of the basins about late Eocene; D, complete filling of the basins with Oligocene deposits, and completion of the Rocky Mountain Peneplain; E, results of the uplift of the beginning of the Miocene—the development of the Prairie Peneplain on the plains, a lesser amount of erosion in the basins, and still less on the Colorado Plateaus. In late Pliocene all of the area was raised to its present position. (Adapted from S. R. Knight.)

very coarse, and all of them are rather sandy. The first filling of the Basin was completed by the middle Eocene (middle Wasatch) and was followed by a second disturbance which folded not only the older beds, but also the lower Eocene deposits. Renewed vigorous erosion on the mountains caused filling of the newly made basins (the Upper Wasatch and Bridger beds).

Sometime in the late Eocene there must have been further uplift, for this second filling period is followed by one of extensive erosion which removed the greater part of the recent deposits and also some of the older marine sedimentary beds. During the Oligocene a third period of deposition filled the basins to the level of the Rocky Mountain Peneplain surface. Following the Miocene uplift the basins were again excavated to their present depths, and at this time the Prairie Peneplain was formed on the weak sediments to the east of the mountains, at a level about 5,000 feet below the Rocky Mountain Peneplain. During this time the surface of the Wyoming Basin was about 3,000 feet below the mountain crests, and the Colorado Plateaus somewhat less. During the Pliocene uplift these several surfaces were raised, and as a result the streams became entrenched. The rivers are superimposed in courses across the granite and strong rock cores of the mountain folds and as yet have not developed lowlands.

The Wyoming Basin is subdivided by mountain ranges into several secondary basins. The Green River Basin has been excavated by the Green River, which has removed much of the Eocene filling and part of the marine sedimentary beds. Remnants of each of the Eocene deposits have been left, especially around the margin of the basin. Oyster Ridge, on the west side of the basin, is an outcrop of a Cretaceous formation almost filled with the shells of fossil oysters. The Red Desert lies in a portion of the basin where the rainfall is less than 10 inches, and the soil is reddish in color. To the west of the Red Desert is a low dome formed in the Cretaceous Period, and just north of the dome is a cluster of young volcanoes, which go under the name of the Leucite Hills (see Fig. 131).

THE SOUTHERN ROCKY MOUNTAINS

The southern section of the Rocky Mountains consists mainly of two parallel north-south ranges: the Colorado and the Wet Mountains, making the eastern, or Front Range; and the Park, the Sawatch, and the Sangre de Cristo Mountains, which form the western of the two ranges.   Associated with these long folded ranges and lying to the southwest are several irregular mountain clusters such

as the San Juan, the
Elk, and the Uncom-
pahgre Mountains.
Between the mountain
ranges are four basins,
known in this region as
"parks." These are
North, Middle, South,
and San Luis parks.

The Colorado Moun-
tains begin in southern
Wyoming as the Lara-
mie Range.   South of
the Wyoming line this
same range is usually
called the Front Range,
and south of the Ar-
kansas River it is called
the Wet Mountains.
All three names refer
to the same fold.   The
Laramie Range is a
simple anticline, the
northern portion of
which is still covered
by sedimentary beds,
and with a gentle slope
up to the mountain
top.   Through Colo-
rado the fold was higher,
and generally on the
east face there are

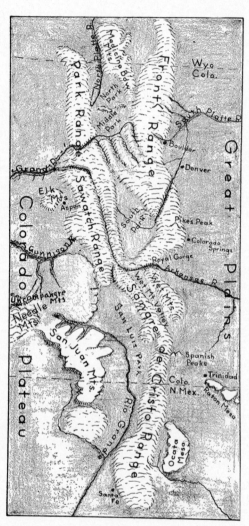

FIG. 141.   Orientation map of the Southern Rocky Mountains.

faults.   Erosion has stripped off all the sedimentary beds down to the granite core, so that the eastern face of the Range is abrupt.   The top of the Range is generally the Rocky Moun-tain Peneplain, but there are many monadnocks on the granite

portion.   Some forty of these monadnocks rise to an elevation
of 14,000 feet, and some 300 reach the 13,000-foot level.   Longs
and Pikes peaks are typical of these monadnocks.   At Pikes

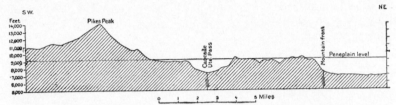

FIG. 142.   Structure section of the Front Range, showing the relations of
Pikes Peak to the Rocky Mountain Peneplain.   (After Cross, U. S. G. S.)

Peak the Rocky Mountain Peneplain is about 9,000 feet above
sea level.   In climbing Pikes Peak, if one stops just above the
9,000-foot level, the sea of ridges all rising to approximately the
same height makes the observer most conscious of the existence
of the peneplain.

FIG. 143.   The Garden of the Gods.   (After Darton, U. S. G. S.)

The main ranges are all anticlinal folds, from which the overlying sedimentary beds were eroded during the development
of the Rocky Mountain Peneplain so that the granite founda-
tions were exposed.   The Miocene uplift raised the mountains
by some 5,000 feet, and the weaker rocks on the Plains and in

the Park basins were later eroded, leaving the stronger granite cores in relief. The floors of the basins were not, however, worn down to the level of the Prairie Peneplain. The Pliocene uplift again raised the region, but here, as in the Wyoming Basin, the rivers have as yet only entrenched themselves.

Close to the mountain front the sedimentary beds underlying the Great Plains are sharply upturned, in places almost to vertical positions. Stronger layers have resisted erosion, so that they form ridges or hogbacks which rise above the Prairie Peneplain level, while the weaker beds above and below have been worn to that level. These hogbacks have a steep face toward the mountain and a lesser slope toward the Great Plains. Beyond the hogbacks the mountains rise abruptly,

FIG. 144. Structure section across the Garden of the Gods. The sandstone between the two arrows is the red Permian bed. (After Darton, U. S. G. S.)

especially in the middle section, because for long stretches the Cretaceous folding was so sharp that the folds broke and faults developed. In some sections the sedimentary beds still extend high up the mountain side and the rise to the mountain top is gentle. On the Laramie Mountains, which are the northern extension of the Colorado Front, where the folding dies out, one may climb to the top of the range without being conscious of more than a fairly heavy grade.

Garden of the Gods.—Just to the north of Colorado Springs is an area where, owing to folding and local faulting, the red sandstone beds of Permian age have been raised into a vertical position. Erosion has removed the weaker portions of the sandstone and the stronger portions have been weathered into many fantastic forms. This area has been set aside as the Garden of the Gods.

Spanish Peaks.—West of Hastings, Colorado, the two Spanish Peaks, East Peak and West Peak, rise just in front of the main range to elevations of 12,708 and 13,623 feet respectively. Each of these two peaks, which lie two miles apart, is part of a mass of lava which spread out as a laccolith under the Cretaceous shales sometime in the middle Miocene, lifting both the Cretaceous and the Eocene far above their normal position. From the lava mass dikes from 2 to 100 feet in thickness

FIG. 145.   The Spanish Peaks as seen from the east.   (After Stose, U. S. G. S.)

radiated on all sides.   Later, erosion removed the overlying beds and divided the laccolith into two masses.   As the Cretaceous shales were removed, dikes were exposed, standing out as walls radiating from the main masses.   These walls range from 50 to 100 feet in height, and most of them radiate from West Peak.

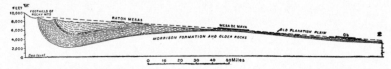

FIG. 146.   Structure section to show the relations of the Raton Mesa lavas to the underlying sedimentary beds.   (After Lee, U. S. G. S.)

Table Mountains.—Another type of volcanic disturbance is seen in North and South Table mountains near Golden, Colorado.   Here, in the Miocene, lava flowed out on the Rocky Mountain Peneplain, covered the upturned and eroded layers of rock, and at the same time dammed Clear Creek. The creek first flowed over the lava, then began cutting into it and finally cut through the lava sheet, dividing it into two masses which now stand out as two tablelands separated by Clear Creek.

Raton Mesa.—South of Trinidad, Colorado, volcanic activity in early Miocene times covered the Rocky Mountain Peneplain with a great sheet (or series of sheets) of lava. These total from 300 to 500 feet in thickness and cover an area 20 miles wide which stretches 80 miles to the east of the mountains. Since the Miocene, erosion has removed so much of the adjoining weak sedimentary rocks (Eocene and Cretaceous in age) that the lava sheets stand from 2,000 to 4,000 feet above the surrounding country. The lava sheets have been cut through

Fig. 147.   Raton Mesa seen from the south.   Raton, New Mexico, in the foreground.   (After Lee, U. S. G. S.)

in many places so as to form groups of mesas. One of the groups includes Bartlett, Barilla, Horse, and Johnson mesas near Raton, New Mexico. Raton Mesa, one of this group, extends nearly to Trinidad, Colorado, and ends in a narrow point called Fishers Peak, which is 9,586 feet above sea level. Fishers Peak is 4,000 feet above the Purgatoire River which flows just below it. This peak is a domed portion of the lava sheet which seems to be the point at which the lava came to the surface, and from which it spread in all directions.

Since the first outpouring of lava, there have been more recent eruptions, as is indicated by lava mesas at lower levels, which could have been formed only after the lowlands they followed had been produced by erosion. The region also includes young volcanoes such as Mount Capulin, whose original form has not been altered by erosion.

Eastward from the Raton group of mesas another group is dominated by Mesa de Maya. Though more extensive, this group of mesas is not so high as the Raton group. To the south and east of the Raton group is Ocata Mesa where Ocata Crater, rising 8,903 feet above sea level, marks the point at which the lava came to the surface. All the flows on which these mesas have developed were poured out on the surface of the Rocky Mountain Peneplain.

The Parks.—Grass-covered depressions within the Southern Rocky Mountains are known as Parks because they are so contrasted with the tree-clad uplands. The rainfall in the higher portions of the Rocky Mountains is sufficient to support a thin, open forest of varying types. Where depressions occur the rainfall is less, and grass is the dominant type of vegetation. Wherever smaller hollows occur in the mountains, due either to the presence of weaker rocks inset into the granite, or to glacial scourings and deposits, parks are found.

One of the best-known parks is Estes Park, whose basin is largely due to glacial action. During the Ice Age glaciers formed in the upper portions of many valleys but did not extend below about 8,000 feet. The snow fields formed cirques, especially on the monadnocks, eroding the peaks into alpine forms; and glaciers flattened and deepened the valleys in their upper reaches. Two glaciers flowing down adjacent valleys came together at about 8,500 feet and formed Estes Park, through which Big Thompson Creek flows. Just below the Park, outside the limit of glacial action, Big Thompson Creek has developed a narrow V-shaped gorge through which passes the road to Estes Park.

The larger parks in the Southern Rocky Mountains lie in basins between the Colorado Range and the Park Range. North, Middle, and South parks are in the syncline formed between these two ranges. This syncline was originally filled by sedimentary beds which have been partly removed by erosion, leaving basins, the floors of which are well below the Rocky Mountain Peneplain, but above the Prairie Peneplain. North and Middle parks were formed as one basin which has

been divided into two parts by a low volcanic ridge known as
the Rabbit Ear Mountains. North Park, about 50 miles long

Fig. 148. The Royal Gorge of the Arkansas River. (After Campbell,
U. S. G. S.)

and with its floor at an altitude of 7,500 feet, is the source of
the North Platte River. Middle Park is smaller and lies a
little higher. In it is Grand Lake, the source of the Grand

River, which flows westward in a canyon through the Park
Range to join the Colorado River. This river, like so many
other Rocky Mountain rivers, has a course which seems to have
been superimposed, the direction of its flow being determined
by the surface of the Rocky Mountain Peneplain. South
Park, just west of Pikes Peak and between 8,000 and 9,000
feet above sea level, is the source of the South Platte River,
which has cut a deep gorge through the Colorado Mountains.
It is another superimposed stream. The western border of
South Park is against the Mosquito Range, a low ridge to the
east of the Sawatch Mountains, which is high enough to prevent
the Arkansas River from entering the Park. This river flows
around the south end of South Park, and then cuts a canyon
through the Wet Mountains known as the Royal Gorge (see
Fig. 148).

The synclinal valley between the Wet Mountains and the
Sangre de Cristo Range, known as Wet Mountain Valley, is a
typical park. Other minor parks are Shaw's, Six Mile, and
Eight Mile, near Pikes Peak.

The Western Ranges.—The western border of the Southern
Rocky Mountains is a series of three major ranges: the Park,
the Sawatch, and the Sangre de Cristo. The Rocky Mountains
end just south of the New Mexico state line, Sante Fe and
Las Vegas being situated at the end of the Sangre de Cristo
fold. The mountains to the south are not anticlinal folds and
were not formed so early as were the Rocky Mountains.

Beginning in the north, the Park Range is an anticline, whose
top was beveled off during the development of the Rocky
Mountain Peneplain. This range is cut into two parts by the
Grand River. The northern part is lower and still retains the
character of an elevated peneplain. The southern part is
higher, and was heavily glaciated—the deep cirques of the east
and west sides approaching each other, so that the divide has
been carved into peaks and narrow ridges of the alpine type.
The north end of the Sawatch Range overlaps the south end
of the Park Range. It too is an anticlinal fold, 2,000 feet higher
than the Park Range, which has been peneplained and re-
elevated. It too was extensively glaciated and was more
strikingly carved into alpine peaks than was the Park Range.

The Sangre de Cristo Range is a narrow anticlinal fold a little over 150 miles long and about 10 miles wide. Its altitude is from 12,000 to 14,390 feet, and it rises from three to five thousand feet above the adjacent valleys. Its narrow base, its abrupt rise, and its alpine peaks together make it scenically the most striking range of the whole Rocky Mountain system.

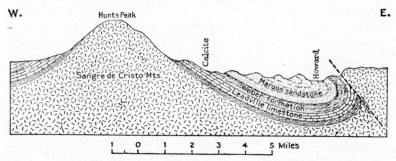

FIG. 149. Cross section of the Sangre de Cristo Range. (After Campbell, U. S. G. S.)

San Luis Park.—West of the Sangre de Cristo Range is a large valley, the San Luis Park, with a broad, apparently flat floor, covered with a scant, almost desert vegetation. It is structurally a synclinal valley between the narrow anticlines of the Sangre de Cristo Range and the broad uplift of the San Juan Mountain group. Like the other parks described above, it was not worn down to the Prairie Peneplain level. Great quantities of detritus have been washed into the valley from the adjoining mountains and deposited in the form of alluvial fans. These have raised the sides of the valley floor, but the fans on the west side are the more extensive, and in consequence the Rio Grande River has been forced over to the easterly side of the basin. On top of the fans, especially on the east side, are heavy deposits of glacial till, owing to morainal accumulation. A series of lava flows from young volcanoes cover these deposits near the New Mexico boundary.

West of the San Luis Park several groups of more or less detached mountain knots, partly folds, partly igneous in origin, form an extension of the Southern Rocky Mountains. These are the San Juan, the Elk, the La Plata, and the Needle Mountain groups.

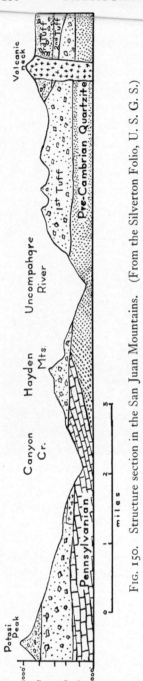

FIG. 150. Structure section in the San Juan Mountains. (From the Silverton Folio, U. S. G. S.)

San Juan Mountains.—The San Juan Mountains are a broad upwarped area, 80 miles long from east to west, and 40 miles across from north to south. The area was domed at the end of the Cretaceous, the top of the dome was eroded off in the making of the Rocky Mountain Peneplain, and the Pre-Cambrian rocks were exposed over much of the area. During a period of volcanic activity the region was covered with tuffs and lava flows to a depth of 2,500 feet, over an area of 15,000 square miles. During a second, and later, period of volcanic activity, 4,000 feet more of tuffs and lavas were spread over the San Juan area. Finally a third outbreak added another 1,000 feet to the accumulated volcanic material.

The whole area was later uplifted, part of it in the Miocene and part of it in the Pliocene, until the Rocky Mountain Peneplain was, with its cover of 6,000 feet of volcanic deposits, approximately 10,000 feet above sea level. Since the uplifts many valleys have been cut, some of them to a depth of 9,000 feet, and many high peaks have been left in relief. Several peaks are over 14,000 feet, and hundreds of them are over 13,000 feet in height. The most rugged portion of this volcanic region is toward the west, the eastern portion having more of the character of a high tableland.

Grenadier Mountains.—The western end of the San Juan uplift is known as the Needle and the Grenadier Mountains. Here the erosion, incident to making the Rocky Mountain Peneplain, stripped off all the sedimentary rocks and exposed a complex of gneisses and quartzites. The peneplain was not so deeply covered with volcanic deposits on the west as it was on the east. During the later uplift it was faulted, and parts of it were raised to an elevation of some 13,000 feet. Erosion first removed the late Tertiary tuffs and then the streams began cutting deep canyons into the gneisses and quartzites, that of

FIG. 151. Grenadier Mountains. Note the peaks all rising to the common peneplain level. (After Cross, U. S. G. S.)

the Animas River being from 3,000 to 4,000 feet deep for a distance of 15 miles. The erosional peaks on the gneiss make the Needle Mountains; those on the quartzite are the Grenadier Mountains. The quartzite has resisted erosion better, and still retains portions of the Rocky Mountain Peneplain at heights of 13,000 feet, with a few peaks rising as monadnocks to 14,000 feet.

The border between the Rocky Mountains and the Colorado Plateaus is not sharply defined in this section. On the Plateaus the sedimentary beds lie nearly horizontal, while in the Rocky Mountains they were extensively folded at the end of the

Cretaceous.   Near the San Juan Mountains, but on the Plateau, are several small groups of elevations which represent early Tertiary volcanic deposits coincident with those in the San Juan Mountains.   Several of these mountains rise to 12,000 feet.

The Henry Mountains are laccoliths which spread out between the layers of the sedimentary beds.   Each intrusion lifted the overlying rocks into a dome.   In some places erosion has since removed the overlying rocks and exposed the lava core, while in other places the uplifted sedimentary layers are still intact.

La Plata Mountains.—In several instances lava was intruded into the layered rocks at several heights, making a series

FIG. 152.   The La Plata Mountains.   (After Campbell, U. S. G. S.)

of sills and dikes.   Such was the case in the La Plata Mountains and in the Rico Mountains, which now stand in relief because of the resistant character of the rocks of which they are composed.   Other areas of a similar type which stand out on the Plateau are the El Late Mountains, the Carrisco Mountains, the Abajo Mountains, and the La Sal Mountains.

The Elk Mountains, north of the San Juan group, have had a slightly different history.   They are a broad anticline of the Rocky Mountain type which was intruded by lavas and covered by tuffs and lava flows.   The volcanic activity occurred before the Miocene, so that the Rocky Mountain Peneplain was formed across both the folds and the volcanic fillings.   This leveled surface was then raised (in the Miocene and Pliocene), until its surface was about 12,000 feet above sea level, with volcanic tuffs and lavas on top of this.   From this uplifted area the Elk Mountains of today have been carved.

Bibliography

For the Northern Rocky Mountains:
Daly, R. A., *North American Cordillera at the Forty-ninth Parallel,* Geological Survey of Canada, Memoir 38, 1912.
Glacier National Park, *Popular Guide,* U. S. Geological Survey, Bulletin, No. 600, 1914.
U. S. Geological Survey Folios: Yellowstone National Park, No. 30; Absaroka Range, No. 52.
U. S. Geological Survey Topographic Maps: Chief Mountain,* Cloud Peak,* Missoula, Helena, Saypo,* for Montana; Coeur d'Alene, for Idaho.

For the Middle Rocky Mountains:
Atwood, W. W., *Glaciation of the Wasatch and the Uinta Mountains,* U. S. Geological Survey, Professional Paper, No. 61, 1909.
Powell, J. W., *Exploration of the Colorado River of the West,* 1874.
Veach, A. C., *Geology and Geography of a Portion of Southwestern Wyoming,* U. S. Geological Survey, Professional Paper, No. 56, 1907.
U. S. Geological Folios: Cloud Peak, Wyo., No. 141; Bald Mountain, Wyo., No. 142.
U. S. Geological Survey Topographic Maps: Fremont Peak, Canyon,* Grand Teton for Wyoming.

For the Southern Rocky Mountains:
Davis, W. M., "The Colorado Front Range," Association of American Geographers, *Annals,* Vol. I, pp. 48–64, 1911.
Fenneman, N. M., *Geology of the Boulder District, Colorado,* U. S. Geological Survey, Bulletin, No. 265, 1905.
Lee, W. T., *Peneplains of the Front Range at Rocky Mountain National Park, Colorado,* U. S. Geological Survey, Bulletin, No. 730, 1922.
U. S. Geological Survey Folios: Anthracite-Crested Butte, Colo., No. 9; La Plata Mountains, Colo., No. 60; Silverton, Colo., No. 120; Rico, Colo., No. 130; Needle Mountains, Colo., No. 131; Laramie-Sherman, Wyo., No. 173; Colorado Springs, Colo., No. 203.
U. S. Geological Survey Topographic Maps: Pikes Peak, Pueblo, Spanish Peaks, for Colorado; Raton, for New Mexico.

For the Wyoming Basin:
Blackwalder, E., "Post-Cretaceous History of the Mountains of West Central Wyoming," Washington Academy of Science, *Journal,* Vol. IV, p. 445, 1914.
Darton, N. H. and Siebenthal, C. E., *Geology and Water Resources of the Laramie Basin,* U. S. Geological Survey, Bulletin, No. 364, 1909.

CHAPTER XXI

THE COLORADO PLATEAUS

South of the Uinta Mountains and west of the Southern Rocky Mountains, and extending to the Basin and Range Province on the south and west, are the Colorado Plateaus. The strata throughout the region are nearly horizontal, but have been elevated to altitudes of from 5,000 to 10,000 feet, in part along a series of north-south fault lines. West-flowing streams have deeply dissected the area and cut canyons of great depth and beauty. In several sections the overlying strata have been stripped away for many miles back from the streams and now face to the south or west in a series of high cliffs. Many of the rocks underlying the plateaus are sandstones of variegated colors (red, white, pink, and chocolate predominating). Where they are exposed in the cliffs and canyon walls, their colors accentuate the beauty of a region where all scenic features are on a large scale. In some sections recent volcanoes and lava flows are numerous. These features, together with the bare rocks, the arid climate (except in the higher portions), and the abundant remains of an advanced prehistoric culture, make this region one of great beauty and interest. The most significant natural and cultural features are preserved in national parks and monuments.

History.—The foundation under the thousands of feet of stratified rocks is the Pre-Cambrian Peneplain made on granites and metamorphic rocks of still more ancient times. On this peneplain were deposited Cambrian marine sediments to a depth of from 200 to 500 feet. During the Silurian and Devonian the region was a land surface and was deeply eroded. In the Pennsylvanian and the Permian the area was again depressed and some 1,500 feet of limestones were deposited over it. Following this there was a long time when the region was an arid lowland basin surrounded by highlands from which gravels and sands were washed into the basin and deposited largely as alluvial fans. The basin also contained some temporary lakes.

By the end of the Triassic 2,000 feet of variegated (red, white, and chocolate) gravels and sands had thus accumulated. In the latter part of the Triassic the winds shifted these sands

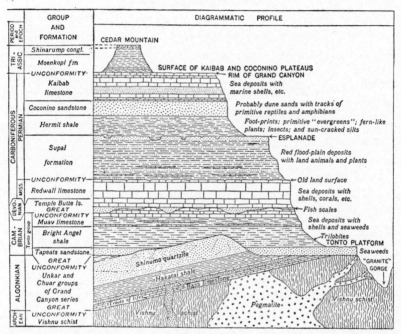

FIG. 153. The rock section as exposed in the wall of the Grand Canyon. (After H. E. Gregory.)

about, making great dunes. During the Jurassic and the Cretaceous, the basin was again depressed and several thousand feet of shales, with some sandstones, were deposited on it. Toward the end of the Cretaceous some of the deposits were continental in character, as is indicated by the presence of beds of coal in them.

In the late Cretaceous, coincident with the uplift of the Rocky Mountains, the area was raised (but not folded), the west being lifted higher than the east and the drop to the east being along a series of monoclinal folds. Then followed "the period of the great denudation," which reduced the whole area to the level of the Rocky Mountain Peneplain. During this period of erosion great quantities of sandy detritus (generally pink in color) were washed from the tops of the Uinta and the Southern Rocky Mountains, and deposited either in low areas next to the mountains, or widely over the plateaus, spreading out as a thick layer of pink beds. It was on this surface that the present rivers developed their courses. As overlying strata were removed, the streams were superimposed on the underlying rocks, whether they were strong or weak. These superimposed streams have maintained their early

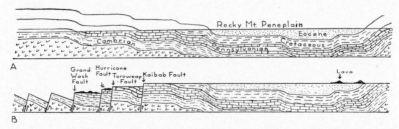

FIG. 154. Sections across the Colorado Plateaus: A, to show the character and amount of folding at the end of the Cretaceous, and the erosion to make the Rocky Mountain Peneplain; B, to show the later fault movements and the flows of lava.

courses which today have no relation to the structures which they cross.

In the Pliocene the region was uplifted and, to the north of the Colorado River, broken by north-south faults into a series of blocks, successively higher to the east. Following this uplift the streams developed a mature surface which is still preserved in the higher section. The greatest uplift came in the Pleistocene, when the area was raised approximately to its present level, and the rejuvenated streams began to cut the deep canyons in which they are now flowing.

Drainage.—The Colorado River is the master stream of the section. It is made by the union of the Green River from the Uinta Mountains and the Grand River from the Southern Rocky Mountains. Its main tributaries are the Little Colorado, San Juan, Dolores, and Gunnison rivers from the Southern Rocky Mountains, all of them streams which flow throughout the year. The tributaries from the west are intermittent streams which rise on the plateaus, and carry water only in the spring after heavy rains. All these streams have cut canyons increasing in depth toward the Colorado River.

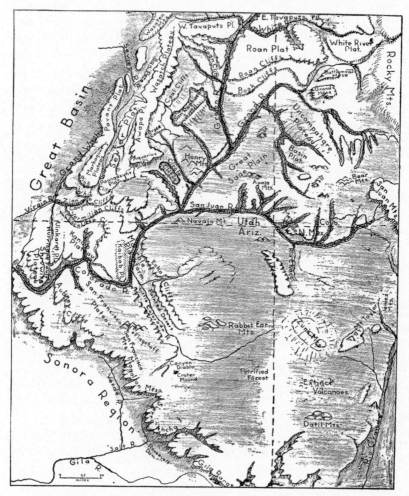

FIG. 155. Orientation map of the Colorado Plateaus.

Grand Canyon section.—The Grand Canyon section of the Colorado Plateaus extends from the Marble Platform to the Grand Wash.[1] (See Fig. 155.) The Colorado River is 2,640 feet above the sea where it leaves the Marble Canyon, and

[1]In this part of the country the term "wash" is applied to a lowland composed either of sands and gravels deposited by intermittent streams, or of alluvial fans built out from the bases of cliffs.

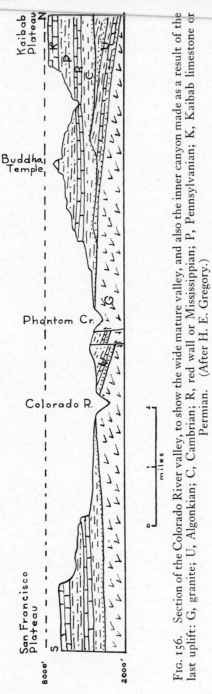

FIG. 156. Section of the Colorado River valley, to show the wide mature valley, and also the inner canyon made as a result of the last uplift: G, granite; U, Algonkian; C, Cambrian; R, red wall or Mississippian; P, Pennsylvanian; K, Kaibab limestone or Permian. (After H. E. Gregory.)

in its 200-mile passage through the Grand Canyon it drops to 1,000 feet at the Grand Wash. The Colorado Canyon is cut through one of the highest portions of the Plateau, its maximum depth below the surface being some 6,000 feet, opposite the Kaibab Plateau, where it is 12 miles wide. Here the river has cut down through all the sedimentary beds, and deep into the Pre-Cambrian granites. About 2,700 feet below the rim a broad platform with mature profiles, known as the Tonto Platform, represents the base level of the Pliocene. As a result of the Pleistocene uplift, the river was rejuvenated, and has cut (and is still cutting) an inner gorge which is now some 2,500 feet deep.

In the Kaibab section the north wall of the canyon is 1,000 feet higher than the south wall. Most of the tributaries are from the north. They have cut side valleys deep into the Kaibab limestone, making the northern rim very irregular in outline. The Coconino sandstone, 310 feet in thickness, and the

Red Wall limestone, 550 feet in thickness, both form vertical walls which may be traced into every side amphitheater. The vertical walls, the large erosional residuals between tributaries, the depth of the canyon, and the bright red and pink slopes of the upper strata, together make the Grand Canyon one of the most renowned scenic features in the world.

The four plateaus north of the Grand Canyon are, from west to east, the Shivwits, the Uinkaret, the Kanab, and the Kaibab plateaus. Each plateau slopes down toward the north from its highest point, adjacent to the Grand Canyon, to the Vermilion Cliffs. These cliffs are the edges of sandstone beds which once formed the top of the plateaus and which have been stripped back to their present position by wind and water erosion.

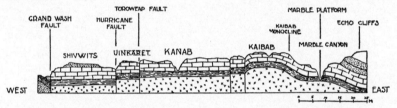

Fig. 157.   The four plateaus on the north side of the Grand Canyon.

Shivwits Plateau.—The western boundary of the Shivwits Plateau is the Grand Wash Fault which extends all along the west side of this plateau country to the Wasatch Mountains. The east side is the escarpment of Hurricane Ledge, which rises 1,800 feet to the level of the Uinkaret Plateau.

The surface of the Shivwits Plateau is about 5,000 feet in altitude and is capped by lava flows and cones, the largest of which, Mount Dellenbaugh, is 6,750 feet high. The western margin is irregular, being cut into by many deep canyons.

Uinkaret Plateau.—The Uinkaret Plateau is only about ten miles wide and fifty miles long. On its surface there are no less than 160 small young volcanic cones, of which several rise from 700 to 800 feet above the plateau surface. The evenness of the Plateau is further broken by Mt. Trumbull, a great mass of lava rising some 2,000 feet above its surface and protecting the underlying sedimentary beds from erosion. Flows from this center underlie the Toroweap Valley and extend to the

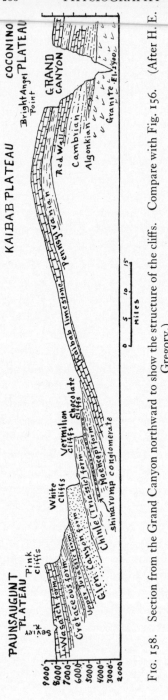

FIG. 158. Section from the Grand Canyon northward to show the structure of the cliffs. Compare with Fig. 156. (After H. E. Gregory.)

edge of the Canyon. The Toroweap Fault escarpment bounds the Uinkaret Plateau on the east. In the south the escarpment is 700 feet in height, but it gradually declines to the north.

Kanab Plateau.—The relatively level Kanab Plateau, about 7,000 feet in altitude, extends from the Toroweap Valley to the fault which bounds the Kaibab Plateau on the west. It is bisected by the deep canyon of Kanab Creek, which is the only nearly permanent stream tributary to the Colorado River on the north side.

Kaibab Plateau.—The Kaibab Plateau, about 35 miles in width, drops down on the east by a monoclinal fold to the Marble Platform. This plateau is 9,300 feet high next to the river but slopes down to the north to a level of 7,500 feet in front of the Vermilion Cliffs. Owing to the height there is sufficient rainfall to support an open forest, but not enough to develop permanent streams. The rain water sinks into the limestone beds and comes out as springs at much lower levels in the canyon walls. The top of the plateau has numerous shallow depressions of the sink-hole type which form grassy parks.

The Marble Platform, east of the Kaibab Plateau, at altitudes

of from 5,000 to 8,000 feet, extends across the Colorado River
to the Echo Cliffs which correspond, in age and character, to
the Vermilion Cliffs. This platform is deeply and intricately
dissected by tributaries of the Colorado River.

The High Plateaus.—To the north of the Grand Canyon
section is a group of plateaus known as the High Plateaus of
Utah. Their southern boundary is composed of a series of
high cliffs extending east and west, and formed on the stronger
rocks, which vary in age from Triassic to Eocene. From south
to north these cliffs are, first, the Shinarump or Chocolate
Cliffs, then the Vermilion Cliffs (both on Triassic rocks), next
the White Cliffs on Jurassic rocks, and finally the Pink Cliffs
formed on Cretaceous and Eocene beds. These cliffs not only
form the southern boundary of the High Plateaus, but also
bound them on the east for 175 miles northward, to the Uinta
Basin east of the Wasatch Mountains.

The High Plateaus are in three series, separated by great
faults. The westernmost series is composed from south to
north of the Markagunt, Tushar, and Pavant plateaus. The
middle series is composed of the Paunsagunt and the Sevier
plateaus; and the eastern series includes the Aquarius, Awapa,
Fish Lake, and Wasatch plateaus.

The western margin of the western series of plateaus is made
by the Hurricane Fault, which here merges with the Grand
Wash Fault. The altitude of the Basin and Range Province to
the west of the fault is about 6,000 feet. Above this level
the plateaus rise 5,000 feet at the south end of the Markagunt
Plateau, from which the plateaus slope down gently toward the
north. The northern portion of this plateau is covered by
a sheet of lava.

To the south the drop is abrupt over the Pink, White, Vermilion, and Chocolate Cliffs. These cliffs are highly dissected,
one of the most highly dissected and picturesque being the
famed Cedar Breaks of the Pink Cliffs. The drainage of these
plateaus is to the south, to the Colorado River. The largest
stream is the Virgin River, whose north fork has cut a narrow
canyon, some 2,000 feet deep, known as Zion Canyon. This
canyon, with its picturesque, nearly vertical walls of red and
white rocks, has been set aside as Zion National Park.

The Tushar Plateau, at an elevation of 10,000 feet, occupies
the middle portion of this upland, especially that part covered
by great flows of lava which have spilled down over the Hurricane Fault, completely obscuring it for some 30 miles. The
Pavant Plateau is somewhat lower than the Tushar Plateau
and is so highly dissected that its level character is nearly
lost.

This series of plateaus not only slopes down to the north,
but also dips to the east, so that there is a lowland adjacent
to the east boundary made by the escarpment of the Sevier
Fault. This lowland is the Sevier Valley, occupied by the
Sevier River and its tributary, the San Pete River, which join
and flow out around the north end of the Pavant Plateau.

From the Sevier Valley the rise to the next series of plateaus
is some 1,800 feet. Sevier Plateau is about 70 miles long, and
is mostly covered with lava sheets. This series also slopes down
to the north and dips to the east to a lowland known as Grass
Valley. Grass Valley has a high fault scarp along the east side
opposite Aquarius and Awapa plateaus, but farther north the
uplift is along a monoclinal fold. The Paunsagunt Plateau,
at an altitude just under 11,000 feet, is developed on top of
the Eocene beds and surrounded by the Pink Cliffs. From
the south and southeast edges one looks down on a myriad of
pinnacles and castle-like spires carved out of these pink sedimentary rocks. The most striking portion of this area is at
the head of Bryce Creek and is now a national monument
named Bryce Canyon.

The southern of the third series of plateaus is Aquarius
Plateau, the highest of all the plateaus, varying in altitude from
10,500 to 11,600 feet. Owing to its height, there is sufficient
rainfall on the plateau to support an open forest. This is the
only one of the several plateaus which was glaciated during the
Ice Age, evidences of which are seen in the cirque lakes and
the glaciated valleys. Its top is protected by a lava cap a
thousand feet thick, from which one can look down to the east
and south to the lower land 5,000 to 6,000 feet below.

The Awapa Plateau is also lava-covered but its altitude is
only about 9,000 feet. It has been described as "an endless
succession of hills and valleys with stony soil." Fish Lake

FIG. 159. Zion Park, Temple of Sinawava. (Courtesy of the National Parks Service.)

Plateau is a narrow area 12 by 2 miles in extent, but with an altitude of over 11,000 feet. The Wasatch Plateau, the most northern of the eastern series, with an altitude of over 11,000 feet, is 75 miles long by 6 miles in width. It is developed on Eocene beds, and is bordered by the Pink Cliffs on the east. On the west it faces the San Pete Valley on a monoclinal fold, the drop being from 5,500 to 6,000 feet.

Uinta Basin section.—From the Wasatch Plateau the Pink Cliffs turn to the east and extend almost to the Rocky Mountains, where they are known as the Roan Cliffs, and a lower cliff, made on Cretaceous beds, is named the Book Cliffs. The plateau above the Roan Cliffs is the Roan Plateau, which is just under 9,000 feet high, and dips toward the north until it is cut by the DeChesne and White rivers. North of these two rivers the same surface, still dipping toward the Uinta Mountains, makes the East and West Tavaputs plateaus. The canyon of the Green River separates these two plateaus as it makes Desolation Canyon, which is over 3,000 feet deep. These several small plateaus and associated lowlands, south of the Uinta Mountains, comprise what is termed the Uinta Basin Section. Branches of the White and Grand rivers nearly isolate the east end of the Roan Plateau, forming the Book Plateau. Two isolated portions of this section near the Rocky Mountains are lava-capped, and go under the names of Grand Mesa, and Battlement Mesa.

Canyon Lands section.—The region between the High Plateaus on the west, the Book Cliffs on the north, the Rocky Mountains on the east, and the San Juan River on the south, is crossed by streams from these highlands, and is so cut into by deep canyons that it is termed the "Canyon Lands." The courses of these streams were developed on the surface of the Rocky Mountain Peneplain and were superimposed on the underlying rocks as the overlying beds were removed. The streams have retained their courses in spite of the faulting during the Pliocene and the uplifts during the Pleistocene. They have removed most of the Eocene and much of the Cretaceous rock from the region, and are now cutting into stronger Triassic and earlier formations.

From the Rocky Mountains come the Grand, Gunnison,

FIG. 160. On trail below Sunset Point, Bryce Canyon. (Courtesy of the National Parks Service.)

Dolores, and San Juan rivers; from the High Plateaus of Utah come the San Raphael, Escalante, and Price rivers; and from the Uinta Mountains comes the Green River—all flowing in deep canyons.

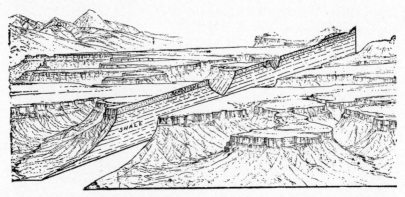

FIG. 161. The Mesa Verde Plateau, topped by the Dakota Sandstone.
(After G. W. Bain.)

Between the San Juan and Dolores rivers are exposed Cretaceous beds which are alternately shales and sandstones. One of these sandstones, the Dakota, holds up the Great Sage Plain, a broad area, which is monotonously uniform, except for the Abajo and La Sal volcanoes, and the numerous minor canyons cutting into its edges.

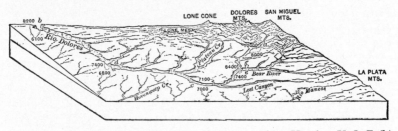

FIG. 162. Block diagram of the Dolores Plateau. (After Hayden, U. S. G. S.)

South and east of the Mancos River is a series of mesas, the northerly ones each topped by one of the higher Cretaceous sandstone beds, while the southernmost mesa, Mesa Verde, is topped by the Dakota sandstone (see Fig. 161). On Mesa Verde, and in the walls surrounding it, there are numerous pueblo and cliff dwellings. The area has been set aside as a National Park.

The Dolores River has a peculiar relation to the plateau across which it flows. Near the head of the river the plateau is 7,000 feet above sea level, and slopes northward until, at the Grand River, it is 8,200 feet high. In consequence the canyon at the head of the river is only 100 feet deep, but at the mouth of the river it has become 2,100 feet deep. Only a superimposed river could develop a valley of this type.

The Uncompahgre Plateau lies between the Gunnison and Uncompahgre rivers at an altitude of 9,000 and 10,000 feet. Its surface is apparently a re-exposed peneplain of a period earlier than the Rocky Mountain Peneplain, for it is developed on early Palaeozoic rocks only, and is only about 1,000 feet above the Pre-Cambrian Peneplain, which is exposed in the Unaweap Canyon.

In the western portion of this section the Green, Fremont, San Raphael, and Escalante rivers all flow in deep canyons cut into the Mesozoic Rocks, which, in several places, have been warped up or down, on anticlinal axes. The Canyon Lands Section contains many features that interrupt the plateau aspect of the region. Laccoliths and dome-like uplifts or swells are numerous. The Henry Mountains are a laccolith whose sedimentary cover has been removed, while Navajo Mountain is a laccolith which is still covered. The most striking dome is

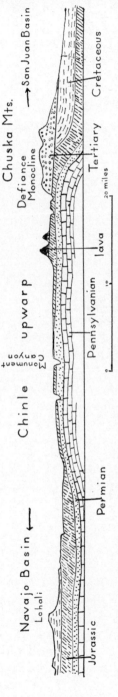

FIG. 163. Section across the Navajo Country, showing its relation to the Rocky Mountain Peneplain, just under the Tertiary. (After H. E. Gregory, U. S. G. S.)

San Raphael Swell, whose top has been eroded off, and which is surrounded by infacing escarpments.

Navajo Section.—The region between the San Juan and Little Colorado rivers is a broad plateau between 5,000 and 7,000 feet high, whose upper surfaces approximate the level of the Rocky Mountain Peneplain. In places there are deposits of sandstone

Fig. 164.   Entrenched meanders of the San Juan River near Goodrich, Utah.
(Courtesy of the Rainbow Bridge–Monument Valley Expedition.)

on top of the peneplain surface, similar in character to those on the High Plains east of the Rocky Mountains.

The Rocky Mountain Peneplain in this region was developed across two synclinal basins, separated from each other by the Defiance Monocline—the western basin being the Navajo Basin, and the eastern basin the San Juan Basin. The dividing line between the two basins is almost coincident with the Arizona-New Mexico boundary, and is accentuated by a mesa-like remnant of Tertiary deposits, known as the Chuska Mountains. In the Navajo Basin an unreduced mass of Cretaceous sandstone stands above the surrounding country from 1,200 to 2,000 feet, with cliffs facing to the north and the east. This is Black Mesa (Zilh-le-jini), whose southern edge is fringed with small mesas occupied by the Hopi Indians.

Between the Little Colorado River and Echo Cliffs erosion has uncovered the deep red Triassic sandstones. This is the Painted Desert, which, with less than four inches of rainfall a year, is almost destitute of vegetation.

The San Juan River runs along the north margin of the Navajo Section, and westward from Bluff, Utah, it has cut a

FIG. 165. The Rainbow Natural Bridge. (After H. E. Gregory, U. S. G. S.)

canyon over a thousand feet deep and with a remarkable set of meanders (see Fig. 164), which are most completely developed near Goodridge, Utah. These meanders developed when the San Juan was an old stream close to base level and were superimposed as the region was elevated. The streams tributary to the San Juan, especially on the south, have also cut deep canyons, so that the region is highly dissected.

The segment of the Navajo Section between Navajo Creek and Piute Creek is the Rainbow Plateau, which is highly dissected by the numerous small streams. As the result of the work of the meandering streams, two striking natural bridges—

the Rainbow Bridge and the Owl Natural Bridge—have been carved from the red and white Jurassic sandstones.

Datil Section.—The country to the south and east of the Little Colorado River is the Datil Section, a nearly level plateau at an altitude of about 7,000 feet, on which are several features of especial interest. The Petrified Forest is a tract some ten miles south of Adamana, Arizona, where thousands of silicified tree trunks have been exposed by the weathering of the red Triassic sandstones. The forest is not preserved *in situ*, as was the standing forest buried by volcanic ashes in Yellowstone Park. It is rather composed of logs which were washed into this area during Triassic times, and buried under conditions which made their preservation possible. This involved burial below the level of the ground water, where dissolved silica (chalcedony) soon filled the cell cavities and pores in the wood, thus making a cast of the interior of the wood. Then, later, the wood itself was replaced by a second infiltration of silica. If the silica differed in color at the two times of infiltration, the wood structure was preserved, even to microscopic details. Generally, in this Arizona forest, though the wood appears well preserved externally, the detail of wood structure is not perfect. However, the colors are such striking reds and browns, and the logs so numerous, that the "forest" is a feature of great interest.

Near Canyon Diablo there is a low rise known as Crater Mound, or Coon Butte. In the center of the mound there is a funnel-shaped crater-like depression about three-fourths of a mile across and 600 feet deep. There are, however, no lava flows associated with the Butte, and the rim is made of upturned beds of limestone.

Two explanations have been suggested as to the origin of this feature. One is that the crater was formed by a steam explosion; the other that it is the scar made by the fall of a large meteor. Numerous pieces of meteoric iron have been found in the vicinity, and drilling has located a large hard mass some 500 feet below the surface, which is thought to be a meteorite. The fact that some of the sand filling the crater is fused strengthens the supposition that the depression was made by an exploding meteor. This must have occurred some thousands of years ago, for lake beds in the crater indicate that a lake, now entirely dried up, must have existed for a long time.

In western New Mexico an elliptical dome, known as the Zuni Uplift, or the Zuni Mountains, rises 2,000 feet above the

FIG. 166.   Silicified logs in the Petrified Forest.   (After Darton, U. S. G. S.)

surrounding country.   It is about 70 miles long and half as wide.   Erosion has removed the top of the dome, and the more resistant top layers make in-facing cliffs of moderate height. Some of these cliffs have been cut into mesas, one of which is the home of the Zuni Indians.

To the east of the Zuni Uplift rises Taylor Mountain, a young volcano, 11,389 feet high, surrounded by several lesser cones. All over this portion of the Datil Section are numerous lava flows, many of which have so protected the underlying weaker beds from erosion that they now form lava-capped mesas.

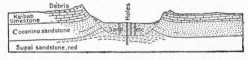

FIG. 167.   Crater Mound.   (After Darton.)

The southern portion of the Datil Section is often described as "the region of extinct volcanoes," because of the large

number of lava flows and of partially eroded volcanic necks.
On the higher portions of the plateau, where the Rocky Mountain Peneplain makes the top surface, these necks rise but little
above the surface; but where erosion has worn away the weak
Cretaceous sediments, these necks make prominent landscape
features. The necks are the remnants of active volcanoes
which made cones and poured out lava at a level some 2,000
feet above the present surface, when the Eocene deposits still
covered all this region.

San Francisco Plateau.—West of the Datil Section, and
separated from it by no distinct boundary, is the San Francisco
Plateau. This is often considered as a part of the Grand
Canyon section because its surface slopes up to the Grand
Canyon where it is some 8,000 feet high. The Plateau is but
little dissected, only a few short canyons, such as Canyon
Diablo and Cataract Canyon, leading either to the Little
Colorado or to the Colorado River. The level, or gently rolling,
character of the surface is, however, broken by the presence of
several hundred young volcanic cones rising above it, especially
in the Flagstaff region. The largest of these volcanoes is
San Francisco Mountain, rising 5,000 feet above the plain to
an altitude of 12,700 feet. The lava cones represent flows of
very recent times, some of the smaller cones being as fresh in
appearance as if they had just been extruded.

BIBLIOGRAPHY

Dutton, C. E., *Tertiary History of the Grand Canyon District*, U. S.
 Geological Survey, Monograph, No. 2, 1882.
Gregory, H. E., *Geology of the Navajo Country*, U. S. Geological Sur-
 vey, Professional Paper, No. 93, 1917.
Gregory, H. E., *Colorado Plateau Region*, XVI International Geologi-
 cal Congress, Guidebook, No. 18, 1933.
Noble, L. F., *Shinumo Quadrangle, Grand Canyon District*, U. S.
 Geological Survey, Bulletin, No. 549, 1914.
Powell, J. W., *Exploration of the Colorado River of the West*, 1874.
Robinson, H. H., *The San Franciscan Volcanic Field, Arizona*, U. S.
 Geological Survey, Professional Paper, No. 76, 1913.
U. S. Geological Survey Topographic Maps: Mesa Verde,* for
 Colorado; Bradshaw Mountains, Bright Angel,* Echo Cliffs, Flag-
 staff, for Arizona; Canyon de Chelly, East Tavaputs, Henry
 Mountains,* Vernal, for Utah.

CHAPTER XXII

THE BASIN AND RANGE PROVINCE

South and west of the Colorado Plateaus, and extending from the Columbia Plateaus on the north, southward into Mexico, and eastward to the Great Plains, is a large area, known as the Basin and Range Province. The province is characterized by hundreds of more or less parallel mountain ranges which are separated by valleys filled to their present level by detrital material washed from the mountains. The mountain ranges are from 40 to 70 miles long, and rise from 7,000 to 10,000 feet above sea level and from 3,000 to 5,000 feet above the valleys. The mountains are all block mountains resulting from faulting and from the tilting of the blocks so that one side is much higher than the other.

The northern portion of this province is the arid Great Basin whose streams do not flow out to the sea. The middle portion, known as the Sonoran Desert, is also arid, but its drainage is dominated by the Colorado River and its most southern tributary, the Gila. The southeastern portion of the province includes the Mexican Highland and the Sacramento section, both characterized by maturely dissected block mountains with intervening aggraded valleys.

History.—The following outline of the geologic history of the province applies particularly to the Great Basin and the Sonoran Desert. The earlier rocks of the region are marine deposits laid down intermittently throughout the Palaeozoic. In the Permian there was a period of folding and mountain building, followed in the Triassic by a period of erosion during which the mountains were worn down to a lowland. Jurassic deposits covered this lowland, and later the region was again mountain-built. The resulting highlands furnished the material which filled the Colorado Sea in the Cretaceous. Erosion continued after the Cretaceous until the region was reduced to a lowland, if not actually to a peneplain. During the Miocene and later, many lava flows covered large portions of the lowland. In the Pliocene came a period of faulting along north-south lines, and the blocks outlined by the faults were tilted so that their edges made the mountain ranges.

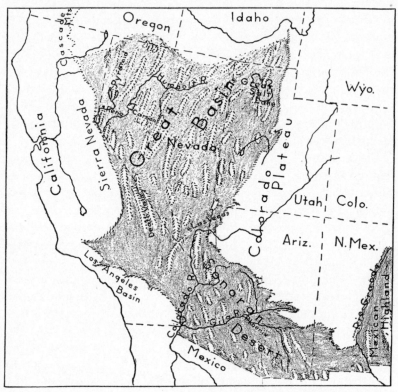

Fig. 168. Orientation map of the Great Basin and Sonoran Desert portions of the Basin and Range Province.

The faulting and tilting of the blocks did not take place simultaneously, but began in the south and progressed northward, so that the southern ranges are older and more eroded than are the northern ones. As a result, the amount of valley filling between the mountain ranges is greater in the south. The mountains are due to repeated movements on the fault planes, and are evidently still being elevated, for earthquakes have been frequently recorded in this region in recent years.

Further, the profiles of many of the rivers are sharply broken, and the shore lines of relatively recent lakes have been faulted and one part raised while the other has remained stationary, or dropped—both indications of recent earth movements.

During and since the faulting and uplifts, erosion has been active, the mountains have been deeply dissected, and the resulting detritus has been deposited in the basins between the mountain ranges, building them up to make the level intermontane flats mentioned above. In places the valley filling is at least 2,000 feet deep. In some places, especially adjoining the older ranges, the detritus makes but a film over the solid rock because the torrential streams, carrying quantities of sand and gravel, scour the bedrock in front of the canyon mouths and erode it to a flat surface. This sort of erosion is termed "sheet erosion."

Playa lakes.—In the intermontane basins the water from heavy rains spreads out to make broad shallow lakes known as playa lakes. Such lakes may be only a few inches or a few feet deep and yet be several square miles in extent. In a few days or weeks the water in these lakes is evaporated and the sand and mud brought into the basin are left behind, thus adding another layer to the floor of the valley.

Playa lakes may contain fresh water, but there is a tendency for each lake formed on the same area to be a little more saline than the preceding one, because each time the water in a lake is evaporated the contained salts are added to the lake deposits. When a lake has become so saline that on drying up it leaves behind a crust of salt, it is a *salina*. Throughout the Great Basin playa lakes and salinas form every year, sometimes in one place, sometimes in another, varying with the distribution of the storms.

Ancient lakes.—The rainfall in this region seems to have varied greatly in recent geological time and to be cyclical in character. There have been times when the rainfall was greater than today, and when large lakes were formed and existed for a long time; and times when there were larger and longer-lived playas and salinas. Almost every basin has old shore lines and shore features which testify to the size of these former lakes.

Lake Bonneville.—Two of these former lakes have an especial interest because their history has been very carefully studied—

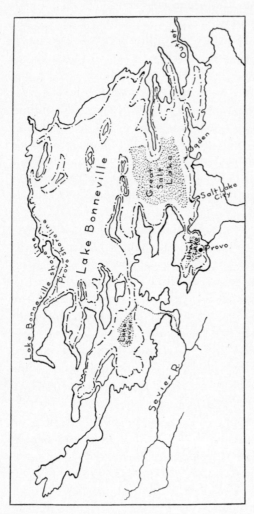

FIG. 169. Outline of Lake Bonneville. The Provo shore line is indicated by the broken line, and the remnant lakes by dotted areas. (After Gilbert, U. S. G. S.)

Lake Bonneville, the forerunner of Great Salt Lake; and Lake Lahontan, of which Lakes Pyramid, Winnemucca, and Walker are remnants.

Great Salt Lake, Sevier Lake, and Utah Lake are existing remnants of Lake Bonneville, which in the Pleistocene, or perhaps even later, occupied at its maximum extent an area of 19,750 square miles in the Great Basin.

In 1850 Great Salt Lake covered 1,750 square miles; by 1869, after a rainy period, it had increased to 2,170 square miles in area; in the period 1901–1904 it was so reduced by evaporation that it almost disappeared. Later it gradually increased to the size of 1850, but in very recent years has again shrunk in size. Though covering so large an area, it averages but 15 feet in depth, with a maximum of 45 feet in the deepest spot.

At an earlier date, during a period of greater rainfall, Lake

Bonneville rose to a level 910 feet above the level of the present lake, submerged what are now the Great Salt Lake Desert, the Utah Lake Basin, the Escalante Desert, Snake Valley, and White Valley, and made islands, or peninsulas, of such mountain ranges as Beaver, House, Confusion, Cedar, and Aqui. After standing for some time at this high level it receded temporarily, only to rise again to 1,000 feet above its present level. At this height it had an outlet through Red Rock Pass into the Snake River and made the highest beach, the Bonneville Beach. As the outlet was over unconsolidated rocks, the channel was rapidly cut 375 feet to a barrier of stronger rocks, and as the outlet was cut down the level of the lake was lowered to the same degree. The lake stood at this lower level for a long time, during which it made its most striking deltas and beaches. These form what is known as the Provo shore line, which is so conspicuous a feature as to be readily noticed by any traveler.

After the Provo shore line was formed Lake Bonneville slowly shrank to the present level, the name Great Salt Lake being applied to it by Fremont in 1843. The shrinking was not uniform, and the lake stood at certain levels sufficiently long to develop a series of shore lines below the Provo level.

After the lake had shrunk below the level of the outlet, the salt content in the water began to increase, both because of the new salts brought in and because of the lesser amount of water to carry the salt. The lake now carries 20% of solids in solution. In 1877 it was 14%, and in 1904, 27%.

Lake Lahontan.—The story of Lake Lahontan is similar to that of Lake Bonneville except that Lake Lahontan never had an outlet. In its maximum development the lake covered over 9,000 square miles of what is now Madeleine Plains, Smoke Creek Desert, Black Rock Desert, and Carson Desert, and extended far up the Humboldt River Valley. At its maximum height the surface of the lake was 530 feet above the present Lake Pyramid, which is 356 feet deep. Between the highest shore line and the present level of Pyramid Lake are well-marked shore lines at 220 and at 110 feet above Pyramid Lake, and weaker shore lines between these levels. None of the remnant lakes in the Lahontan Basin are nearly as saline as is Great Salt Lake. This is in part due to the fact that they overflow from time to time into adjacent basins; but the primary cause is that Lake Lahontan has completely dried up several times, each time burying its salts under a mantle of mud. This is indicated by borings in the bottom of the lake basin, which show several recurring sequences of salt, mud, and gravel.

Pyramid Lake is so slightly saline that it is inhabited by lake trout. Apparently this condition is due to the fact that from time to time Pyramid Lake rises and overflows into the Smoke Creek Desert, where the overflow evaporates and where the salts have accumulated. Pyramid Lake is fed by the Truckee River, which flows out of Lake Tahoe in the Sierra Nevada, and which divides before entering Pyramid Lake, part of its water going to feed Winnemucca Lake. Carson Lake is fed by the Carson River, also flowing from the Sierra Nevada. In the spring this river brings so large an amount of water into the lake that it expands and overflows into the Carson Desert to make Lower Carson Lake, which dries up before the summer is far advanced. The Carson Desert with its playa lake is also known as the Carson Sink. The Humboldt River rises in the Ruby and the Humboldt Mountains, and in spring its water spreads out to make Humboldt Lake at the west, or lower, end of the river. Humboldt Lake generally lasts through the summer, but in dry years may evaporate completely. The water in this lake is but moderately saline, because it, like Carson Lake, occasionally overflows into an adjacent basin, where evaporation takes place and the salt accumulates.

The Lahontan Basin is peculiar in that algae lived in the waters of Lake Lahontan and deposited large quantities of calcareous tufa, sometimes in sheets, sometimes in towering masses. The calcareous tufa is of a somewhat different type for each stage of the lake's existence.

Owens Lake.—Owens Lake, in the southern part of the Great Basin, was once much larger, its surface standing 220 feet higher than at present. At that time it had an outlet to the south. The lake has since shrunk in size, and has become a little more saline than the ocean. The lake was fed by Owens River, but this river has been taken over by Los Angeles for its water supply; consequently Owens Lake is fast becoming more saline, and will eventually disappear.

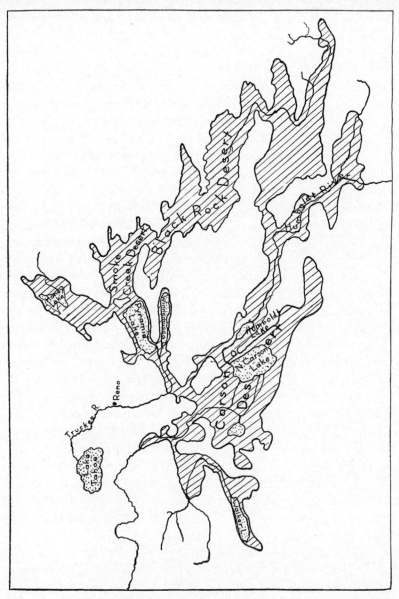

Fig. 170. Outline of Lake Lahontan. The remnant lakes are indicated by dotted areas. (After Russell, U. S. G. S.)

279

Other playa lakes.—In southern Oregon there is a group of typical playa lakes—Warren, Goose, Silver, and others—all of which, less than 25 feet in depth, and covering several square miles, expand and contract with the varying rainfall, occasionally drying up completely.

In addition to the lakes which have been mentioned, there are hundreds of basins which contain playa lakes at times, and which in periods of greater rainfall have had lakes which existed for years. Most of these lakes have left salt deposits as they have dried up, and hence the soil of the basins is strongly alkaline.

Death Valley.—Between the Panamint Mountains on the west and the Spring and Amagos Mountains on the east is Death Valley, which is the result of the down-faulting of a block. The depression thus formed has been only partially filled by valley deposits, and the floor of Death Valley is 276 feet below sea level at the lowest point—the lowest land in America. This valley, 135 miles long and from 3 to 10 miles wide, was once filled by a lake fed by streams from the adjacent mountains. This lake had no outlet, and when its water evaporated, valuable salts were deposited to a depth of several feet in places. These salts were for a time an important source of borax. Later, richer deposits were found in an adjoining basin, and the Death Valley borax deposits are no longer worked. West, east, and south of Death Valley are numerous basins which contain either borax, soda, or potash.

Sonoran Desert Section.—To the south of the Great Basin, and extending southeastward to near Tucson, Arizona, is the Sonoran Desert Section. The western portion of the section is the Mohave Desert—a region of interior drainage. The eastern portion is drained by the Gila River, which, with its tributaries, heads in the higher Mexican Highland lying between the Sonoran Desert and the Colorado Plateaus. In this broad area, mountain-building took place earlier than in the Great Basin; the mountain blocks are more deeply eroded, and the intervening flat lands (lying between 1,000 and 2,000 feet in altitude) are wider and more extensive

The Mohave River rises in the San Bernardino Mountains and flows for about one hundred miles north and east across the

Mohave Desert. Much of its course is through underground gravels, and it appears as a surface stream only when it encounters relatively impervious rocks. It ends at the Soda Lakes.

The portion of the Sonoran Desert drained by the Gila River is largely composed of plains, and the subdued mountain ranges are few as compared with those in the Mohave Desert or the Great Basin. Portions of the Gila Desert have been irrigated through the building of reservoirs in the higher areas to the east. The most famous irrigation project in this section is that found along the Salt River, whose waters are impounded by Roosevelt Dam, in the highlands to the east of Phoenix, Arizona.

The Salton Basin.—In southern California, between the Chocolate Mountains on the east and the Coast Ranges on the west, is a basin some 2,000 square miles in extent, with its lowest point 246 feet below sea level. This is the Salton Basin or Sink, which includes the famous irrigated Imperial Valley. The Salton Basin was originally a portion of the down-faulted basin now occupied in part by the Gulf of California. The Colorado River, with its heavy load of detritus, emptied into the east side of this gulf near Yuma, Arizona, and gradually built forward a delta until eventually the Salton Basin was separated from the Gulf of California. Once isolated, the water in the upper basin evaporated until a small but extremely saline lake, known as the Salton Sea, remained. The sea is surrounded by a large basin, which is all below sea level. The soil of the basin is alluvium from the Colorado River, and the shore lines left at different levels by the old Salton Sea are readily seen. In the north end of the basin are large areas where the loose soil has been picked up by the wind and piled into extensive sand dunes.

As the Colorado River flows across its broad low delta on its way to the Gulf of California, it normally follows a southern distributary. If, as has happened several times in the past, the river shifts its course and follows a northern distributary, it flows into the Salton Sink, filling it until it overflows.

Irrigation ditches have been built from the head of the delta to carry water to the Imperial Valley. In 1905, after a period of unusually high water in the Colorado River, the inadequate head gate gave way and the river poured its waters into the Salton Basin, and the Salton Sea rose 67½ feet, expanding to an area of 443 square miles and submerging the Southern Pacific

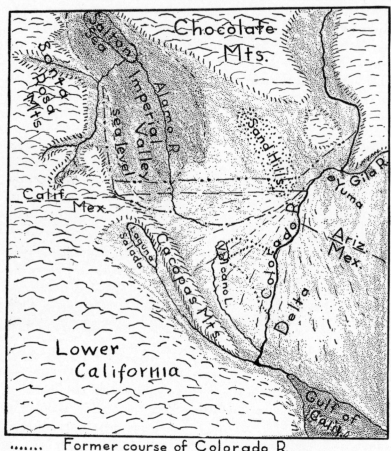

.... Former course of Colorado R.
—·—· Present Imperial Valley Canal
—··—·· Proposed All-American Canal

FIG. 171. The Colorado River delta and the Imperial Valley.

Railroad and the salt works on the shore.   It was a year and a half before the river could be brought under control and turned back into its regular channel (by the efforts of the railroad company).   Immediately the lake began to shrink in size, and its level fell, and is still falling, at the rate of about five feet a year.

Colorado River.—The valley of the Colorado River, from the Colorado Plateaus at the Grand Wash to the Gulf of California, has been cut across mountain ranges and detritus-filled basins without conforming to structure or slopes. The layers of filling in the basins are often tilted, sometimes as much as 30°. The ridges are composed of granite, lava, or volcanic ash. These facts taken together seem to indicate that at some time in the past the region as a whole was covered with detritus to a level above that of the highest of the ridges. On this plain the river established its course, and when the plain was raised

Fig. 172.   The Colorado River at the site of Boulder Dam.   (After La Rue, U. S. G. S.)

(probably at the time of the elevation of the Colorado Plateaus), the river became superimposed. Since the uplift the Colorado River has cut its channel down to the present level, forming canyons through the strong rocks, and wide basins where the material was unconsolidated.

Boulder Dam.—When the damming of the Colorado River was first considered, Boulder Canyon was chosen as the site of the great dam—and the name Boulder Dam is still used, in spite of the fact that the dam was finally built a little lower down the river in Black Canyon, not far from Las Vegas, Nevada, and 95 miles below the Grand Wash. In this stretch the river level drops at the rate of about five feet to the mile. The dam is 729 feet high and will raise the level of the water 600 feet. The lake thus formed will furnish water for irrigating

the Imperial Valley and other sections, and a water supply for
the city of Los Angeles. The flooding to which the lower river
basin has been subjected in the past will be controlled by im-
pounding the flood waters. The lake will become a settling
basin for the heavy load of detritus carried by the Colorado
River, and thus its capacity will be constantly lessened.

Mexican Highland.—Lying east of the Colorado River and
south of the Colorado Plateaus, and extending beyond the
Rio Grande, is a broad area known as the Mexican Highland.
While the dominant features of the highland are block mountains and intermontane basins, in sections near the Colorado
Plateaus the rocks have been so faulted that it is almost im-
possible to work out either the geological or the physiographic
history. Mineral deposits, especially of copper and silver,
have accumulated in the fault fissures. Extensive areas owe
their form to volcanic activity; and lava plains, isolated volcanoes, and laccoliths, are numerous. Since the lava flows,
which probably occurred in late Miocene times, there have been
further uplifts, and long periods in which some of the mountains were worn down to their roots. In many cases the lava
flows so protected the underlying weaker beds that numerous
tablelands developed, but these have been now deeply eroded.

Sacramento Section.—Between the Rio Grande Valley on the
west and the Pecos Valley on the east is a highland region
known as the Sacramento Section, or Trans-Pecos Highland.
It is characterized by block faulting, as is the Basin and Range
Province as a whole. The mountains are, in general, young.
Many of them are plateau-like in character and are but slightly
dissected. Others have now been eroded into mature forms.

In the Cambrian and the Ordovician this region was below
sea level and received deposits of sandstone and limestone,
which were largely removed by erosion during the Silurian and
Devonian periods. During the Pennsylvanian and the Permian more than 5,000 feet of sediments, mostly limestone,
were laid down over the section. It was then raised above
sea level for a time, but in the Comanchean was again depressed
and was covered by from 300 to 400 feet of shale and sandstone.
The Comanchean deposits thicken toward the south. Before
the Cretaceous the region was raised well above the sea, perhaps

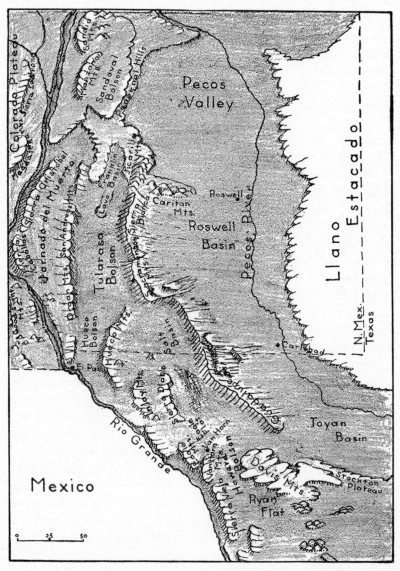

FIG. 173. Orientation map of the Mexican Highland portion of the Basin and Range Province.

285

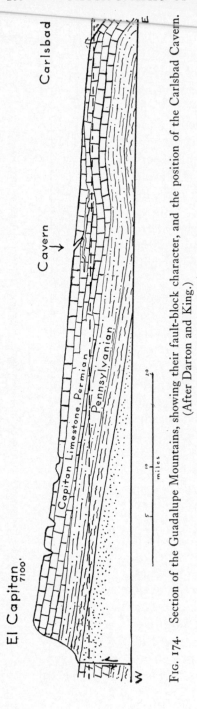

FIG. 174. Section of the Guadalupe Mountains, showing their fault-block character, and the position of the Carlsbad Cavern. (After Darton and King.)

slightly folded; and from its surface was contributed a part of the sediments which filled the Colorado Sea. Erosion continued over this area until either late Pliocene or early Pleistocene, and a peneplain was well developed.

At this period, long after the folding of the Rocky Mountains, and after the faulting of the rest of the Basin and Range Province, this section was broken by faults, and blocks were tilted into their present positions.

The mountains of this section have a general north-south trend, and are arranged in four series from east to west. The first and third series have steep fault faces toward the west, and a gentle dip to the east, and the second and fourth series have fault faces toward the east and a gentle slope to the west. The first series of blocks forms a fairly continuous range, made up of the Jicarilla Mountains, the Sierra Blanca, the Sacramento Mountains, and the Guadalupe Mountains, together with the lesser Delaware, Davis, and Santiago Mountains—the series reaching to the Rio Grande.

Some 50 miles west of the first series is the San Andreas,

Organ, Franklin group of mountains, which have their steep face to the east, and extend to the Rio Grande Valley.   Running southeast along the river is a set of smaller ranges lying between the first and second series.   These include such ranges as the Hueco Mountains, the Sierra Diablo, and the Eagle Mountains.   The third series consists of the Sandia and the Manzona Mountains, together with Sierras Cristobal and Caballos.   These have their fault faces toward the west and the Rio Grande.   Across the river, and facing east, are the Sierra Landrone, the Magdalena Mountains, the Mimbres Mountains, and the Goodsight Mountains.

Bolsons.—Between these series of mountains lie many debris-filled basins known as *bolsons*.   The bolson between the Hueco Mountains and the Franklin Mountains is the Hueco Bolson.   This extends north from El Paso, Texas, widening out to make the Tulorosa Bolson, which is 90 miles wide in the south and narrows to 40 miles in the north.   In this northern portion are several recent volcanoes, from which lava flows extend southerly for 70 miles, making what is known as "the malapais country."   Near the southern end of the malapais country is a great salt marsh, covering an oval area of some 500 square miles, south of which occur the famous "white sands," formed of wind-drifted grains of gypsum.   The sand came originally from a dry lake basin even more extensive than the salt marshes.   The south end of the bolson is covered by reddish and brown sands as far as the Rio Grande, which crosses the bolson in a channel from 200 to 500 feet below its surface.

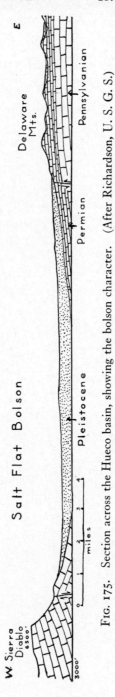

FIG. 175.   Section across the Hueco basin, showing the bolson character.   (After Richardson, U. S. G. S.)

Between the Guadalupe Mountains and the Sierra Diablo lies the Howard Bolson, also known as the Salt Lake Basin. In the north end of this bolson are the Howard Lakes, or rather salt marshes, used for hundreds of years by the Mexicans as their source of salt. These marshes represent the lowest part of the bolson and are 3,600 feet above sea level. From this height the bolson slopes up to the north to Eagle Flat, and to the south to Ryan Flat, each about a thousand feet higher than the marshes.

In the depression between the San Andreas Mountains and the Sierra Cristobal lies the famous bolson known as the Jornado del Muerto, a name given it in the pioneer days on account of the numerous deaths of travelers attempting to cross its dry and barren sands. In the northern part of the bolson depressions hold water several months, but seldom throughout the year. In the southern end of the basin are several recent volcanic cones, the Donna Anna Hills and the San Diego Mountains, from which extensive lava fields have flowed.

Carlsbad Cavern.—The Guadalupe Mountains are typical of the first series of ridges in the Sacramento section (Fig. 174). They are made up mostly of the Pennsylvanian and Permian limestones, and slope gently down to the east from an altitude of 7,100 feet at the crest. Surface water has seeped into the limestones and made many caverns, of which the most famous is Carlsbad Cavern in the east slope of the Guadalupe Mountains. This cavern is outstanding because of the size of some of its chambers, the largest being 4,000 feet long, 625 feet wide, and 350 feet high. Usually before a cavern reaches such a size as this, the roof falls in, but this chamber is so far beneath the surface that its roof is still intact. In general this is a dry cavern, and the drip deposits are somewhat limited, but in certain chambers are extensive stalactites formed partly of calcite and partly of gypsum, both of which are abundant in the Permian beds of the mountain.

Rio Grande Valley.—The Rio Grande flows between the third and fourth series of ranges. From San Luis Park southward the general course of the river is through a series of eight basins connected with each other by progressively deeper canyons. The river and its alluvial plains are from 200 to 300 feet below the level of the bolsons which it once helped to build.   Flowing through so much unconsolidated soil, the Rio Grande is one of the most heavily loaded streams in the United States.   For a time the river flowed through the Jornado del Muerto, but it has been diverted to the west of the Sierra Cristobal.

FIG. 176.   Valley of the Rio Grande at El Paso, Texas, showing its passage from the Mesilla Bolson to the Hueco Bolson across the south end of the Franklin Mountains.   (After Hill, U. S. G. S.)

The fault faces of the mountain ranges west of the Rio Grande all are toward the east while their more gentle western slopes tend to merge into the level surface of the Colorado Plateaus.

Just west of the Rio Grande, in southern New Mexico, is a group of recent volcanic cones with associated lava flows.   To the south of these vol-canoes are three "holes" which have been com-pared with Crater Mound.   The largest of them is Kilbourne Hole, two miles in diameter, 300 feet deep, and with

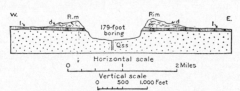

FIG. 177.   Kilbourne Hole.   (After Darton, U. S. G. S.)

a rim about 150 feet high.   The opening is surrounded by the same sort of material as is found in the bottom of the hole. It has the appearance of being the crater formed by a volcanic

steam explosion which was not accompanied by any flow of
lava.   Hunts Hole and Phillips Hole are similar but smaller.

BIBLIOGRAPHY

For the Great Basin:

Gilbert, G. K., *Lake Bonneville*, U. S. Geological Survey, Monograph,
No. I, 1890.

Jones, J. C., "Origin of the Tufas in Lake Lahontan," *Bulletin of the
Geological Society of America*, Vol. 26, p. 392, 1915.

Louderback, G. D., "Basin Range Structure," *Bulletin of the Geological Society of America*, Vol. 15, p. 289, 1904.

Russel, I. C., *Geological History of Lake Lahontan, a Quaternary Lake
of Northwestern Nevada*, U. S. Geological Survey, Monograph,
No. 11, 1885.

U. S. Geological Survey Topographic Maps: Carson Sink for Nevada;
Fish Springs, Sevier Desert, for Utah.

For the Sonoran Desert:

LaRue, E. C., *Water Power and Flood Control of the Colorado River*,
U. S. Geological Survey, Water Supply Paper, No. 556, 1925.

Lee, W. T., *Geological Reconnaissance of Part of Western Arizona*,
U. S. Geological Survey, Bulletin, No. 352, 1908.

McDougal, D. T., *The Salton Sea*, Carnegie Institution Publication,
No. 193, 1914.

U.S. Geological Folios: Globe, Ariz., No. 111; Bradshaw Mountains,
Ariz., No. 126; Clifton, Ariz., No. 129.

U. S. Geological Survey Topographic Maps: Needles Special, Salton
Sink, Camp Mohave, for California; Roosevelt for Arizona.

For the Mexican Highland:

Darton, N. H., *Guidebook of the Western United States, Southern
Pacific Lines*, U. S. Geological Survey, Bulletin, No. 845, 1933.

Darton, N. H., and King, P. B., *Western Texas and the Carlsbad
Caverns*, XVI International Geological Congress, Guidebook, No.
13, 1933.

Hill, R. T., *Topographic Atlas of the United States, Texas*, Folio No. 3,
1900.

U. S. Geological Survey Folios: El Paso, Tex., No. 166; Van Horn,
Tex., No. 194.

U. S. Geological Survey Topographic Maps: Deming, Columbus, for
New Mexico; Salt Basin, Van Horn for Texas.

CHAPTER XXIII

COLUMBIA AND SNAKE RIVER PLATEAUS

Between the Northern Rocky Mountains and the Cascade Mountains there is a broad plateau country of more than 200,000 square miles, whose character is determined by great lava flows, which cover its surface to an average depth of more than half a mile. The Columbia Plateaus, as this region is called, may, for convenience, be divided into two sections—the one dominated by the Columbia River, and the other by the Snake River.

The lava flows.—Before the occurrence of the lava flows the region was composed of block mountains, similar in character and in history to the block mountains of the Great Basin. Beginning in the Miocene and con-

FIG. 178. Orientation map of the Columbia and Snake River lava plateaus.

tinuing until very recent times, fluid lavas have, at intervals, risen to the surface through fissures and numerous necks, and covered to varying depths the surface as it then existed. After each flow there was a period during which the lava surface was weathered to soil, or deposits accumulated in lakes due to the damming of streams by the flows. Each later flow buried the earlier surfaces, and at points there may now be seen ten or fifteen separate flows, separated by soils, by lake beds which

291

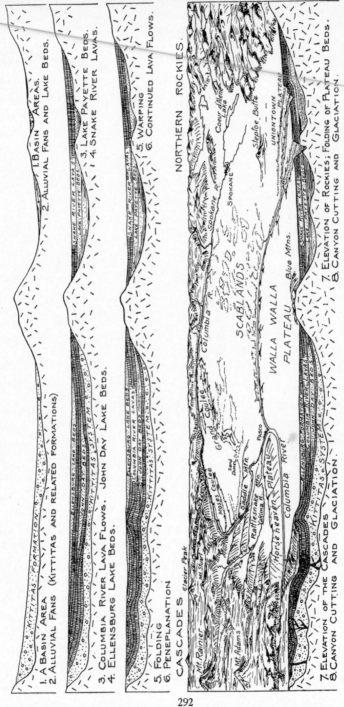

1. A BASIN AREA.
2. ALLUVIAL FANS (KITTITAS AND RELATED FORMATIONS)

3. COLUMBIA RIVER LAVA FLOWS. JOHN DAY LAKE BEDS.
4. ELLENSBURG LAKE BEDS.

5. FOLDING
6. PENEPLANATION

7. ELEVATION OF THE CASCADES.
8. CANYON CUTTING AND GLACIATION.

1. BASIN AREAS.
2. ALLUVIAL FANS AND LAKE BEDS.

3. LAKE PAYETTE BEDS.
4. SNAKE RIVER LAVAS.

5. WARPING
6. CONTINUED LAVA FLOWS.

7. ELEVATION OF ROCKIES; FOLDING OF PLATEAU BEDS.
8. CANYON CUTTING AND GLACIATION.

FIG. 179.   Eight stages in the development of the Columbia Plateaus.   (Courtesy of A. K. Lobeck, from *Atlas of American Geology*.)

often contain fossils, or by other evidences of a long-continued erosional period.

In general the flows in the Columbia River basin are older than those in the Snake River basin, some of the latter being so recent that the lavas are not appreciably weathered. The periods between flows must have been hundreds or even thousands of years. In many places the volcanic cones from which the flows took place now rise from 200 to 300 feet above the general surface, but as their bases are from eight to ten miles in diameter, the slopes of the craters are scarcely noticeable.

In a few places mountains still project above the lava, having been so high that they were not buried by the flows. The Blue Mountains and the Strawberry Mountains are instances.

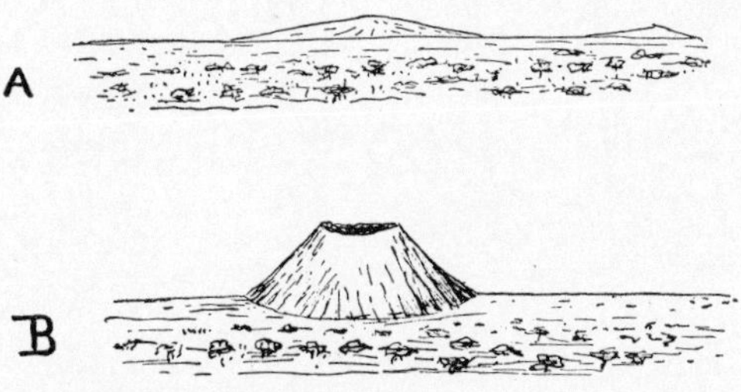

Fig. 180. Two types of lava eruptions in the Columbia Plateaus: A, a cone of the very fluid basalt lava; B, a cone of the viscid rhyolite lava.

Warped surface.— The surface of the lava ranges in altitude from 6,000 feet on the east margin of the Snake River basin to below sea level at the junction of the Columbia and Snake rivers. These differences in height are due more to warpings than to variations in the thickness of the flows. These warpings took place both during the time the lava flows were being poured out and since their occurrence. When the Cascade Mountains were raised to their present height, the earlier flows were also raised; these are now to be seen high up on the sides of the Cascades. At the same time there must have been a sinking of the lava surface in the basins, for thousands of cubic miles (estimated at 100,000) of lava were transferred from within the earth to the surface.

The rivers on the Plateaus, especially the Snake River, do not follow courses consequent to the present surface, but have cut canyons through upraised ridges. They must have inherited their courses from a time when the Plateau surface was markedly different from what it is today.

SNAKE RIVER PLATEAU

The Snake River Plateau is generally level, except for occasional volcanic cones rising from 200 to 300 feet above its surface. These recent cones are associated with characteristic basaltic flows. In places the most recent flows present a surface of broken, ragged, scoriaceous lava. One such area has been set aside as the Craters of the Moon National Monument.

Fig. 181. Thousand Springs on the north side of the Snake River canyon. (After Russell, U. S. G. S.)

In a few cases older cones of less fluid, rhyolitic lava rise to notable heights, the bases of these cones being buried in the later basalt flows. East Butte is such an old volcano, rising 2,350 feet above the level of the plateau.

Snake River.—The Snake River, rising in the Middle Rocky Mountains, flows out on the Plateau at an altitude of about 6,000 feet and has no marked valley for about 100 miles. Then at American Falls it drops 50 feet into a shallow trench which it follows for sixty miles. At Twin Falls it drops 180 feet, and two miles farther on at Shoshone Falls it drops 210 feet into a deep canyon. There is another drop of 25 feet opposite the mouth of Salmon River, making the Salmon Falls. All the falls are over the edges of resistant sheets of lava. In the 300 miles above the Salmon River the Snake River has no tributaries from the north. Streams rising in the Rocky Mountains flow out onto the lava surface and eventually either dry up or sink into the ground. The ground water seeps into the soil layers, or into the scoriaceous lava between the more dense lava flows, and a little above the entrance of Salmon River comes out on the side wall of the canyon to make the famous "Thousand Springs." These springs double the volume of the Snake River. The greater part of the water enters the river from the top of the scoriaceous lava layer, which outcrops 185 feet above the level of the river.

Payette Lake.—West from its junction with the Malade River, the Snake River for many miles cuts through the sandy

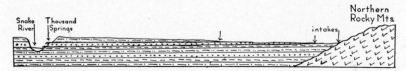

FIG. 182. Diagram of the lava beds between the Northern Rocky Mountains and the Snake River, to show how the Thousand Springs are caused.

deposits of a buried lake of Miocene age known as Payette Lake. This lake has been extinct since early Pliocene. The lake beds are a thousand feet in thickness and contain numerous interbedded thin lava flows which entered the lake from time to time without destroying it. This old lake is exposed only in the canyon walls of the Snake River and its tributaries. The margins of the lake are today 3,500 feet high where first exposed, and 2,500 feet in altitude where the Snake River leaves the Payette basin; indicating that the lake basin, once level, has since been deformed.

Owyhee Mountains.—In southwestern Idaho the canyons are deep and wide, and their side walls are terraced, each terrace being held up by a strong layer of lava. Between the Owyhee and Snake rivers rise the Owyhee Mountains, a range some 30 miles long and 8,000 feet high. This is one of the ranges which rise above the later lava flows and lake beds. A part of the altitude of the mountains is due to an uplift since the lava flows, as is indicated by the fact that the lava surfaces slope in all directions down and away from the mountain base, which is 5,000 feet above sea level.

Island Ranges.—The Snake River, on crossing the eastern boundary of Oregon, turns northward, and enters the Columbia River lava field.   In eastern Oregon the lava plateau surface is broken by several mountain ranges which, though surrounded by lava flows, were never completely buried.   Of these the most striking are the Blue Mountains, running a little east of north, and rising to an altitude of 8,650 feet, 3,000 feet of which lies above the lava plain.   Between the Blue Mountains and the Seven Devils Mountains, which are western outliers of the Salmon River Mountains, are several lesser island mountain ranges, such as the Eagle Creek (Wallowa), Elkhorn, and Greenhorn Mountains.   The Strawberry Range, farther to the south, also belongs to this group.

Snake River Canyon.—The Snake River, flowing across this broken stretch of lava fields at an altitude of about 6,500 feet, has cut a canyon which in places is more than 5,000 feet deep. The height of the river where it enters this stretch at Weiser, Idaho, is 2,100 feet; at Lewiston, Idaho, it is 700 feet.   The canyon is about 15 miles in width, the upper and wider part being in the lavas, while the lower narrower portion is in the granites and gneisses below the lavas.   In depth, width, and precipitousness of slopes, this canyon rivals the Grand Canyon of the Colorado, but it does not have high colors, the walls being of black lava.   The canyons of the Salmon and Clearwater rivers from the Idaho side and those of the Grande Ronde and Powder rivers from the Oregon side are almost equally striking.

COLUMBIA RIVER PLATEAU

At Lewiston the Snake River turns west and flows in a canyon of decreasing depth until it joins the Columbia River near Pasco, Washington, where the altitude is but 381 feet.   This is the low point of the Columbia River Plateau, the lava surface being below sea level, and the altitude being due to the river silts which here bury the lava.   From this point the Plateau rises in all directions, being 3,500 feet high on the north where it meets the Rocky Mountains, and 6,000 feet high on the west, where the lava overlaps the sides of the Cascade Mountains.

In this region the lava flows are old, probably mostly of Miocene age, and they have disintegrated into a deep soil over which is a cover of fine loess, borne by the wind from the more arid sections to the southwest. From the Snake River to the Spokane River the surface is rolling, and rises to an altitude of 3,500 feet on the east and north. The rolling character is due to the numerous valleys, which formerly had streams, but

FIG. 183. The scablands of Oregon. (Courtesy of J. Harlan Bretz.)

which are now dry because the infrequent rainfall sinks at once into the ground and develops no streams. This is the Palouse Country, famous as a wheat-growing region. The lava surface of this plateau is broken by but one projection—Steptoe Butte, a peak of quartzite rock which rises through the lava and stands 1,000 feet above its surface.

Coulees.—The Columbia River flows westward from its junction with the Spokane River until it reaches the Cascade Mountains. Thence it turns southward along the margin of the mountain range, until it cuts through Saddle Mountains, where it turns southeast to join the Snake River.

The area embraced in this loop, while it has the same early history as the rolling hills around Spokane, differs in that it is dissected by a complex of "coulees." These coulees are river channels, now dry, made by the Columbia River during the Glacial Period. At that time the Columbia River was forced out of its channel by glaciers which pushed out from the Cascade Range, especially out from the Okanogan Valley and across the Columbia River Valley. The normal drainage was augmented by water from the melting of the glaciers, and as a result a stream, or several streams, of great volume flowed for a long time across the sloping lava surface toward the low point at Pasco. These streams not only stripped off the decayed lava and loess on the surface, but in places removed one or more of the lava layers. The channels, or coulees, cover some 2,000 square miles of territory within the Big Bend of the Columbia. They branch and then reunite like the channels in an aggraded river valley. Between the coulees are many isolated remnants of the early surface, with the soil surface intact. These, however, are not available for agriculture, as the rainfall here is less than in the Palouse Country. This region is known as "The Scablands." Two of the larger channels, Moses Coulee and the Grand Coulee, seem to represent the main channels of the river.

Grand Coulee.—The Grand Coulee is the most striking abandoned river valley in the world, being about 50 miles in length and about 1,000 feet in depth. Its continuity being broken midway by a structural basin, it may be divided into an upper and a lower coulee. In the lower coulee there is a dry waterfall, 400 feet in height and $3\frac{1}{2}$ miles in width, below which is a gorge formed as the crest of the waterfall retreated northward. The lower falls were the largest of which we have any record. Today the channel is dry, but the brink of the falls appears as if the water had just been withdrawn. In the gorge several lakes occupy what were once plunge pools under the cataract. The most northerly of these lakes contains fresh water and occasionally overflows, but the lower pools are increasingly saline. The upper coulee is the gorge made by a waterfall which worked back until it met the canyon of the Columbia River. Whether the two waterfalls were coincident is unknown, but the upper falls made a gorge about 500 feet deep, and the lower falls made another gorge of equal depth,

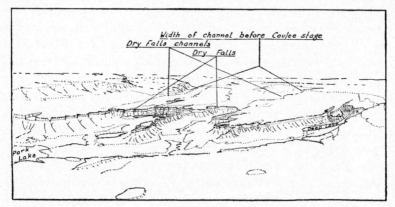

FIG. 184.   The great dry waterfalls in the Grand Coulee.   (After G. W. Bain.)

to the present edge of the abandoned rim.   The withdrawal of the water from the coulee channels was probably sudden, and occurred when the glacial ice had retreated far enough to permit the Columbia River to return to its old channel.

Ellensberg region.— In the angle between Saddle Mountain and the southeast-flowing portion of the Columbia River is an area in which the normally level surface of the plateau is interrupted by seven or eight anticlinal folds, which extend

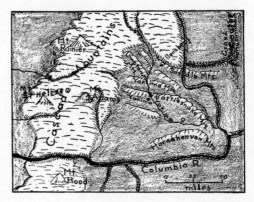

FIG. 185.   The Ellensberg region and the course of the Yakima River.

to the east from the Cascade Mountains, and which rise from one to three thousand feet above the plateau level of 1,000 feet.   The tops of these ridges have been heavily eroded, and the resulting detritus filling the adjacent valleys is in places 1,200 feet deep.

The Ellensberg section is dominated by the Yakima River, which flows across ridges and lowlands without conforming to

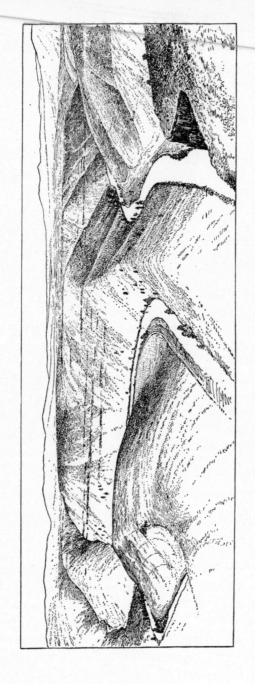

Fig. 186. The Yakima River and a structure section across the basin. (Courtesy of A. K. Lobeck, from *Atlas of American Geology*.)

the present surface forms.   It may be an antecedent stream, but more probably has been superimposed.   The Yakima River receives a subsequent tributary from each lowland it crosses. The Yakima, rising in the Cascade Range, brings to a region of slight rainfall a steady supply of water for irrigation.   This irrigated region, with its rich soil of decomposed lava, has become famous for its fruit-growing.

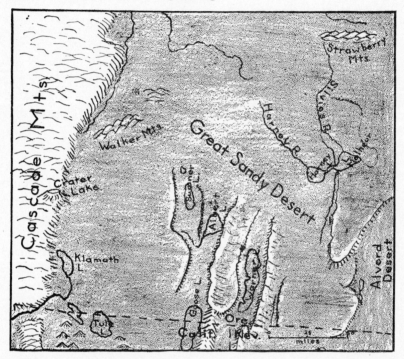

FIG. 187.   Orientation map of the southern portion of the Columbia Plateaus.

North Central Oregon.—To the south of the Columbia River in North Central Oregon the plateau surface is composed of highly disintegrated old lavas capped by loess and volcanic ash brought from the south by the wind.   Where the soil layer is thick it is rich, and is devoted to wheat-growing by dry-farming methods.   The section is drained by the Deschutes and John Day rivers, both flowing from the south in canyons from 500 to 2,000 feet deep.   The volume of the Deschutes River and its tributaries is largely due to water which seeps out of vesicular layers of lava, as do the Thousand Springs on the Snake River. Along the John Day River are deposits of loess and volcanic ash dating back to the Oligocene, in which are preserved the fossils of a great number of land animals.

Harney Section.—The southwestern corner of the Columbia Plateaus, including the Great Sandy Desert, is known as the Harney Section. It is an area of some 8,000 square miles, at an altitude of about 4,000 feet, and with interior drainage. The surface is covered with 70 or more feet of decayed lava, the fragments of which are locally called "gravel" when coarse, and "sand" when fine. The central and west portions of the section are sprinkled with volcanic cones, most of which are under 200 feet in height. Some of them are remnants of old volcanoes, while others are young volcanoes.

Two fairly large lakes lie on the plateau—Lake Harney and Lake Malheur. All the water which falls on this portion of the plateau either sinks into the ground or evaporates from these two lakes. Ordinarily the two lakes are separate, but after heavy rains Lake Harney may overflow into Lake Malheur. As a result, Lake Harney is fairly fresh, while Lake Malheur is strongly saline. Lake Malheur is prevented from flowing into the Malheur River by a young flow of lava, which, however, rises but ten feet above the lake level. In prehistoric times the Malheur River was doubtless the outlet of the lake, but in historic times the level of the lake has never been high enough to permit it to overflow this barrier.

BIBLIOGRAPHY

Bretz, J. H., *The Grand Coulee*, American Geographical Society, Special Publication, No. 15, 1932.

Bretz, J. H., *The Channeled Scablands*, XVI International Geological Congress, Guidebook, No. 22, 1933.

Russell, I. C., *Reconnaissance in Southeastern Washington*, U. S. Geological Survey, Water Supply Paper, No. 4, 1897.

Russell, I. C., *Snake River Plains of Idaho*, U. S. Geological Survey, Bulletin, No. 199, 1902.

U. S. Geological Survey Folios: Ellensburg, Ore., No. 86; Silver City, Idaho, No. 104.

U. S. Geological Survey Topographic Maps: Manpa, Silver City, Weiser, for Idaho; Moses Lake, Pasco, Spokane, for Washington; Mitchell, Pine, for Oregon.

CHAPTER XXIV

THE CASCADE–SIERRA PROVINCE

The Cascade Mountains and the Sierra Nevada are usually considered as one province, not because they have the same history throughout, but rather because they make a continuous highland separating the Columbia Plateau and the Great Basin on the east from the Great Valleys of Washington, Oregon, and California on the west. Because of the differences in their history the Cascade Mountains and the Sierra Nevada will here be considered separately.

CASCADE MOUNTAINS

The Cascade Mountains begin just north of the Canadian boundary line and extend to the Feather River in northern California. In northern Washington the Cascade Range is about 100 miles wide, but it gradually narrows so that through Oregon it is but half that width. The mountain tops represent an upwarped peneplain surface, rising above the Interior Lowlands of Canada, the Columbia Plateau, and the Willamette River and Puget Sound troughs of Washington and Oregon. The northern end, some 8,000 feet high, slopes downward toward the south, and in southern Oregon and northern California is buried under numerous lava flows. The north end of the Cascade uplift is divided into three lobes by the Pasayten and Skagit rivers—the lobe to the east of the Pasayten River making the Okanogan Mountains; that between the Pasayten and Skagit rivers making the Hozomeen Mountains; and the lobe to the west of the Skagit River making the Skagit Mountains. The Okanogan Mountains were highly ·dissected by streams before the Ice Age. The peaks all rise to the peneplain level of 8,000 feet, but numerous glaciers which occupied the valleys above 6,000 feet gave the mountains a rugged alpine aspect. The Hozomeen Mountains and the Skagit Mountains are less dissected, and have preserved much more of the original peneplain surface, but at altitudes of only 5,000 to 7,000 feet.

Volcanoes.—On top of the uplifted Cascade peneplain stands a series of volcanoes of much later origin, beginning with Mount Baker (10,827 feet) in the north, and including, to the south, Glacier Peak (10,436 feet), Mount Rainier (14,408 feet), Mount Adams (12,470 feet), Mount Hood (11,225 feet), Lassen Peak (11,437 feet), and several other peaks. The more northern of these volcanoes are isolated peaks, from which only enough lava was poured out to make the cones. To the south the amount of extruded lava is progressively greater, until the southern end of the Cascade Range is completely buried under lava flows, and near Lassen Peak the secondary cones are numbered by the hundreds. The lava of all these cones is viscid andesite, which did not flow in the thin sheets characteristic of the basalts of the Columbia Plateau.

The volcanoes of the Cascade Range are all young, being in part, at least, of postglacial age. Lassen Peak was in eruption in 1914 and again in 1919. Both Mount Baker and Mount St. Helens were reported by Fremont as active in 1843. Mount Baker was active in 1854, 1858, and 1870.

History.—The history of the Cascade Mountains begins with the deposition of marine shales and limestones in the Pennsylvanian and earlier periods. In the Permian these were highly folded and intruded by granites. From then until the Eocene this region was eroded approximately to a peneplain. Then followed a period of deposition of epicontinental sands and gravels. A second folding followed, accompanied by the deposition of tuffs and some lava flows. Then there was a second period of erosion until the Pliocene, during which time the surface was again reduced to a peneplain. This surface developed in part on the old granites and metamorphosed shales and limestone, and in part on the continental sandstones and lavas, and was warped in the Pliocene into a flat-topped ridge to make the Cascade Mountains. The uplift occurred early enough in the Pliocene so that the streams had cut deep valleys into the sides of the range before the Ice Age came on.

Lake Chelan.—A little south of the rugged Okanogan Mountains, a multiheaded glacier once occupied the valley of the

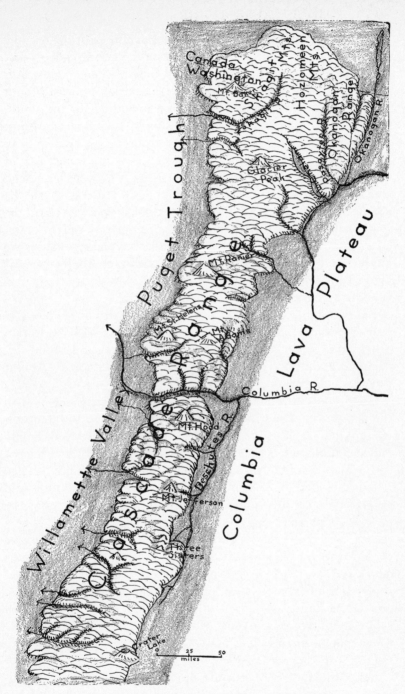

Canada
Washington
Mt. Baker
Skagit Mts.
Hozomeen Mts.
Pasayten R.
Okanogan Range
Okanogan R.
Puget Trough
Glacier Peak
Mt. Rainier
Mt. St. Helens
Mt. Adams
Lava Plateau
Cascade Range
Columbia R.
Willamette Valley
Mt. Hood
Deschutes R.
Columbia
Mt. Jefferson
Three Sisters
Crater Lake

0   25   50
miles

FIG. 188.   Orientation map of the Cascade Mountains.

Chelan River, deepening and widening it, and also pushing out
across the Columbia River. When this glacier withdrew, it
left a high moraine across the lower end of the valley, and Lake
Chelan was formed back of the barrier. Lake Chelan is a
beautiful, narrow lake 65 miles long, its lower end lying just
outside the mountains, and its upper end enclosed between
oversteepened glaciated walls. The surface of the lake is
1,079 feet above sea level, and as it varies in depth from 1,000
to 1,400 feet, the bottom of the lake in places is below sea level.

Fig. 189. View in the High Cascades, showing the level sky line. (After
Willis, U. S. G. S.)

This depth seems to be due, not to sinking of the region, but to
the gouging effect of the ice, which must have been over 4,500
feet thick.

Columbia River Gorge.—One of the striking features of the
northern Cascades is the magnificent canyon which the Columbia River has cut through the range. The river is but 100 feet
above sea level as it enters the mountains on the east side, and
it drops to sea level just after leaving the mountains. The
course of the river has been explained as a typical example of an
antecedent stream, which maintained its course as the mountain
rose; but Hodge's recent studies give quite a different interpretation. His theory is as follows: After the Miocene lava flows

there was no single large river developed on the new surface, but the drainage was carried by several small streams
which either emptied into arid basins, or followed unknown
channels. In the Pliocene the mountains rose and the lava
flows were both folded and faulted. The course taken by the
Columbia River was due to faulting. East of the Cascade
Mountains there were several east-west faults, between which
blocks were dropped, so that the northern edges were lower
than the southern edges. The Shaniko block (see Fig. 190),
on which lie the Deschutes and John Day rivers, has Antelope

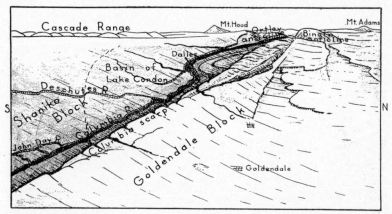

Fig. 190. Diagram to show the tilted fault blocks which diverted the
Columbia River to its present course. (Adapted from Hodges.)

Scarp as its south edge, while the north edge is depressed and
faces Columbia Scarp, which is the upraised edge of the next
block. The Columbia River developed its course on the depressed portion of the Shaniko block, just under the Columbia
Scarp, which rises from 350 to 3,000 feet above the river. Thus
guided, the Columbia River flowed, in the Pliocene, past its
present entrance into the mountains to a sag in the mountain
belt. In the Pleistocene, eruptions, during which Mount Hood
and its adjacent peaks were formed, poured lava across the
river's course, damming it and forming a great lake, named
Lake Condon. When the lake rose high enough so that it overflowed the lava dam at an altitude of about 1,900 feet, it began
to cut the gorge by which it now crosses the Cascade Range.

"The Cascades" are a series of rapids in the river about 40

miles east of Portland, Oregon. These are caused either by
the river not having completed its channel cutting, or by a

FIG. 191. Airplane view of the Dalles portion of the Columbia River.
Celilo Falls in the foreground. (Courtesy of the U. S. Army Air Corps.)

landslide at this point. Both explanations have been offered,
but as yet neither is established as correct.

Mount Rainier.—Mount Rainier (14,408 feet) may be taken
as typical of the volcanoes on the top of the Cascade Range.

FIG. 192. Long-distance airplane view along the top of the Cascade Mountains (approximately 227 miles): 1, Mt. St. Helens; 2, Mt. Washington, Ore.; 3, Mt. Jefferson, Ore.; 4, Mt. Hood, Ore.; 5. Mt. Rainier, Wash.; 6, Mt. Adams, Wash.; 7, Three Sisters. Mt. St. Helens and Mt. Rainier are totally invisible to the naked eye. (Courtesy of the U. S. Army Air Corps.)

It is no longer active, but it is conical in form because it is so young that weathering has not changed its contour. Owing to its height, it has a perpetual snow cap, from which some 48 glaciers flow down to the platform on which it stands. The lesser peaks, like Mount Hood, also have snow caps, but these are not extensive enough to develop into glaciers.

Crater Lake.—South of the Columbia River Gorge the top of the peneplain is never over 7,000 feet high, and its elevation diminishes southward, so that in middle Oregon it is 6,000 feet at Crater Lake. This lake, 6,117 feet above the sea, occupies the crater of a former volcano. It is a caldera lake, five to six miles in diameter, walled around by lava cliffs, which rise from 500 to 2,000 feet above its surface, and which slope away from the rim on all sides. The evidence indicates that a high volcano, named Mount Mazama, has lost its top because it was engulfed, probably due to the fact that the lava beneath escaped through some vent near the base, and the volcano no longer was supported. The water in the lake is 2,000 feet deep, and from its center a recent small cone, known as Wizards Island, rises 763 feet above the lake level.

Southern Cascades.—South of Crater Lake the peneplain surface is nowhere visible, as it is covered by flows of andesitic lava, by tuffs, and by other evidences of volcanic action. Between the southern end at Feather River and the Pitt River fifty miles distant are over 120 volcanoes, including Lassen Peak and Mount Shasta. Mount Shasta (14,380 feet) is a cone just past its youth, with a snow cap and five glaciers, the longest of which, $2\frac{1}{2}$ miles long, descends to the 9,500 foot level. While the height of the mountain has not been lessened by erosion, canyons, some of them several hundred feet deep, have been carved on the sides of the mountain. A secondary peak, a mile and a half distant and called Shastina, is a perfect cone, which was evidently formed during recent eruptions.

The southern end of the Cascade Range is not distinctly marked off from the Columbia Plateau. Both are of volcanic origin, but the Cascade Mountains are about 1,000 feet higher, and are made of fresh, viscid, andesitic lavas, while the Columbia Plateau is composed of old, eroded basalt lava.

Fig. 193. Crater Lake and Wizards Island. (After Diller, U. S. G. S.)

Fig. 194. Mount Shasta (right) and Mount Shastina (left) from Sisson,
California. (After Diller, U. S. G. S.)

THE SIERRA NEVADA

The Sierra Nevada extends from the Feather River south to the Mohave Desert as a high mountain barrier, 400 miles in length and about 80 miles in width in the widest section. The Sierra Nevada is a great easterly-facing fault block with a peneplained upper surface. The eastern summit of the block is from 6,000 feet to 11,000 feet high, from which the western face slopes down to, and under, the Great Valley of California.

History.—The first stage in the history of the Sierra Nevada was the deposition of several thousand feet of strata in the Pacific Ocean during the Palaeozoic Era. These deposits were later highly folded and uplifted, and then worn down to a peneplain by the beginning of the Jurassic. This level surface then sank below the sea, and shales and limestones of Jurassic age were laid down unconformably on it. A second period of mountain-building followed, during which great masses of granite were intruded into the sedimentary rocks of the region and metamorphosed them. This granite intrusion made one of the largest batholiths to be found in America.

Through the Cretaceous and the early Eocene, erosion removed several thousand feet of the metamorphosed rocks and exposed the granites over three-fourths of the area. This was followed by a period of volcanic activity as a result of which a large part of the surface was covered by volcanic ash and lava flows, especially in the north. In the Oligocene the country was slowly warped up, and erosion, which continued into the middle Miocene, carried away a part of the volcanic material. The erosion surface which was developed is preserved only on the high peaks of the southern part of the Sierra Nevada, and is sometimes referred to as "the sub-summit plateau."

The Miocene period of erosion was followed by a second set of lava flows, after which began the faulting that first outlined the Sierra Nevada block and raised the eastern edge to an altitude of about 3,000 feet. Following the uplift a new lower peneplain, called the Sierra Peneplain, was developed over some 70 per cent of the surface. Above this surface numerous monadnocks, especially in the south, rise approximately to the level of the sub-summit peneplain.

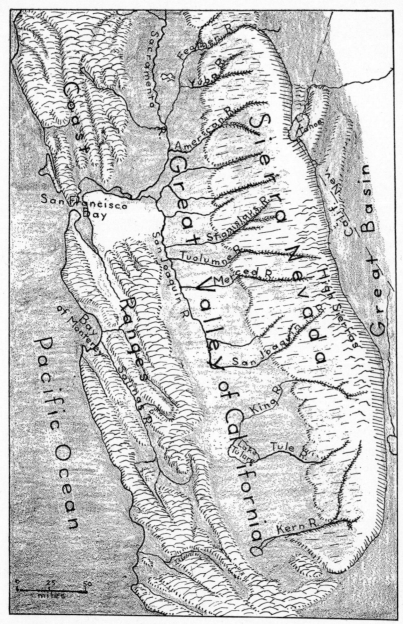

FIG. 195. Orientation map of the Sierra Nevada.

At the end of the Pliocene a vigorous uplift tilted the Sierra Nevada block approximately to its present position, and the streams were rejuvenated and cut deep V-shaped valleys. During the Ice Age the higher northern parts of the range were covered by snow fields, from which glaciers flowed down the

valleys in places to the 3,500 foot level. As the glaciers advanced and retreated with changes of climate, they deepened the river valleys and changed their cross profiles to the U-shape characteristic of glaciated mountain valleys. A few small glaciers are found on the higher northern peaks of the range today.

Fig. 196. Block diagram to show the structure of the Sierra Nevada. (U. S. G. S.)

The material eroded from the Sierra Nevada block in recent geologic time was carried westward into the ocean, and deposited in thick sedimentary beds. As the Sierra block was tilted, these beds slumped and were folded in a most complex manner (see Fig. 205). Later they were uplifted and faulted to make the Coast Ranges. Between the Coast Ranges and the Sierra Nevada block was left a wide depression which has since been so deeply filled with detritus brought by streams from the Sierra Nevada that it is now above sea level. From this lowland, known as the Great Valley of California, the peneplained surface of the Sierra Nevada slopes upward at the rate of 100 to 200 feet to the mile.

The streams from the Sierra Nevada block flow southwesterly in conformity to the slope of the block, and doubtless acquired their courses as a result of the tilting of the peneplain. Near their heads some of the rivers have tributaries from the north, or the south, which represent courses retained from pre-Pliocene times. At high altitudes the valleys are mature and the surface is rolling. From about 8,000 feet down to the limit of glaciation the valleys are U-shaped canyons, some over 4,000 feet deep. Below the ice limit the valleys are typically V-shaped.

General features.—In general the surface of the Sierra Nevada is a composite surface, in which are recorded the several stages in its geological history. In the highest areas are some remnants of the surface preceding the Oligocene uplift. These are seen as flat-topped monadnocks, rising from 2,000 to 3,000 feet above the rest of the surface, especially in the southern portion, and are known as "the High Sierras." The most famous peak is Mount Whitney (14,496 feet), the highest peak in the United States. In the middle and northern portions of the range monadnocks of lesser height were formed in the same period. Then there is a general level to which the ridges and river-divides rise, and which represents the Miocene or Sierra Peneplain. After this level was developed in the late Miocene, there seem to have been some minor warpings and changes of level, for many streams deposited gravels in their channels, in depths as great as 100 feet. During the volcanic eruptions which immediately followed, lava flows covered some of these gravels to depths of hundreds of feet, especially in the northern portion. These flows filled depressions and gave the surface an unusually level appearance. This surface was lifted approximately to its present position and the streams at once began to deepen their valleys.

The fault on the east side of the Sierra Nevada is a branching fault. In the north the Grizzly Mountain and Diamond Mountain blocks, which belong to the Sierra mass, were separated from it by secondary faults which split off from the main fault. The Carson Range in Nevada is a block which only dropped part way on the fault plane.

Lake Tahoe, in the angle between the Carson Range and the Sierra Nevada, lies

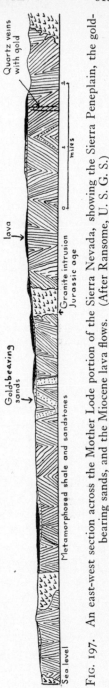

FIG. 197. An east-west section across the Mother Lode portion of the Sierra Nevada, showing the Sierra Peneplain, the gold-bearing sands, and the Miocene lava flows. (After Ransome, U. S. G. S.)

at an altitude of 6,225 feet.   The lake is 1,650 feet deep; its formation was due to a lava flow across the north end, above which the water had to rise before the lake could overflow into the Truckee River.   On the west side, Lake Tahoe is bounded by high cliffs, which mark the Sierra Nevada Fault, while the east shore is on the barren eroded granites of the Sierra surface. South of the Carson Range the main Sierra Nevada Fault is simple, and the rise from the Great Basin to the top of the range is in one abrupt step.   At the south end of the range the fault bends around to the west and feathers out.

The gold belt.—The "gold belt" of the Sierra Nevada lies south of the latitude of San Francisco and consists of a strip of highly metamorphosed rocks of the Pennsylvanian and Jurassic periods.   The gold occurs in numerous quartz veins which penetrate the Jurassic rocks in all directions.   These veins were formed while the rocks were being metamorphosed as a result of granitic intrusions.   Most of the original deposits were removed by erosion in the Eocene and Miocene periods and were either carried to the sea or deposited in river gravels. Some of the gravels which were deposited in the late Miocene river beds were later buried by lava flows.   These beds have been revealed by erosion, and have been extensively mined for gold.   The stream gravels deposited during the Ice Age were the source of the gold mined in the placer mining days of California from 1849 to 1860.

The canyons.—The Merced, the Tuolumne, the Kings River, and other streams have cut canyons in the median portion of their courses half a mile or more deep.   These stream- and glacier-cut gorges form some of the most striking scenic features of the Sierra Nevada.   The canyon of the Tuolumne River makes the Hetch-Hetchy Valley; that of the North Fork of Kings River makes the Tehipete Valley; that of the South Fork of Kings River makes the Kings River Canyon; and that of the Merced River makes the Yosemite Valley.   This last is typical of all these valleys, and, having been made into a national park, is best known.

Yosemite Valley.—All of the Yosemite region is composed of granite from which the overlying sedimentary and metamorphic rocks had been eroded as early as the Eocene.   The region had

been worn down in late Miocene approximately to the Sierra
Peneplain, above which stronger cores of granite, such as Half
Dome, North Dome, and El Capitan, rose about 900 feet. The
tops of these monadnocks, rising approximately to the same
height, represent the sub-summit peneplain referred to earlier
in the chapter. At the time of the Sierra Peneplain the streams
flowed in broad shallow
valleys. (See Fig. 198.)
At the end of the Mio-
cene the region was
lifted so that its east-
ern edge was 3,000 feet
high. The streams be-
came rejuvenated and
made new valleys, that
of the Merced River
being cut some 700 feet
below its "broad val-
ley" stage. The side
streams also deepened
their valleys, but to a
lesser extent. During
this erosion the differ-
ences in strength of the
several granites be-
came apparent.

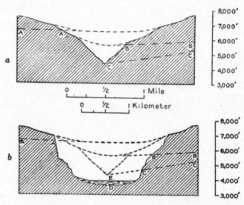

FIG. 198. (a) Generalized profiles of the
Yosemite Valley before glaciation: The upper
shallow profile is the Miocene valley; the
middle profile is the Pliocene valley; and the
deep V-shaped canyon is early Pleistocene.
Side profiles, A–A, B–B, and C–C, are side
valleys left hanging after each rejuvenation
of the area. (b) Profile of the Yosemite Valley after glaciation: D is the rock floor, and E
the lake deposits. (After Matthes, U. S. G. S.)

The next uplift, at
the end of the Pliocene, further rejuvenated the streams, and
the Merced River cut a narrow canyon inside its previous
double valley to a depth of some 1,300 feet. The side streams
also cut canyons, but not so deep, and so entered the Merced
over cascades or waterfalls. Then came the snow fields and ice
of the Pleistocene, from which a glacier flowed down the Merced
Valley and another down the Tenaya Valley, the two uniting
through the Yosemite section and extending down to the 4,000-
foot level. This glacier deepened the Yosemite Valley some
600 feet at the lower end and 1,500 feet at the upper end, and
widened it to half or three-quarters of a mile. The walls
of the valley, which rise in places as sheer precipices, 3,000

feet high, were made vertical by the erosion of the ice at the base.

The glacier must have advanced through the canyon at least two or three times. At the end of the last advance it left a terminal moraine blocking the lower end of the canyon. A lake which occupied five and a half miles of the canyon basin

FIG. 199. Bird's-eye view of the Yosemite Valley directly after the Ice Age: RC, Ribbon Creek. EC, El Capitan. EP, Eagle Peak. YC, Yosemite Creek. IC, Indian Creek. R, Royal Arches. W, Washington Column. TC, Tenaya Creek. ND, North Dome. BD, Basket Dome. MW, Mount Watkins. E, Echo Peak. C, Clouds Rest. SM, Sunrise Mountain. HD, Half Dome. M, Mount Maclure. L, Mount Lyell. F, Mount Florence. BP, Bunnell Point. CC, Cascade Cliffs. LY, Little Yosemite Valley. B, Mount Broderick. LC, Liberty Cap. SD, Sentinal Dome. G, Glacier Point. SR, Sentinel Rock. SC, Sentinel Creek. CR, Cathedral Rocks. BV, Bridal Veil Creek. LT, Leaning Tower. DP, Dewey Point. MR, Merced River. (After Matthes, U. S. G. S.)

FIG. 200. Bridal Veil Falls, a hanging valley. (After Matthes, U. S. G. S.)

formed behind this moraine, and lasted until it was filled almost to its present level by detritus brought into it by the Merced and Tenaya rivers. The depth of the lake beds has not been measured, but is estimated to be between 100 and 300 feet in the central portion. Since the filling of the basin some flood-plain material has been added to its surface. Mirror Lake is not a remnant of the postglacial lake, but is the result of a rock fall, which has temporarily dammed Tenaya River.

The erosion of the wide-bottomed Yosemite Canyon involved the under-cutting of the ends of the tributary streams. As a result the entering valleys are left as hanging valleys, and the streams now come into the valley over waterfalls of great, but varying, heights, the most famous being Bridal Veil, Yosemite, and Ribbon Falls.

BIBLIOGRAPHY

Diller, J. S., *Mount Shasta—a Typical Volcano*, National Geographic Society, Monograph No. 8, 1897.

Hodge, E. T., "The Columbia River Fault," *Bulletin of the Geological Society of America*, Vol. 42, pp. 923–984, 1931.

Matthews, F. E., *Geological History of the Yosemite Valley*, U. S. Geological Survey, Professional Paper, No. 160, 1930.

Reid, J. C., *Geomorphogeny of the Sierra Nevada Northeast of Lake Tahoe*, University of California Publications, Dept. of Geology, Vol. VI, pp. 89–161, 1911.

Willis, B., *Physiography and Deformation of the Wenatchee-Chelan District*, U. S. Geological Survey, Professional Paper, No. 19, 1903.

U. S. Geological Survey Folios: Lassen Peak, Calif., No. 19; Truckee, Calif., No. 39; Bidwell Bar, Calif., No. 43; Mother Lode, Calif., No. 63; Ellensburg, Wash., No. 86; Mount Steward, Wash., No. 106; Snoqualmie, Wash., No. 139.

U. S. Geological Survey, Guidebooks of the Western United States: Bulletin No. 611 for the Northern Pacific Route; No. 612 for the Overland Route; No. 614 for the Shasta Route; No. 845 for the Southern Pacific Lines.

U. S. Geological Survey Topographic Maps: Ellensburg, Mount Rainier National Park, Snoqualmie,* for Washington; Mount Hood and Vicinity for Oregon; Bidwell Bar, Lassen Peak,* Mount Whitney, Shasta,* Truckee, Yosemite,* for California.

CHAPTER XXV
THE PACIFIC BORDER PROVINCE

The Pacific Ocean is bordered by a series of mountain ranges. Between these coastal ranges in the west and the Cascade Mountains and the Sierra Nevada on the east there are wide valleys known as the Puget Trough and the California Trough, separated by the Klamath Mountains.

The most northern coastal mountains are the Olympic Mountains, which are separated from the Oregon Ranges by a lowland which extends as far south as the Chehalis River. The Oregon Ranges begin as a low upland, and rise toward the south, to a height of about 3,000 feet at the Rogue River. Both in the Olympic Mountains and in the Oregon Ranges the tops of the mountains all come to approximately the same height, with a few monadnocks rising above the general level. This would indicate that the same Pliocene peneplain which makes the top of the Cascade Mountains was developed in these mountains. The Puget Sound region and the Willamette Valley together form a synclinal trough, partly buried by alluvial deposits of younger age. We may think of the Oregon Coast Ranges, the trough, and the Cascade Mountains as forming parts of the same uplifted peneplain.

Olympic Mountains.—The Olympic Mountains have as yet been inadequately studied, because of the difficulties of access owing to the dense forest which covers the lower 4,000 feet of this mountain group. The rocks, like those of the Cascade Mountains, are Palaeozoic in age, and have been folded and partly metamorphosed by the intrusions of granite. The mountains of Vancouver Island are a continuation of this group; but the ranges of British Columbia are to be thought of rather as a continuation of the Cascade Range. The Olympic region was eroded to a peneplain before the Eocene, and then was uplifted. During the uplift there may have been some lava

321

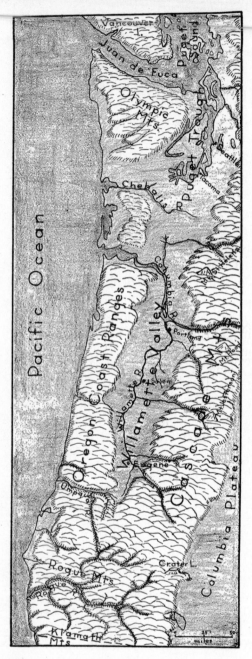

FIG. 201. Orientation map of the Coast Ranges and the valleys of Washington and Oregon.

flows. In the Pliocene the greater part of the area was reduced to a peneplain surface, which has since been elevated to an altitude of 4,000 feet. In the central part of the area a group of monadnocks rise to from 7,000 to 8,000 feet—the highest being Mount Olympus at 8,150 feet.

Oregon Coast Ranges.—The Oregon Coast Ranges differ in their history from the Olympic Mountains in that after the pre-Eocene peneplain was completed, the whole area (together with much of the Puget Trough) was depressed below sea level, and throughout the Eocene sands, shales, and limestones were deposited on top of the pene-plained surface. These Eocene beds reach a thickness of from 7,000 to 12,000 feet.

In the Coos Bay region is an area some 30 miles long by 12 to 15 miles wide, on which, during the late Eocene, swamps formed. These were several times depressed and buried by marine sedimentary beds, and their vegetation changed to coal beds. These coal beds are important, because they form the only coal deposits on the west coast of the United States. The sedimentary beds were later intruded by lavas at different times. The first of these was a black lava (diabase), which spread out in sills and dikes between the layers of sandstone; while some of the later intrusions simply lifted, or invaded, the sandstones without making sills. The intrusions were accompanied (or followed) by gentle folding, which raised the area above sea level. Erosion then reduced the uplifted region to the Pliocene peneplain, with a few monadnocks left rising above its surface. These monadnocks are generally masses of lava, such as Mary's Peak (4,097 feet), Saddle Mountain, and Larch Mountain; but a few, like Mount Tyer, are unreduced masses of sandstone.

Superimposed rivers.—The Chehalis, the Columbia, the Umpqua, and other rivers of this region generally flow from the east toward the west in courses which are not adjusted to either the strength or the attitude of the rocks which they cross. They mostly rise in, or near, the Willamette Valley, and cross from sandstone to lava and back to sandstone several times. This would indicate that they were developed on the Pliocene peneplain, and have been superimposed on the various rock layers as they have cut their valleys down. At present these rivers, especially those toward the south, flow in narrow valleys across the lava, and in wide mature valleys in the sandstone areas.

Puget Trough.—The trough between the Coast Range and the Cascade Mountains is divided into two portions—Puget Sound and the Willamette Valley. Both portions had a common origin as a synclinal trough between the ranges. Originally this basin had the Pliocene peneplain as a surface;

Fig. 202. Section across the Coast Ranges near Coos Bay, Oregon. (After Diller.)

but after the uplift of the ranges the southern portion of the basin was partially filled by silt brought down by the rivers, especially by those from the Cascade Mountains.

The two portions of the trough owe their distinctive characters to the effects of glaciation. There were two advances of the Continental Glacier in this region (the Admiralty and Vashon epochs), with a rather long interglacial period (the Payallup). During each of the advances of the ice the land stood at about the same height as today, but in the Payallup epoch it was 1,000 feet higher than at present. In both glacial advances the main body of the ice came from the north with lesser contributions from the east. The moraines and other deposits of the first advance were heavily eroded and dissected by the streams of the Payallup period. All around Seattle the hills, ridges, and lakes owe their origin to the moraines, till, and outwash plains of the last glaciation. During the uplift period the rivers converged toward what is now Puget Sound, cutting deep valleys in the earlier alluvium. These valleys are now the "canals" which traverse the sound, making waterways from 600 to 900 feet deep. When the ice advanced the second time, lobes followed these valleys upstream, and thus prevented them from being filled.

When Puget Sound was filled with ice, the water from the melting glaciers flowed to the sea by way of the Chehalis River, around the upper part of which there are outwash plains, still covered with gravel. Just before the final retreat of the Ice Sheet, the land stood lower than it does today; and the sea covered all the Puget Trough. The Columbia River was then a strait connecting the valley with the ocean. Between the two advances of the continental glacier the valley floor stood higher than at present, as is evidenced by the occurrence of marine fossils 1,000 feet up on the sides of the valley.

Wave-cut terraces.—The ocean side of both the Olympic Mountains and the Oregon Ranges presents a series of wave-cut terraces, the highest one being at the present time 1,500 feet above sea level. Below this are several others at intervals of from 200 to 300 feet. Each terrace must represent a period of stability, during which the waves had time to carve the mountain sides. The terraces also indicate that a large part of the uplift of the region was so recent that the wave-cut forms have not been obliterated by weathering. However, not all of the movements in the region have been upward. One of the latest has been downward, as is indicated by the fact that the mouths of all the rivers from the Strait of Juan de Fuca southward have been drowned. The Chehalis River is drowned for 50 miles inland; the Columbia River for 140 miles; the Umpqua River for 25 miles; and the Coquille River for 30 miles. Further, each river extends as a submerged channel out to the edge of the continental shelf.

Willamette Valley.—The glaciers did not extend into the Willamette Valley, but its surface is covered with a thin layer of alluvium deposited when it was flooded at the end of the last glaciation. The few erratic boulders in the alluvium were probably dropped by icebergs which floated into the flooded valley. Around Portland are numerous hills made of lava, which rise from 700 to 1,000 feet above the surface. These seem to be monadnocks which rose above the level of the Pliocene Peneplain when it was warped down to make the floor of the valley. The Willamette River is a comparatively sluggish stream, with its braided channel choked by the large amount of sediment which it carries.

Klamath Mountains.—Along the Pacific Coast from the Rogue River Mountains to the first range south of the Klamath River, and reaching east to the Cascade Mountains, is a mountain cluster known as the Klamath Mountains. These are not related either to the Oregon Coast Ranges or to the California Coast Ranges. This group of mountains is opposite that part of the Cascade Mountains which is most completely covered by lava flows. In age they correspond to that of the Blue Mountains on the Columbia Plateau and of the Sierra Nevada, so they may represent a western extension of the Sierra Nevada Range. The rocks forming the mountain cluster are either Palaeozoic, or Mesozoic (through the Jurassic) in age. They have been intensely folded and metamorphosed by the intrusion of granites, as were the Sierra Nevada. In early Comanchean times the whole region was raised above the sea and erosion began. The divides have many ridges and peaks which, rising approximately to the same level, indicate an old peneplain surface known as the "summit," or Klamath Peneplain. If reconstructed, this peneplain would rise in altitude from 1,700 feet in the northwest to 6,000 feet where the Klamath Mountains meet the California Coast Ranges.

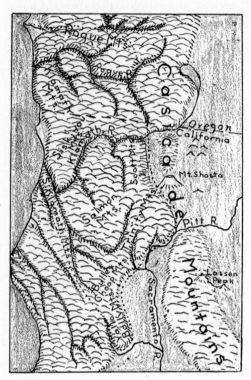

FIG. 203. The Klamath Mountain region.

The northeast corner is 4,000 feet high, and rises to the south so that the Salmon Mountain peaks reach heights up to 6,000 feet, while those of the southeast corner, the Yolo Bally Mountains, rise to 7,000 feet.

After the Klamath Peneplain was completed, at a date which can only be estimated, but which was probably sometime during the Miocene, this surface was uplifted and a set of broad mature valleys, which locally might be designated as peneplains, was developed. These surfaces are not continuous from one river valley to another, but seem to indicate an incomplete peneplain of Pliocene age.

However, long before the Pliocene peneplain could be completed, a series of uplifts took place and the rivers made narrow inner gorges with a series of terraces at intervals all the way up to 1,500 feet above the present sea level. The rivers of the Klamath region show no adjustment to the structure or strength of the rocks, and probably their courses were superimposed from the Klamath Peneplain. There was some glaciation on the highest peaks and ridges, but glaciation has dominated neither the forms of the mountains nor those of the valleys.

California Coast Ranges.—The California Coast Ranges form a highland nearly 400 miles in length and about 50 miles in breadth which extends from the Eel River in the northern

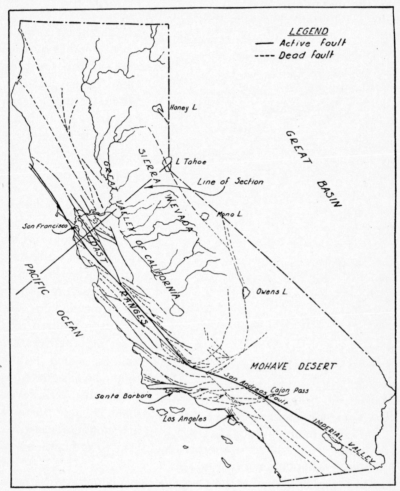

FIG. 204. The active and dead faults of California. (After G. W. Bain.)

part of the state in a general direction of S.30°E. nearly to Point Conception, where it meets the east-west ranges of the Los Angeles section. South of the Los Angeles section is a small area of upland, similar in character to the Sierra Nevada, which forms the northern end of the Lower California peninsula (see Fig. 195). The California Coast Ranges are composed mostly of Cretaceous and Tertiary sediments, partly marine and partly continental in origin. These sediments were deposited on an early erosion surface which had been developed on the metamorphosed Jurassic rocks. The beds have been alternately folded and eroded several times and since the Pliocene have been greatly faulted.

The Cretaceous to late Pliocene sediments—generally some 20,000 feet in depth; in the San Francisco region 24,000 feet deep—all are the result of erosion of the Sierra Nevada. Some of these beds are marine; some are lake beds; some were deposited as alluvial fans and flood plains; and a small portion is volcanic ash. The deposits seem to be largely piedmont accumulations of detritus which at different times have sunk, and at other times have been folded in complex ways. After each movement the material was eroded, and then covered with detritus. This mass of rocks of complex origin and history was faulted in the Pliocene, and the blocks thus formed were raised to various altitudes. Erosion surfaces later than the Jurassic peneplain seem to represent local lowlands rather than a broad peneplain, for they cannot be traced from one block to another.

The northern part of the California Ranges is a broad upland from 1,600 to 2,100 feet above the sea, subdivided into ranges by rivers such as the Eel and the South Klamath, which have their courses adjusted to fault lines. Farther south four distinct ranges may be distinguished from west to east—the Marin, the Sonoma, the Napa, and the Yolo. The Marin Range extends to San Francisco Bay at the Golden Gate.

The alignment of the subordinate ranges and of the many longitudinal valleys in the Coast Ranges is due to faulting. Faulting began in the Pliocene and has continued to the present. The best-known fault is the San Andreas Fault, which extends over 500 miles from Cape Mendocino in the north to the Salton Sea in the south, and which perhaps bounds the depression occupied by the Gulf of Lower California. A great earthquake due to movement along this fault took place in 1906 and caused extensive damage in San Francisco and its vicinity. The movement was mostly horizontal, and fences, roads, railroads, and other structures were offset where they crossed the fault line. The motion took place on the east side of the fault plane, points to the north of the focus being moved north, and points to the south moved south, as though the block had suddenly expanded. A strong movement took place on the Las Trampas Fault in 1848, and on the Franklin Fault in 1812. More recently there have been movements on some of the lesser faults, as at Santa Barbara and at Long Beach.

The California Coast Ranges rise abruptly from the ocean along a line that seems to be due, at least in part, to faulting. The, shore line is everywhere steep and unbroken. Wave-cut terraces occur at numerous levels up to 1,500 feet, suggesting that between the periods of elevation the land was stationary for a time. A submarine platform extends from 25 to 50 miles off-shore to a depth of 5,000 feet, and then the ocean floor slopes steeply to a depth of 12,000 feet. The evidence seems to be that this platform is not a continental shelf built up by sedimentation, but that it is the result of a deformation of the land.

San Francisco Bay region.—The region about San Francisco Bay may be best described as composed of a group of fault blocks. The uplifted Montara block and several smaller blocks to the east together form the peninsula of San Francisco. The depressed San Francisco block to the east forms the southern arm of the bay, and includes the Santa Clara valley to the south, while on the east of the bay is the raised Berkeley Hills block.

A river formed by the union of the Sacramento and the San Joaquin rivers maintained its course to the ocean across these

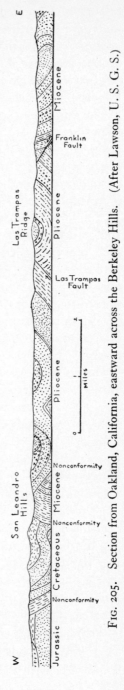

Fig. 205. Section from Oakland, California, eastward across the Berkeley Hills. (After Lawson, U. S. G. S.)

blocks. A recent depression caused the valley to be drowned back to the junction of the two rivers, thus forming the two arms of San Francisco Bay. The amount of this depression is indicated by the depth of the channel, which is 414 feet

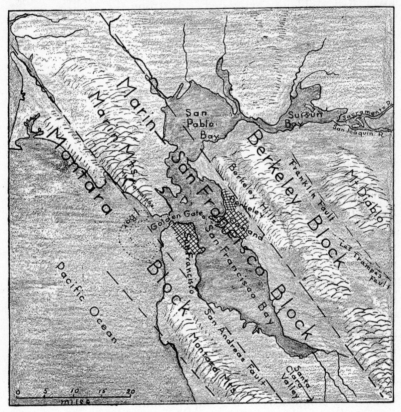

FIG. 206. The system of block faults in the San Francisco Bay region. (Adapted from Lawson, U. S. G. S.)

in the Golden Gate. The downward movement here is in contrast to the general uplift of the Coast Ranges and may have been caused by the concentration at this point of the detritus brought by the rivers. Just outside of the Golden Gate there is a great bar which is thought to be the submerged delta of the river.

The mountains around San Francisco Bay are about a thousand feet in height, but the Berkeley Hills to the east rise to 1,500 feet, with some peaks rising above that level. Farther east the higher Diablo Range, culminating in Mount Diablo at 3,849 feet, continues southward into the Temblor Range, and that in turn becomes the San Emigdio Range. These three ranges forming the western boundary of the Great Valley were elevated on fault planes along their eastern fronts.

The Berkeley Hills Range is an off-shoot of the Diablo Range, which it joins some 50 miles south of Suisun Bay. The Hamilton Range, on which the Lick Observatory is situated, also merges into the Diablo Range. Its western face is made by the Oakland Fault, which also marks the east margin of the Santa Clara Valley. The Montara block, which extends to Monterey

FIG. 207. San Francisco Bay from the Berkeley Hills. (After Lawson, U. S. G. S.)

Bay, includes several ranges: the Montara Range on the west expands into the Santa Cruz Range, and this range in turn continues inland as the Gabilan Range, which extends to the south end of the Diablo Range. The west front of the Gabilan Range is a fault face, to the west of which is a down-dropped block, making the Salinas River Valley.

South of Monterey Bay the coast is made by the Santa Lucia Range. At Point Conception the Coast Ranges bend to the east, as is illustrated by the San Raphael Range, the eastern end of which is opposite the southern end of the Sierra Nevada. The Los Angeles Ranges to the south have had a different history, and will be described later.

The Great Valley.—Between the Coast Ranges of California and the Sierra Nevada lies the Great Valley of California, 500 miles in length and averaging 50 miles in width. It is a structural valley, between the deeply depressed western portion of the Sierra block and the uplifted blocks which make the easternmost Coast Ranges. The valley, which has existed since before the Miocene, has been partially filled with detritus brought down by streams from the bordering ranges and deposited as deltas where the valley was submerged, and as alluvial fans where it was above sea level. The major portion of the filling has come from the Sierra Nevada, for the heavier rainfall occurring on the west sides of the ranges has caused many large streams to flow from the Sierra Nevada, whereas from the Coast Ranges only two minor streams flow into the Sacramento River, and none into the San Joaquin River. The depth of the fill in the Great Valley is not definitely known, but wells drilled to 2,000 feet have not reached bed rock. In places around the margin Miocene marine sediments outcrop on the surface.

Sacramento Valley.—The northern half of the Great Valley is drained by the Sacramento River, which comes out of the Klamath Mountains near Redding, California, at an altitude of about 500 feet. For the first 25 miles it flows in a broad valley, 100 feet below the level of the valley floor. Just above Red Bluff the river crosses an upland belt from 10 to 15 miles in width, formed by a low anticline which crosses the valley at this point. Below Red Bluff the character of the river changes. It no longer flows below the level of the adjacent country, but meanders over its flood plains with a grade of less than a foot to the mile. Like the Mississippi River, the river and its tributaries have built up levees on either side of their channels. As a result there are numerous sloughs near the river, and between the levees of the Sacramento River and those of the tributaries are a number of basins, such as American Basin, Sutters Basin, and Butte Basin. Near San Francisco Bay some of the basins are submerged, or are swamps; this fact, together with the braided character of the rivers, has given the section the name of "the Island Country."

The Marysville Buttes, just west of the town of the same name, form the one interruption to the generally flat aspect of the Sacramento River valley. These buttes are the remnants of a volcano which was active either in late Pliocene or early Pleistocene time. The residual necks rise some 2,000 feet above the surrounding country in an area about four miles in diameter. Lava and tuffs are distributed about equally on all sides of the necks, and the buttes make a circle some ten miles in diameter.

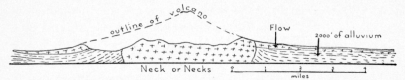

FIG. 208. Section to show the structure of the Marysville Buttes. (After Lindgren, U. S. G. S.)

San Joaquin Valley.—The southern half of the Great Valley is drained by the San Joaquin River, formed by streams from the Sierra Nevada. Each of these streams has built a great alluvial fan out into the valley, and these fans have spread until they unite along the whole mountain front. They have pushed the San Joaquin River well over to the west side of the valley.

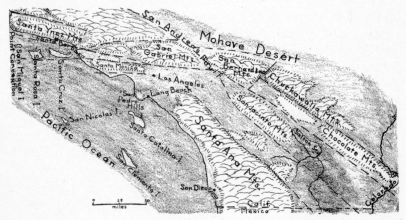

FIG. 209. Orientation map of the Los Angeles Basin.

In the case of the smaller streams the water sinks into the sands and gravels of the valley before it reaches the San Joaquin; and even the larger streams lose much of their water in crossing the valley.

The fan of Kings River forms a dam across the valley, back of which Tulare Lake, fed by waters from Kings River and the Tule River, has formed. The rate of evaporation in the southern San Joaquin Valley is so great that Tulare Lake has never overflowed into San Joaquin River in historic times. In like manner, fans of the Kern River farther south have caused Kern and Buena Vista lakes, neither of which has an outlet. These lakes are all shallow playa lakes surrounded by tule (*Scirpus lacustris*) swamps.

The Los Angeles Ranges.—South of the San Raphael Range is a group of mountain blocks and intervening lowlands. The ranges in the north are made of Cretaceous and Tertiary rocks,

FIG. 210.   The San Bernardino Mountains; San Bernardino Peak to the left.
(After Darton, U. S. G. S.)

like the Coast Ranges, but they trend east-west. The ranges to the south and west are composed of granites and metamorphic rocks, as are the ranges of the Mohave Desert, but are formed by a continuation of the same faults as make the Coast Ranges. The ranges surround a lowland, known as the Los Angeles Basin, or the Valley of Southern California.

From Point Conception the Santa Ynez Range, extending east for more than 60 miles, is outlined by faults of which the southern one coincides with the coast line. The Santa Monica Range also trends east-west and is bounded by faults. Between these two ranges is a narrow down-dropped block, which continues out to sea as the "Channel." The "Channel Islands," Santa Cruz, Santa Rosa, and San Miguel, are remnants of the submerged block, but the sea bottom about them is by no means so deep as in the "channel." The islands of Santa

Catalina and San Clemente are also remnants of submerged blocks. Recently a survey of the sea bottom near these islands disclosed a submerged canyon, of the Grand Canyon type, and of almost as great depth. The date when this island area was submerged seems to have been middle to late Pleistocene, for fossil elephant bones which belong to late Pleistocene types have been found in Santa Rosa Island. The last movement of these islands seems to have been upward, for wave-cut terraces are found almost to the highest points on the islands, which are 1,000 feet above present sea level.

The San Gabriel Mountain block includes some 700 square miles of granite and metamorphic rocks which rise in places to an altitude of 6,000 feet. The block is so deeply and completely dissected that it must have been elevated at an earlier time than the neighboring blocks. In composition it seems to be similar to the Mohave Desert mountains.

San Bernardino Mountains.—The San Bernardino Mountain block is also made mostly of granite and belongs to the Mohave Desert type. The upper surface is rolling, and valleys are not yet deeply incised in it. Toward the west the top surface is at an altitude of 6,000 feet, but farther east is a ridge, terminating in San Bernardino Peak (10,660 feet) at the northerly end and in San Gorgonio Peak (11,485 feet) at the southern end. On the latter peak are cirques and moraines down to the 8,500-foot level—the result of alpine glaciation in the Pleistocene. This is the most southerly occurrence of the Ice Age glaciers in the United States.

Farther to the south is the San Jacinto Range with many crests from 7,000 to 9,000 feet high, and to the east of this range is the Santa Anna Range, both of the Mohave type. Between these ranges lies the Los Angeles Basin with several arm-like extensions reaching in between the ranges. All these basins are being filled with alluvial deposits, which in many places are already hundreds of feet thick.

There seem to have been two periods of deformation in this region: an earlier and less violent one in the Miocene; and a second more vigorous one in the Pleistocene. After the Miocene movements the ocean occupied most of the present-day lowlands and extended into the Mohave Desert. The eastern

basins were filled with Pliocene and Pleistocene deposits, largely
of a continental character.   The Los Angeles Basin, however,
was under the sea all through the Pliocene.   During the Pleistocene disturbance the several blocks of this section were raised
to somewhere near their present positions, and since that time
there have been lesser movements along the fault lines, and
some folding of the less coherent beds in the basins.

FIG. 211.   The Rancho La Brea tar pits.   (After Darton, U. S. G. S.)

Both the Miocene and the Pliocene marine deposits in the
Los Angeles Basin, with a thickness of from 7,000 to 8,000 feet,
contain great quantities of petroleum, and where favorable
structures for segregation of the oil have developed, oil fields
of major importance have been found.   Such structures have
resulted from that western remnant of an old block, the San
Pedro Hills, moving inward to the west.   The sedimentary
beds between the San Pedro block and the San Gabriel and
other blocks were gently folded during the Pleistocene.   This
primary folding is complicated by lesser cross folds and some
minor faults.   As a result of the crossing of the two sets of folds
low domes were formed, of which there are a score in the Los
Angeles Basin.   Figure 212 shows a section along the coast
cutting three of these oil-producing domes.   One from San

Pedro Hills to Los Angeles would appear very much the same.

Rancho la Brea.—At the edge of the city of Los Angeles an oil-bearing dome, crossed by a small fault, permitted part of the petroleum to seep to the surface, where it formed a lake in Pleistocene times. The volatile portions of the petroleum evaporated and left an asphalt deposit known as the Rancho la Brea asphalt lake. Until very recently animals walking on the hardened portions of the lake surface would break through when they came near the center, and would become entangled in the less solidified tar. Their struggles brought birds and beasts of prey to the spot, and they too would be caught in the tar. When an attempt was made to use the asphalt for commercial purposes the bones of these animals were discovered; some were recognized as animals of the Pleistocene, and some as belonging to recent times. The tar pit was bought and presented to the city of Los Angeles, which has filled a great museum with the thousands of skeletons found there.

Oil fields.—The oil on the south side of the fault did not escape to the surface, and this section is now being developed as one of the lesser oil fields of the basin. The Long Beach, or Signal Hill, dome is one of the most spectacular oil centers

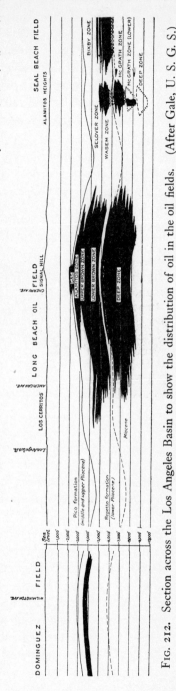

FIG. 212. Section across the Los Angeles Basin to show the distribution of oil in the oil fields. (After Gale, U. S. G. S.)

found anywhere, partly because it is a very large producer, and partly because it lies under land which had been subdivided into small city lots and which belonged to hundreds of people. Each lot owner tried to get his share of the oil, and the result was a forest of oil derricks. As a result of the drilling of so many wells the production soon began to decline. The field will, however, produce for a long time, for deep drilling has revealed several zones of oil below the one first found. A contrast to this extravagant mode of production is seen in the Domingues field, where the oil was discovered on undeveloped land. Here the oil field is being developed slowly, wells are spaced widely, and plans have been worked out for a long continuation of production.

BIBLIOGRAPHY

Bryan, K., *Sacramento Valley*, U. S. Geological Survey, Water Supply Paper, No. 495, 1923.

Fenneman, N. M., *Physiography of the Western United States*, 1931.

Lawson, A. C., *California Earthquake Commission Report*, Vol. I, 1908.

Mendenhall, W. C., *San Joaquin Valley*, U. S. Geological Survey, Water Supply Paper, No. 222, 1908.

XVI International Geological Congress, Guidebook No. 15 for Southern California, 1933; Guidebook No. 16 for Middle California and Western Nevada, 1933.

U. S. Geological Survey Folios: Marysville, Calif., No. 17; Tacoma, Wash., No. 54; Coos Bay, Ore., No. 73; Redding, Calif., No. 138; Santa Cruz, Calif., No. 163; San Francisco, Calif., No. 193.

U. S. Geological Survey, Guidebooks of the Western United States: Bulletin No. 614 for the Shasta Route, 1915; No. 845 for the Southern Pacific Lines, 1933.

U. S. Geological Survey Topographic Maps, Tacoma,* for Washington; Coos Bay, Portland,* Rosenburg, for Oregon; Lompoc, Oceanside, San Mateo,* Santa Cruz, Tamalpais,* for California.

INDEX

INDEX

(Heavy-faced type indicates the page where a major subject is taken up.)

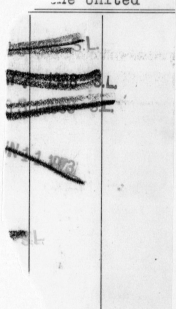

omis

the United

S.L.

S.L.

S.L.

S.L.